Dragons
more than a myth?
by
Richard Freeman

Illustrated
by
Mark North

Typeset by Mark North, Designed by Mark North and Jon Downes for CFZ Communications
Using Microsoft Word 2000, Microsoft Publisher 2000, Adobe Photoshop CS.

First published in Great Britain by CFZ Press

CFZ Press is a division of:

CFZ Communications
15 Holne Court,
Exwick,
Exeter.
EX4 2NA

ISBN: 0-9512872-9-X

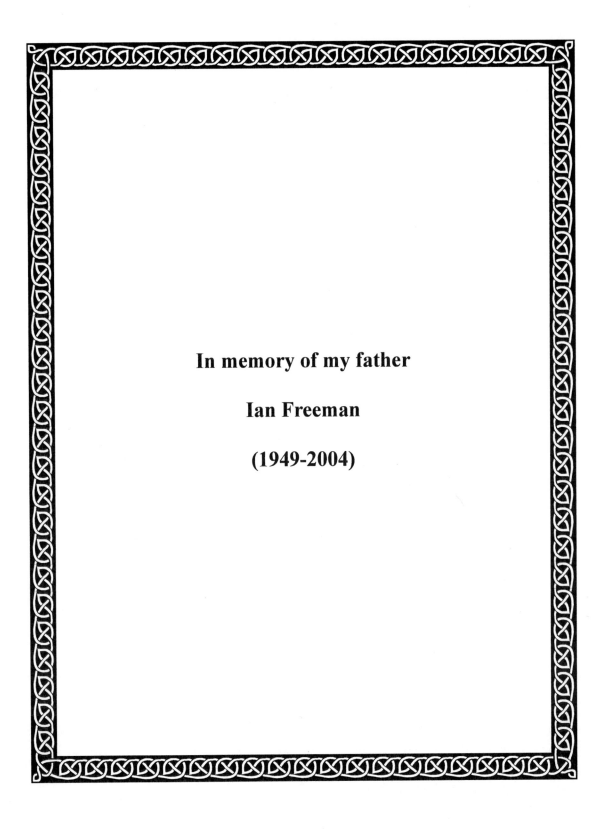

In memory of my father

Ian Freeman

(1949-2004)

Out - out are the lights - out all!
And, over each quivering form,
The curtain, a funeral pall,
Comes down with the rush of a storm,
While the angels, all pallid and wan,
Uprising, unveiling, affirm
That the play is the tragedy, "Man,"
And its hero the Conqueror Worm.

The Conqueror Worm by Edgar Allan Poe (1843)

CONTENTS

ACKNOWLEDGEMENTS

My thanks go to the following people for their assistance in this book: Dr. Gail Nina Anderson, Neil Arnold, Rupert Bunts, Dave Curtis, Jon Downes, Lisa Dowley, Matthew Hall, Mike Hallowell, Tony Healy, Corinna Jones, Steve Jones , Graham Inglis, Graham King, Mark North, Peter North, Darren Naish, Chris Moiser, Gary Opit, Nick Redfern, Pene (cousin Penelope) Rowe, Dr. Karl Shuker, Dave Sutton, Tessie (*The Bald Dog*) John Tindsley, Paul Vella, Anthony Wallis, and to *Joy Division*, to whose music this book was written.

FOREWORD

Dragons are everywhere. Stories of these impressive and fearsome creatures come to us from every corner of the globe – from Norse mythology and Chinese folklore, to Christian allegory and contemporary fantasy. They can be seen on Ming Dynasty vases, in medieval heraldry, Renaissance paintings and even in the earth itself in the case of the great Serpent Mound of Adams County, Ohio.

Here in modern-day Britain, a fiery red, arrow-tailed dragon looks down from the national flag of Wales; and the City of London is presided over by a number of splendid winged examples of the species (even if David Icke believes they're just another clue to the Queen's reptilian heritage, and a global financial conspiracy!)

Richard Freeman has certainly felt the appeal of the Dragon; and as a knowledgeable herpetologist and reptile-lover, a self-confessed Goth, a keen student of the paranormal, and one of the country's few practising cryptozoologists, he is, perhaps, in ideal position to consider the creature in all its bewildering aspects – which is precisely what he does in this wide-ranging and fascinating book. Here, he offers us the full gamut of Dragons – from basilisks to wyverns, giant crocodiles to salamanders – in its multifarious mythological and zoological forms and an in-depth study of sightings both ancient and modern, unearthing along the way some truly bizarre tales, such as that of the gwibers of Wales or the 19th century dinosaur bone hoax of the Barnum-like Dr Albert Koch.

Of course, the book also attempts to answer those most intriguing of questions: What are dragons? And, do they exist today?

Freeman provides a variety of possible answers, examining evidence both zoological and anecdotal, as well as looking at those cases of high strangeness that force us to consider the possibility that Dragons may well emerge from that *terra incognita* of the human unconscious, or even from some little-understood parallel realty.

Although in the course of this book we discover that Richard Freeman is a man who once spent a good deal of time 'feeding' a tulpoid spider-deity – the Goth side of his personality clearly to the fore at this point. He can also, from similar hands-on experience, tell the difference between Naga bones and elephant teeth. And the latter quality, I'd say, is one devoutly to be wished for in a guide who offers to take us through the forests of the Lost World to the Dragon's very lair...

David Sutton
Editor
Fortean Times
16th March 2005

INTRODUCTION

Why is it that on a pleasant summers day - when a breeze tosses clouds briefly across the sun - we freeze? In that moment, instinct tells us to stop dead. The sight of a huge shadow, sweeping across the landscape, fills us with an awe and dread that we cannot place. These feelings, however fleeting, are real! Some fast-moving '*thing*' in the sky - big enough to blot out the sun; the hairs on the back of your neck rising, the feeling that someone just 'walked over your grave. Where do these sensations come from? It is almost as though vast ebon wings are soaring above you. Wings that carry a fear hidden in mankind's collective memory. A fear of something so terrifying it burnt itself onto our species' mind thousands of years ago.

This is a book about impossibilities - a book about the physical reality of creatures consigned to mythology since the Renaissance. This is a book about *real* dragons. But this is *also* a book written by a professional zoologist – a man who has worked with over four-hundred different species of animal, from spiders to elephants, and it is this knowledge of animal behaviour that brings a *new* angle to the ancient science of dracontology.

For example the freezing instinct mentioned earlier? This same freezing behaviour has been observed in lemurs on Madagascar. It is believed to be a defensive mechanism evolved to thwart the predations of eagles. The Madagascan eagle species feed mainly on fish or snakes, so at first this behaviour confused zoologists. That was until the remains of now-extinct gigantic eagles - adapted for preying on lemurs - were discovered. Despite their predator's absence, the lemurs retained the defensive behaviour. But what has that got to do with us?

Perhaps, like the lemurs, this is instinctive behaviour possibly due to some kind of racial memory. But surely there was never a flying predator big enough to be a threat to man.....

PART ONE

TYPES OF DRAGON

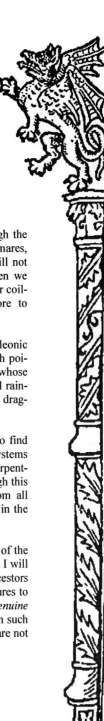

What is a dragon?

An absurd question - we all know The Dragon. It rampaged through the stories and fairy tales of our youth. It haunted our childhood nightmares, and took centre-stage in our games and imagination. What child will not recall *Smaug* - the awesome villain in Tolkien's *The Hobbit*? When we think of dragons, we imagine them in a European, medieval setting, or coiling through clouds of the ancient Orient. But there is *far* more to dragonkind than this.

The dragon is found in *every* culture on earth, and comes in a chameleonic array of shapes and guises. Some are crawling, limbless horrors with poison gas as breath and acid as blood. Some are tiny crested serpents whose very gaze can strike a man dead. Others still are bejewelled, ethereal rain-gods whose breath brings life-giving moisture. All these things are dragons, all these and many, many more.

In October of 2000, (The Chinese Year of The Dragon!) I set out to find such a monster. I travelled to the rivers, jungles, and remote cave-systems of northern Thailand, in search of the Naga - a 60 foot, crested serpent-dragon of ancient Buddhist and Hindu legend. As we progress through this book, I will reveal what I discovered, together with evidence from all across the globe that supports my thesis - the existence of Dragons in the 21st Century.

In the first section of this book we will embark on a worldwide tour of the draconic menagerie. We will look at each kind of dragon in turn, and I will retell some of the legends pertaining to each species. To our ancestors these were not just stories but very real accounts, accounts of creatures to be feared or revered. Good or evil, the dragon was above all a *genuine* beast. We will also see an example of a contemporary encounter with such a beast. Join me now as we take a closer look, but be warned: these are not children's tales. We know the dragon…or at least we *think* we know.

CHAPTER ONE

Dragons and Dragonkind

"You too, the dragons who shine with golden brilliance...you move on high with wings, and chasing herds, you tear apart massive bulls, constricting them in your coils. Even the elephant is not safe from because of his size; you condemn every animal to death."

Marcus Annaeus Lcanus (AD 39-65)

THE TRUE DRAGON OR FIREDRAKE

This is *the dragon* - the beast that springs instantly to mind at the mention of the word. Also known as the Heraldic-Dragon, it is the most ubiquitous, formidable, and magnificent of its race. We know it from its appearance in countless books and stories, and from its combat with St George and other 'heroes'. It is a gigantic reptilian quadruped, that dwarfs the largest elephant into mouse-like insignificance. Its whole body is covered with titanium-hard scales, and bares a huge pair of leathery, bat-like wings. The back is crested and spiny, the tail long and whip-like. All four legs terminate in cruelly-clawed talons, like those of some outsized bird-of-prey. Most horrific of all is its head. Atop a long, sinuous neck, it has massive jaws lined with razor-sharp stiletto-like teeth. The cold eyes are hypnotic, drawing in its hapless prey, both man and beast. The head is crowned with regal horns. It lairs in deep caves, forests, lakes, and seas. It is indeed a master of all elements.

The true-dragon was originally an immortal beast of god-like power and cosmic significance. Indeed, many did battle with Gods such as Typhon, (the bane of the Greek pantheon - arch foe of Zeus), and Tiamat of Babylonia, who battled the God Marduk.

In latter legends they became more mortal - but *still* immensely hard to kill! The true-dragon had but one vulnerable-spot, and this was seldom same on any two dragons.

The firedrake's most potent weapon is its breath. Great jets of flame erupt from its jaws; flame hot enough to melt stone - like butter under a blow-torch. Lakes boil, and flesh becomes a wisp of carbon beneath the dragon's flame.

The firedrake is known also for its gigantic hoards - veritable mountains of treasure that the monster accumulates during its indefinite life-span. Pillaged from castle strongholds and treasuries; coins, jewels, goblets, mirrors, be-jewelled swords, sceptres and crowns, form the firedrake's precious bed.

They are also the most magickal of dragons. The true-dragon can shapeshift, often taking the form of another animal or a human. They can self-heal wounds at an amazing rate, and their blood is acidic and venomous. Many can become invisible, and speak the languages of other creatures (including man). Some can change size, growing from a tiny lizard into a huge-monster in the twinkling of an eye. Most are malevolent, cutting vast-swathes of death and destruction through whole countries. But a few have been more kindly disposed to mankind.

The true dragon is best known in Europe, western Asia, and north Africa.

La Vibria – The Dragon of Catalonia.

When the Moorish forces were finally crushed by Charlemagne's Army in 801 AD, and driven from the Catalonian region of Spain, they left behind a nasty surprise. As a means of vengeance upon their victors, the warriors of Allah left behind them a young dragon called *La Vibria,* in a cave in the Massif of Saint Llorrenc.

The reptile grew at an alarming rate, becoming both cunning *and* powerful. He also grew wise in all matters of the occult, (as was the nature of his kind). Soon he sallied forth in the night, on vasty, ebony wings, to bring the shadow of death upon the religion. Falling from the night-sky he razed whole towns with his flaming breath, toppled the mightiest towers with his tail, and reduced lush crops to stubble. Rending with tooth and claw, *La Vibra* gorged himself on shepherds and their flocks, snatched guards from castle-ramparts, and slaked his thirst in the blood of maidens.

The town of Terrassa had fell foul of the dragon's depredations more than any other. Eventually the townsfolk offered a reward to anyone who could deliver them.

There was no shortage of brave men who sought to deliver Catalonia from the scourge. The Catalonians were no cowards. Many a champion rode forth to the cheers and adulation of the masses. None returned. Occasionally a steed - mad with fear and frothing at the mouth - was found - its saddle torn and bloody.

Monks, wizards and holy-men too, tested their spells and faith against the dragon. They fared no better. Neither sword nor prayer could bow the beast.

Eventually, Count Jofre el Pilos, Governor of the territory, decided to tackle the monster himself. Dressed in thick armour, and astride a huge black-horse, he rode from his castle and into the desolation that had spread out like an ebon-tide from the dragon's lair. His steed shied and whinnied at the edge of the black desert, but the count forced it to ride on.

About him the earth was black and scorched. The rocks were twisted into outlandish shapes where the dragon's fire had melted them, making the stone run like hot-wax and then cool into fantastic forms. There were no trees or grass. Indeed, the count spied no living thing amidst the desolation - even flies were absent.

At last he saw a bird. A large rook busily ripping at the eye of a blackened-corpse. The count wondered why the carrion-bird should be the only life surviving near the dragon's lair. Then he recalled the shapeshifting powers attributed to dragons. He called the brute by name. His deceit uncovered, the dragon abandoned his disguise.

Scarlet spines like gargantuan rose-thorns sprang from the bird's spine. A forked-tongue flickered from the ever-widening maw, as the beak became jaws, and teeth like Moorish-scimitars sprouted from the gums. As the thing swelled, the bird-lizard's feathers hardened into blood-coloured scales. Clawed forearms unfolded as the neck lengthened. The pinions sloughed feathers, in favour of leather and unfurled like vasty sails. Where a rook once stood, was 80-feet of fang, claw, scale and muscle - glowing with a ruddy, igneous lustre.

The Count's mind recoiled from the uncanny sight, as his steed reared up screaming in wild-eyed panic. He hurled a hefty spear at the dragon as it slinked closer with a liquid grace. The weapon clattered off the saucer-sized scales with a metallic clang. Again, the horse reared - protesting at the dragon's approach. The animal's panic saved the Count's life, as a jet of white-hot fire sprang from *La Vibria's* jaws. Instead of striking the Count's side, it torched the unfortunate-horse's belly. The animal's innards were boiled in its own vital-juices, and exploded from its belly in a spray of scalding gore. The horse was dead before it hit the ground, and pinned the scorched count beneath it.

The giant-reptile moved in for the kill. Its tooth-studded maw swept down upon the count. The nobleman desperately swung up his shield. The massive jaws clamped onto this, instead of his body, and reared up crumpling the metal like eggshell. Dire spume fell from the furnace-mouth, and spattered onto the count, burning like drops of molten-lead.

Discarding the tattered shield, the dragon swung his head around, and struck again. Half-blinded by heat and smoke, cruelly burnt, and with several bones shattered, the count thrust up his sword in desperation - expecting naught but death. But as the jaws snapped shut about him like a titanic rat-trap, his blade pierced the roof of the monster's mouth.

La Vibria withdrew - hissing like a thousand pans of water spilt on a thousand hot-stoves. He clawed at the stinging irritation in his mouth, the acidic-blood already gnawing at the metal. With a fantastic beating of his wings that caused a maelstrom in the air, the monster lifted-off. He whirled frantically in a wild aerial-dance, as he tried to pluck the sword from his jaws. Heedless of his erratic-flight he careered into a mountainside and exploded. Hundreds of tons of rock came crashing down the mountainside. A shower of black ichor fell like a searing rain, and there followed a profound silence.

When the townsfolk finally dared to creep to the dragon's lair, they found the count, unconscious. They took him back to Terrassa, and nursed him back to health. The mountain into which *La Vibria* had crashed was named *Puig de la Creu* (Peak of the Cross), and the count's battle was recorded for posterity on the sculpted door of Sant Iu in Barcelona Cathedral.

The Green Dragon of Longwitton

In the grounds of Longwitton Hall, near Rothbury, Northumberland were three wells. They were known for miles around, on account of the medicinal properties of the water. They were the scene of a midsummer-festival, when people assembled to drink the miraculous waters.

One day, a ploughman, weary from toil, came to the wells to sup. To his horror, he discovered a gigantic, green, dragon, with its long whip-like tail coiled about one of the wells. It was lapping the water from another well, with its long, black, forked-tongue, in the manner that a dog laps at a bowl of water.

Upon seeing the man, the creature seemed to melt from sight before his eyes. The terrified ploughman knew that the monster was still present, and watching him due to the rhythmic-hiss of its breathing. Shaking - as if struck with the palsy - he fled home.

Soon word of the dragon got about. A few people claimed to have seen it, but mostly it stayed in its invisible state - betrayed only by its sibilant breath and the heat of its flames. Unlike many of its peers, The Longwitton Dragon did not deal wholesale destruction to the area, but stayed by the wells. It barred all who came to drink at them, guarding the water as other dragons guarded treasure.

Finally, a wandering knight happened into Longwitton. He was none other than Sir Guy of Warwick; a redoubtable champion, who had slain many giants and monsters throughout England and The Holy-Land. Sir Guy listened to the local people's pleas, and rode out to fight the dragon.

Guy had a great advantage. He was carrying with him some magickal eye-ointment that had been given to him by a wizard. Once rubbed into the eyes, it rendered all *invisible* things *visible*.

Guy could plainly see the dragon lying next to the wells. It was a formidable beast - larger than the greatest elephant that he had seen in The Holy-Land. It was covered in iridescent green scales, punctuated by toad-like poison-glands. The leather-wings were folded against its body, and its elongate tail coiled off into the shadows. The huge head bore a great crest or fin, and the jaws were liberally furnished with ivory-daggers. Between these teeth, a livid green venom trickled, (doubtless having its genesis in the twin venom-sacs that hung below the dragon's jaws). Its green, glowing eyes, flickered, and the smoky-nostrils twitched at Guy's approach.

With a supreme effort Guy stayed calm. He wanted the dragon to *think* that it was still invisible to him, and catch the fiend off-guard. Rearing onto its hind-legs - like an immeasurable bird - the dragon dashed forward. But Guy was ready, and whirled his horse about, and charged. He aimed his lance at the dragon's flank, but the 15-foot weapon glanced off the diamond-hard scales. the dragon seized the lance in one of its clawed forelegs, and snapped it like a reed. The toothy-head flashed down, and only Guy's shield saved him from the dragon's razor-fangs. Drawing his sword, he slashed at the head, but the scales turned his blade back. Again the dragon lunged - jaws agape. This time, Guy parried and hacked at the dangling venom-sacs. He slashed one open - releasing a gout of smouldering green poison. But - to his horror - the wound healed before his eyes. The flesh grew back into place in seconds. Guy pulled back, knowing that he was outclassed. As he retreated, the dragon breathed a great cone of flame - blistering his flesh beneath the armour.

Guy and his steed staggered back to the village defeated. But he was a man of honour, and promised the villagers that he would face the beast again the next day. After rest, recuperation and the dressing of his wounds, he returned to his foe.

This time the dragon was ready, and charged forward snorting flames. Guy hurled a spear at the crested head, and it lodged in one of the flaming-nostrils. As his nemesis shook its head in irritation, Guy rode around it, and swiped at the toad-like growths that sprouted in rows between the scales. His blade tore them. and more of the evil green liquid ran in rills down the monster's side. But once again, the wounds closed like the mouths of monks. The dragon swatted the knight aside like a fly with one of its massive wings, as it plucked the spear from its snout. The ghastly head - larger than a flour barrel - struck out, and snapped-up the knight. Fangs pierced armour, and the dragon shook Guy like a terrier worrying a rat. It then contemptuously threw him aside, and returned to the well.

This time, Guy *crawled* back to the village. Despite the protests of the worried peasants, he vowed to finish his task the next day.

Despite both man and horse being much the worse-for-wear, the pair rode out for a third time. Guy was cautious this time and watched the dragon from afar. He noticed that it always kept the tip of its tail in one of the wells. He then remembered the curative powers of the well, and realized that *this* was the source of The dragon's self-healing power. Guy formed a plan.

He galloped towards the wells shouting his challenge to the monster. Enraged, it reared up releasing a blast of flame. Guy and his steed, (a veteran of battle), stayed just beyond the reach of the flames, but Guy let out a scream as if he had been injured. Another blast followed. Again, the knight was *just* out of range - but yelled in mock agony. He slumped in his saddle - as if mortally-wounded - his horse *seemed* lame and slow. Bellowing in triumph, The dragon reared up, and bounded forwards - reckless in its bloodlust. Sure enough, the end of the tail was drawn *clear* of the well.

As the beast bent to swallow, the rider plunged his blade through the attacker's throat. As it withdrew - gurgling horribly - he spun his horse about so that it was between the dragon and the well. Dodging the flailing claws, he rode between its legs, and jabbed the poison dripping warts on the monster's belly. Caught by surprise, the creature staggered to one side and fell. Its massive tail whipped around, and slashed horse and rider repeatedly. Guy backed away to a safe distance and drew his bow. As the beast regained its feet he sent an arrow through its eye and into the brain. The brute collapsed. Even as he watched, Guy saw the huge body begin to dissolve, (as if eaten away by acid). Soon, nothing was left, but a smoking, oily pool, seeping into the ground. But eventually, the water of the wells quenched the acrid-slime.

Mythology aside, could anything *resembling* these horrors from mankind's past, actually exist? The true-dragon or firedrake, is the most elusive and rarely reported of modern dragons, but they still raise their scaly-heads from time to time.

One such creature was encountered by Captain W H Bartlett, Second Officer Joseph Ostens Grey, and the crew of the cargo steamer *Tresco,* on May 30th 1903. The ship had left Philadelphia two days earlier. Ninety miles off Cape Hatteras, the water became disturbed and oily. A group of forty sharks passed the ship, and looked as if they were fleeing some unseen pursuer. About an hour later, what was at *first* thought to be a wreck, came into view. As the *Tresco* drew closer, a frightful head on a long-neck - *"as thick a cathedral pillar"* – rose-up. The beast resembled nothing so much as a dragon from a medieval-bestiary. It was some hundred-feet long, and about eight-feet wide in the middle, where the body thickened. Two fan-like wings grew from the sides of the body, and it was covered by large, oval scales the colour of greening antique bronze. Second Officer Grey takes up the story:

"There was something unspeakably loathsome about the head, which was five feet long from nose to upper extrem-ity. Such a head I never saw on any denizen of the sea...Underneath the jaw seemed to be a sort of pouch, or drooping skin... The nose, like a snout upturned, was somewhat recurved... I can remember seeing no nostrils or blow-holes. The lower jaw was prognathous, and the lower lip was half projecting, half pendulous. Presently I no-ticed something dripping from the ugly lower jaw. Watching I saw it was saliva, of a dirty drab colour... While it displayed no teeth, it did possess very long and formidable molars, like a walrus's tusks... It's eyes were of a red-dish colour... They were elongated vertically... They carried in their dull depths a sombre baleful glow, as if within them was concentrated all the fierce menacing spirit that raged in the huge bulk behind."

The dragon thrashed the water with its tail, but did not attack. Presently, it turned and made off having thoroughly terrified everyone on board.

THE WYVERN

The Wyvern resembles the true-dragon in many ways. It is a reptilian, winged monster that brings death and destruction. It fulfils the same roll in legends as its relative - a guardian of treasure, and an obstacle to be defeated by a hero. The main difference between the two creatures, is that the Wyvern bears only two legs, as opposed to the dragon's *four* legs. Many wyverns sport scorpion-like stings in their tails. They have a bat's wings, and a snake-like head and neck. The legs are eagle-like, with curved-talons. The head is often furnished with horns or a crest.

Wyverns were believed to be disease vectors, spreading pestilence wherever they appeared. Plague outbreaks and illnesses of both humans and livestock were blamed upon them. *Some* wyverns breathed fire in the fashion of true-dragons. Others spewed forth a noxious poison-gas.

On the whole, they seem to be smaller than firedrakes, and lacked many of their magickal powers. Despite this they were formidable monsters in their own right and were the terror of medieval Europe.

The Horror of Cynwch lake

Cynwch lake was a mile-long body of water that lay beneath the shadow of the mountain, Moel Offrun in Clwyd, north Wales. This tranquil spot was disturbed one day when a wyvern took up residence in the lake. Death had come to Cynwch.

It was an appalling beast with an undulating neck and a humped back. It had two clawed-legs, and a pair of wings, but it neither walked nor flew. It moved in a jerking, humping, slither that was appalling to behold. It crawled like a vast caterpillar across the slopes of Moel Offrun, its body oozing a rank slime as it went. It would come heaving out of the lake and slither along the shores looking for prey. It was easy to tell were the wyvern had been due to the trail of gelatinous-slime it left behind it like some demonic slug.

The creature's breath was a billowing-cloud of green gas. So toxic was this, that the wyvern could overpower and kill the largest horse or bull with one jet. In its predatory forays, the wyvern took both livestock *and* their owners. What it did not eat, it left in contorted-death with its sickening-vapour.

A local warlock - The Wizard of Ganllwyd - decided that the menace should be dealt with. In past attempts, all who had challenged it in single-combat were soon overcome by its breath, and fell dead! The wizard reasoned that The Monster must be tackled from a distance. He hired archers with mighty longbows to riddle the wyvern with arrows. But their quarry seemed to have some sixth-sense, and when the bowmen were present it never appeared.

And so it went on - fruitless hunts, and further depredations. One day - when the archers were not in the area - the wyvern slithered from the lake to bask in the sunshine. It slithered far from the shore, and stretched itself out amidst the heather. It so happened that a young shepherd-boy called 'Meredydd', was moving his depleted-flock to pastures further away from the lake. in the hope of saving them from the wyvern. When he stumbled across the sleeping fiend sprawled-out like a lazy cat, his blood ran cold. He could hear its hissing breath, see greenish-vapour twisting-up from its nostrils, and observe the body rise and fall as it glistened like wet leather in the sunlight.

The boy kept his nerve, and realised that the creature's carelessness had given him an opportunity to rid his community of the peril. He ran – frantically - the two miles to Cymmer Abbey and told the monks of his discovery. He asked to borrow the magickal-axe kept there to wield against the slumbering-terror. The monks lost no time in agreeing to his request, and he hurried back to the spot - praying that the beast had not awoken.

Lady Luck was with Meredydd, and the wyvern still slept. Creeping closer, he approached upwind of the monster, so that the foul vapours from its nostrils were blown away from him. Hefting the huge two-handed axe above his head, he swung it down with every ounce of strength that he could muster, against the slimy neck. The axe cleft the loathy-head from the body. Meredydd leapt back as black blood fountained out, searing the heather. The head let out a shrill shriek, and the jaws snapped impotently. The body thrashed and convulsed like a headless-chicken, showering the surrounding vegetation with its corrosive vital-juices. Gradually, the thrashing became twitching, and finally the thing lay still. The wyvern of Cynwch had been defeated - *not* by a knight's sword or a wizard's spells - but by the luck and bravery of a lowly shepherd lad.

The deserts of the southern United-States are about as different as you can get to the soggy, cold-climes of Medieval-Europe. But it was *here* - in the mid 1970s - that a wyvern-like creature - dubbed *the Big-Bird* - terrorized the Rio-Grande valley, for a period of several months. Perhaps the most startling encounter, took place at 10.30 pm on January 14 1976. Perhaps Armando Grimaldo had heard of the *Big-Bird* sightings, of the mutilated-livestock. If he had, then he probably did not believe them. Had he done so, then he would not have been sitting alone outside after dark. He had come to visit his estranged wife - Christina - at her mother's house. Whilst Christina slept inside, Armando sat in his mother-in-law's back yard. He vividly remembers what happened next.

I heard a sound like the flapping of bat-like wings, and a funny kind of whistling. The dogs in the neighbourhood started barking. I looked around but I couldn't see nothing. I don't know why I never looked up. I guess I should have, but as I was turning to go look over on the other side of the house, I felt something grab me, something with big claws. I looked back and saw it and started running. I've never been scared of nothing before but this time I really was. That was the most scared I've ever been in my whole life.

Armando made it to a tree in the yard, and hid beneath it. His attacker flapped away into the night. Awakened by his frantic-screams, Christina flung open the back-door as her husband collapsed in, and hysterically told her that he had been attacked by 'something from the sky'. By the time that The Police arrived, Armando was in such a state of shock that he could only mumble one word - *pajaro* - the Spanish for 'bird'.

As he recovered, Armando gave the police a description of the thing that had attacked him. It had huge bat-like wings, featherless, leathery skin, a muzzle full of sharp teeth, hooked-talons, and malevolent eyes that glowed red in the dark. Armando had escaped with nothing more than a ripped shirt and – doubtless - some weeks of bad-dreams.

▶ *Early depictions of wyverns can be found on this 11th century tympanum (door mantle) at St. Lawrence Church, Wynford Eagle, Dorset, England.*

THE WYRM OR LINDORM

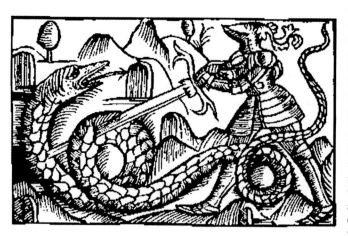

This creature must challenge The Fire-drake as one of the most widespread of dragonkind. The wyrm is essentially a gigantic-snake of mind boggling dimensions. In Scandinavia, it was believed that lindorms, (as they were known there), grew from ordinary-snakes. As the snake grew beyond the norm, it took to dwelling in lakes. The growth of a lindorm never stopped but continued throughout its lifespan - which unless slain - was virtually indefinite. As the lindorm reached truly *fantastic* proportions it would eschew its lake for the open-sea and become a sea-serpent. Finally, its coils would become so vast, that they would drag it to the sea-bed under its own weight. In Norse-Mythology, the greatest of these serpents was the *Jormungandr* or Midgard-Serpent. This lindorm was *so* huge, that it encircled the whole-world in its coils, and needed Thor - The God of Thunder - to finally put paid to it. Vast serpents were the adversaries of many gods in many cultures.

The breath of the wyrm was poison gas rather than fire. They often possessed hypnotic-powers and the ability to rejoin severed-sections of their bodies. The *most* dangerous weapon in the wyrm's arsenal however was is steely, constricting coils. These could squeeze the life out of an elephant or hug the sides of a hill with such force they would leave their imprint there for centuries afterwards.

Back in Scandinavia – lindorms were believed to encircle churches in their coils, and crush them. This seems to hearken back to true dragon as an ancient pagan symbol. Here too, we find another fascinating piece of wyrm-folklore. Towns menaced by a lindorm would often breed a gigantic-bull of unnatural size and strength, that would be sent out to fight the lindorm. Goring with its horns, and stamping with its hooves – whilst its foe bit and constricted with its coils - the fight usually ended in the death of both combatants. This has several interesting modern day analogues. Some of the colossal-snakes in South America (which we shall examine in-depth in Chapter Three), are known as *mano toro* or the 'Killers of Bulls', due to their habit of feeding on steers.

A copy of the journal *The Field*, ran a story in the mid 19th Century of a remarkable combat between an American alligator *(Alligator mississipiensis)*, and a group of domestic bulls. The 'gator had sized a bull by the snout, causing the animal to bellow in fear. Several other bulls came to its aid, and began goring and trampling the attacker. The alligator lashed out with its tail and jaws. Finally the alligator lay dead. But all about it lay the bulls - legs shattered and snouts ripped. Accounts like these strengthen the idea that some legends *may* have a basis in the truth.

The Wyrm of Loschy Hill.

On the wooded hill of Loschy - near The Parish of Stonegrave, north Yorkshire, there dwelt a wyrm. It lay coiled about the hill, still as death mostly, but every so often it would uncoil and slither down the hill - like a river of quicksilver - to hunt in the surrounding countryside. It's bite was as lethal as a thousand adders, causing its victims to swell and bloat in their death agonies. Men feared its coils even more, for once in its tenacious grip even the greatest of beasts would soon be reduced to little more than a skin-bag full of shattered bone. Warriors - lucky or skilful enough to avoid its fangs and coils - invariably failed to slay it. For, if the beast was hacked in two - the halves would merely join back together once more - leaving the creature intact.

The wyrm's 'reign of terror' reached the ears of Sir Peter Loschy - a famous knight who vowed to lay low the beast that haunted his namesake hill. Loschy was an artful and a well read man. He knew of other dragon-slayers before him, and of the tricks that some of them had employed to gain victory over their stronger foes. Loschy had his blacksmith weld razor-blades all about his suit-of-armour, (as other knights had done before combat with a wyrm). He then rode with confidence to the hill, dismounted, and sought the wyrm.

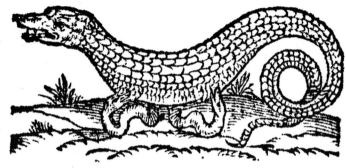

Twilight had drawn-in, and the hill was bathed in an eerie violet light. Strands of mist began clawing up from the damp-earth, and twisted around the trees like vaporous-fingers. The nightjars began their churring, as the knight thrust deeper into the wooded-hill. Here and there, Sir Peter saw great-furrows in the vegetation, where the wyrm had crawled. The tracks were as wide as an ale-keg.

Suddenly, the nightjars ceased their chorus and a musky smell crept into the air. Beneath his helmet Sir Peter felt the hairs on his neck rise. Then he heard the dragging, crashing, sound of the thing's *huge* body as it hurtled through the undergrowth towards him. Spinning around, he caught a brief glimpse of the wyrm as it bore down on him. It had scales like tarnished bronze, glowing orange spheres for eyes, shark-like teeth in a head as broad as his shoulders. Before he could raise his blade, the wyrm had whipped several loops of its body around him and began to tighten them.

As the wyrm squeezed, its own massive muscularity forced the razors through its scales and into its body. The coils slackened, and the beast retreated - rills of inky blood trickling from dozens of puncture-marks in its flank. As Sir Peter watched, the wounds miraculously closed - healing within seconds. To his horror, the serpent turned again, and rushed *back* at him. Once more, the powerful body encircled him. Once more, the razors bit deep, forcing the reptile to retreat. But its wounds healed *almost* as soon as they were made.

Peter staggered out of the woods, and crawled onto his horse. It was a stalemate! Neither foe seemed able to harm the other. He rode home, and spent a sleepless-night poring over his books. The next day he returned, not with his horse but with his favourite hunting-dog - a noble and intelligent beast who would face the largest boar.

This time he reckoned to have the element of surprise, and slipped through the forested-slopes as quietly as his spiky armour allowed. He found the terror coiled about a rocky-outcrop. Before it could rear its venom-dripping jaws, he swung his broadsword, and hacked off a section of the serpent's tail. Instantly, Sir Peter's hound snatched up the wriggling section and ran away with it. Fleet as a hare the dog ran until it was out of The Wyrm's reach, then dropped his loathsome burden.

Meantime, the Knight parried the wyrm's snapping-jaws and sliced *another* section from the body. The dog dashed in and dodging the beast's maw, seized the second section. Again, he carried his gruesome-trophy away, and dropped it in the bushes.

And so it was. *Master* hewing away at the wyrm's coils, and *hound* disposing of them. Soon, the bushes were writhing with pieces of wyrm-flesh, and the beast itself was little more than a head! Finally, the lurid glare of the eyes flickered and died, and the snapping jaws lay agape in mute death.

Catching his breath, Sir Peter turned to his trusty ally and bent to congratulate him. The dog licked his master's face as he had done countless times before. This time, however, his tongue was caked with the wyrm's blood. Un-knowingly the brave animal transferred some of the poison to his master. When farmers and villagers dared to steal up the hill next day, they found the knight and his best friend lying dead beside each other.

In Thailand, a creature very like the lindorm is reported right up to the present-day. It is known as the naga. In the year 2000, I travelled through Thailand in search of the naga. On my expedition, I interviewed many eyewitnesses. The most impressive was a sighting that occurred around 1990 at close-quarters, around a mile beneath the ground!

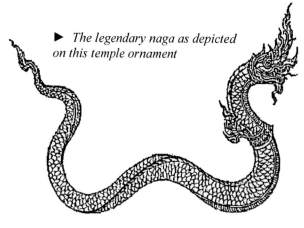

▶ *The legendary naga as depicted on this temple ornament*

Mr Pimpa Suvakhun - an elderly man from a remote village in the jungles north of Nong Khai - took me to the spot of his encounter some ten-years earlier. A modest entrance led to an antechamber, and on to the strangest place that I have ever been. By candlelight Pimpa led me through a network of labyrinthine-tunnels. My guide told me that they went on for almost ten miles beneath the jungle-swathed mountains. Mostly we were bent-double in the cramped passages. Sometimes we were compelled to go on all-fours or *even* to crawl like snakes on our bellies through the primal-slime. Where the passages widened, we passed fantastical rock-formations - some like Greek-pillars, others like outlandish guillotines. All were festooned with wreathes of jasmine - in honour of the sacred serpent.

Finally we came upon a tunnel through which an underground-river flowed. I estimated that we were about a mile beneath the surface. Mr Suvakhun related how he had been exploring these caves some ten-years previously. Upon turning into this particular cavern, he was horrified to see an immense-snake crawling *out* of the water and into another channel. The head was hidden in the shadows, but the visible-portion of the body was 18 metres, (60 feet) long! I asked him how thick the snake had been. The old man indicated that its height from the ground had been almost three feet - giving the naga a girth as large as an oil drum! Pimpa shrunk back against the wall - paralysed with terror - as the gigantic-reptile slithered past him with agonizing-slowness. Its scales were clearly visible - black with a green, iridescent sheen.

In the shadows, Pimpa's hand fell upon something. After the massive animal had disappeared, he looked at it. It was a semi-precious stone. Upon his return to the surface he had the stone mounted on a naga-shaped ring - and he wears it to this day. Despite the fear he had felt upon seeing the naga, Mr Suvakhun believed that the monster had brought him luck. Prior to his adventure he had been poor, and hardly able to feed his family. Soon afterwards, however, he was given some land and now is a successful farmer.

I met others with similar stories to tell, and later in this book we return to Thailand, discover more evidence and eventually come to a conclusion on the nature of the naga and giant snakes worldwide.

THE BASILISK OR COCKATRICE

Of all dragonkind, the basilisk is probably the most arcane. Its genesis involved a series of events so unlikely that, (luckily for man), they conspired only rarely to create one of these baleful monsters. It was believed that occasionally - in old age - a rooster could lay an egg! If such an uncommon-egg were to be incubated by a snake or toad, then a basilisk would hatch out - to bring death into the world!

The basilisk is one of the smallest of the dragon-tribe but one of the most lethal! Its death-dealing powers came *not* from fiery-breath or tooth and claw but from its withering-glare. Any creature that caught the eyes of the basilisk, would fall dead from the uncanny-power of its vision. There was but one exception to this - one animal that could withstand this 'look of death'. That animal was the weasel! It was believed that God never created a bane, without creating *some* cure for it, (like the stinging-nettle and the dock-leaf). Ergo, even the basilisk could be tackled by someone who *knew* its weaknesses. The monster's own gaze was as lethal to itself as to any other creature. Hence, its *own* reflection would kill it stone-dead! Equally - for some cryptic-reason - the sound of a cock-crowing at dawn would also kill The Basilisk.

These monsters came in a variety of shapes. They first appeared in the bestiaries of the Dark-Ages. It was described as a tiny-serpent about a foot in length, bearing a crown or crest upon its head to denote it as The King of Serpents. The deserts of North Africa and the Middle East were reputed to have been created by basilisks, whose glare was *so* terrible that all vegetation withered under it, and even solid rocks were split and sundered into sand.

Later reports of basilisks came in from Europe. As the centuries passed, the basilisk's form changed. Sometimes it was portrayed as a lizard with a rooster's head, or as a large lizard with six legs and a crown upon its head. The commonest form that these later basilisks took, was that of a huge-rooster with the tail of a serpent or a lizard. Sometimes these beasts sported horns or antlers. In *this* form they were known as the cockatrice.

The Basilisk of Saffron-Walden

No-one knew where the basilisk had come from. The repulsive-bane just *appeared* one day, close to the Essex town of Saffron-Walden. Perhaps it had travelled back un-noticed amidst the luggage of some knight, returning from The Crusades? Maybe it had been brought back as an egg by some innocent fool who believed it to have been lain by some exotic bird. It could *even* have hatched out on some remote-farm, and killed the landowner before he could send warning to the town.

It mattered little, for now the thing had the town under siege. No-one dared wander beyond the town's outskirts. Few had seen the beast and lived. The ones that had done so described it as being but a tiny serpent, not more than a foot long. It was black and yellow in colour, with glowing red eyes and a sharp beak. Its head was adorned with white-spots arranged like a crown.

Despite its diminutive stature, the basilisk had done as much damage to the surrounding countryside as any plague or army. Its lethal eyes could strike a man down from a mile distant. They blackened the grass and withered the trees. Every living thing coming within its sight perished. Even *rocks* were split in twain - as if struck by lightning - when the basilisk's eyes fell upon them.

Killing the monster seemed impossible. Few could get *near* to it without it seeing them, and striking them dead. One man had caught the terror as it slumbered and struck it with a spear. But *so* deadly was the Basilisk's venom, that it leapt up the shaft of the weapon, and killed the man - leaving the monster relatively unscathed.

The townsfolk were held hostage by the serpent, until a wandering-knight, (whose name history does not recall), happened into town. Upon asking about the strange state of affairs, the locals told him their sorry tale, and in-formed him how lucky he was to have arrived unseen by their foul nemesis. The knight felt it his duty to help, but was at a loss as to how to tackle such a powerful foe, but he knew that his *greatest* weapon was *not* the sword, *nor* the mace, but his wits.

He took some humble-lodgings at a tavern in the town, and that night he paced his room like a caged-lion, racking his brains for a way to get close enough to the basilisk so that he could destroy it. Come the morning, he strode confidently from his inn. He visited the smithy and asked the blacksmith to join him in a drink. Likewise he visited the glassblower, and extended the same invitation.

As the three men sat about a table in the inn drinking what little was left of a substandard-ale, The Knight ex-plained his plan. He bade the glassblower to create for him many small mirrors. He asked the blacksmith to fasten these to all parts of his armour. Thus, he was encircled in mirrors, and should the basilisk gaze upon him, it would find its own lethal eyes burning back at it many times over.

The knight strode out in his crazy suit-of-mirrors. Like a living-crystal, he threw rainbow-arcs as he moved. Crowds of people gathered, as their shining-saviour strode out into the desolation.

His rainbow-nimbus brought the first colour to the countryside in months. It had seemed that the basilisk had drained off the colour as well as the life! The twisted dead-trees, the split rocks, the dry grass; *all* were shades of a bleak-grey. Bodies of men and beasts littered the road. A travelling-apothecary and his mule, a band of gypsies, a priest; *all* with the same mute horror on their dead-faces. None of the bodies were rotting - even *flies* died under the basilisk's eyes.

Finally, he came upon a tiny, ruined chapel, door sundered and windows gaping, glassless - like eye-sockets. At his approach, something stirred in the shadows. There was a dry rustling, like dead leaves. A shape was peeling itself from the darkness; it came slithering closer. A snake of diminutive proportions crawled into view. In lieu of jaws it had a bird-like beak, and was striped in black and gold, like some exotic serpent of the Far-East. Its eyes began to glow with some self-created light, bathing the chapel in a ruddy lustre.

The Knight snapped his own eyes shut, and desperately fought the urge to turn and flee. Suddenly, the air was rent by a strangled scream - almost like that of a child - accompanied by a violent thrashing sound. Full ten minutes *after* the sounds ceased, the knight finally opened his eyes. There it lay. It was astounding that so little a creature could have brought so much death and pestilence. Barely a foot long - it was now a weak and limp little thing.

Thus, it came to pass that the knight's cunning had delivered the people of Saffron-Walden from the basilisk. To commemorate the great deed, brass effigies of the basilisk were made, and, together with a tablet retelling the saga, were displayed in the town's church until the time of The Civil War.

From the 1930s to as recently as the 1980s, basilisk-like creatures have been reported in Italy. These include a eight foot green and yellow "dragon" seen near Montrose - north of Rome in 1935. One local man claimed to have seen it every ten to fifteen years since he had been a boy. Near to the town of Flori, a farmer reported being chased by a fifteen-foot lizard with searing-hot breath. The beast chased him for two-hundred yards, as he ran for his life - its searing exhalation at his heels. In 1975 at Goro a farmer hoeing tomatoes, came upon a ten-foot long, snake-like lizard, as thick in girth as a dog. When he returned with the police, the beast was gone but its tracks were clearly visible. Thankfully, these modern day basilisks seem to lack the death-dealing attributes of their legendary for-bears.

THE AMPHIPTERE

The amphipteres were legless winged-serpents. They could range in size from around one foot long, to *gigantic* beasts that dwarfed the greatest pythons. In Egypt they could be found along the banks of the Nile, guarding frankincense trees. Even the *smaller* amphipteres were dangerous as they had a lethally venomous bite. The ibis bird was believed to be the chief enemy of the smaller kinds of winged-serpents, and often devoured them. These birds were said to have been tamed, and used to destroy infestations of amphipteres.

Wales was home to many of the larger variety. Here they were known as 'gwibers' and legends of them in Wales actually out-number the more familiar type of dragon that we see even today on the Welsh flag. The Welsh had some strange folklore pertaining to the genesis of the gwiber. It was believed that serpents loved milk, and would - given the chance - suckle from cows. Women's milk was favoured even more, but if a serpent drank the milk of a *woman*, it would grow into a gwiber. Nursing-women had to be careful not to let any of their milk fall to the floor where a snake might lap it up, or to fall asleep on the ground where a snake might reach their breasts.

Another strange quirk of Welsh gwiber tales, is that they are *never* killed by a knight or any sort of nobleman. It is *always* a shepherd, farm-hand or some other peasant-lad who puts paid to the gwiber with his wits.

The Gwiber's Curse

There was much cause for celebration at the great house in Penmynydd, Clwyd. A son and heir had been born to the aristocratic family, and a banquet was to be held in the child's honour. All the gentry and the richest merchants in the county were in attendance, and the finest fare and sweetest ale put strain on the enormous tables in the great hall.

But not *all* guests were noblemen or merchants. One of the most venerated men there on that fateful night, was a wizard! As was the custom, the mage had been invited in order to perform a divination - to look into the future, and to predict the child's fate. The grey-skinned, wizened, old man sat hunched in a corner - slurping ale through his silver beard - and gnawing at a leg of honeyed-mutton.

When the time of the divination came, he rose to his feet and strode into the centre of the room. He was an imposing figure - well over six feet tall - and with pallid, lupine eyes. His purple robes rustled as he reached into their folds, and produced a calf-skin sack. From the sack he took a bowl - carved from jet - a number of bottles, and a beeswax candle.

He poured water into the bowl, followed by what looked like ink. Then he lit the candle, sat cross-legged before the bowl, and stared intently at the swirling shapes in the water. Presently, he took up the candle and began to drip the molten wax into the inky-water.

A worried look stole across his face - visible *even* under his flowing whiskers. Finally, he took up the bowl, and tossed the contents into the fire. The burning logs spat like wildcats, and the flames guttered.

"What have you seen, Wizard?" bellowed the child's father, in concern and anger.

"Your son shall never reach manhood! He will die from a gwiber's bite," replied the Sorcerer. Then, he swung his cloak about him, and strode through the doorway, leaving a confused and worried audience behind him.

The family were angered, but they knew better than to doubt the words of a wizard. What could they do? How does one go about cheating fate? Presently, a plan stole into the mind of the father. The gwiber, (and other dragons), were now uncommon in Wales, and so he had been told, (erroneously), extinct in England. So it was, that with some regret, he sent the boy to be raised by relatives in the land of their ancestral foes.

It was some years later that a gwiber raised its head in the county. It had appeared on a remote farm, perhaps unwittingly suckled by the farmer's buxom wife, and grown fat upon her milk. The monster killed and ate the farmer, his wife, his children, and his livestock. It made its lair in the now empty farmhouse, and made expeditions upon its leathery-pinions into the surrounding country in search of more prey.

News of this quickly reached aristocratic ears, and a price was put upon the gwiber's scaly head. The child's parents realized that this beast - here on their doorstep - must be the monster of The Wizard's prophecy. If it could be killed, then their son could return to Wales and take up his rightful title.

Many warriors tried. All fell venom-bloated to the dust, chain-mail or breast-plate riddled with puncture-marks. It fast became apparent that The Gwiber could not be defeated by mere   force.

Many of these confrontations had been watched by a teenaged farm-hand - with dreams of grandeur - who had slipped into some nearby woods. He noticed that when - unmolested by would-be heroes - The gwiber was a creature of habit. It flew from its lair early each morn to hunt, and it returned before nightfall. Upon its return, the monster - fat from the flesh of its victims - would crawl rather than fly. A trough had been ploughed through the dirt where it had slithered.

By and by, the bright lad formulated an artful plan. First, he borrowed his mother's great brass-pan, and polished it until its surface reflected like a mirror. Then, he took his father's finest spade, and dug a pit across the gwiber's track. He laboured hard for hours until he had excavated a deep hole. He then lowered the polished pan into the hole. Gathering branches, leaves and grass, he covered the pit the best he could. Taking the spade home he swapped it for the great axe that his father used for hewing trees in the forest. He returned to the farm, ensconced himself in some bushes, and waited.

He heard his foe before he saw it. A loathsome, ponderous dragging-sound, like a massive, heavily-loaded sack, being dragged along the ground. The noise made his hackles rise, and he found himself in a cold-sweat. Soon the thing hove into view. First, the furtive snake-head, fork-tongue flickering, jerking side-to-side, eyes like globes of gold-fire. Then, the elongate body, coiling horizontally, gorged on human gore, and patterned in black-and-grey diamonds. The bat-wings were folded against its sides.

It seemed to hesitate at the rim of the pit. The boy watched for agonizing moments before the gwiber heaved its way onto the frail covering. With a crash it pitched downwards into the hole. Hissing in surprise, the gwiber was confronted in the pit by another gwiber. It was obviously a rival, seeking to drive it from its lair, and from the good hunting-grounds. The enraged serpent struck, its poison festooned fangs piercing copper. But the rival was still alive and rampant. Again and again the gwiber's head flashed out to bite at its enemy. Again and again the foe endured. In a frenzy, The Monster unleashed a Berserker-fury at its own reflection in the brass pan until it was blackened by venom, warped by strikes, and riddled with fang-marks. Finally, the gwiber saw its rival's image no more, and ceased – exhausted - from the fight.

The boy waited, as silence reigned for several minutes, before creeping to the edge of the pit. The serpent lay prone, its venom and energy spent. Uttering a prayer under his breath, he leapt down into the pit. Hoisting up the great axe, he swung it down onto the gwiber's neck. The body shuddered weakly, and the scales rasped, the head rolled away - the golden-glow in the hypnotic-eyes fading.

And so it came to pass, that the boy made his fortune. His fiscal reward lifted his social status and secured him for life. He married the prettiest girl in the village, and lived happily ever after. But the tale of the gwiber's curse does not end there.

As the news of the county's deliverance spread, The lord and lady of the great house in Penmynydd, sent for their long-banished son. The boy had grown into an arrogant, spoiled teenager. Upon his arrival back in Penmynydd, the first thing that he demanded, was to see the carcass of his fallen nemesis. He was shown the skeleton of the monster that had been saved for posterity. Sneering and gloating at his "victory", the youth took a kick at the gwiber's skull. One of its six-inch fangs sliced through the leather of the boy's boot. Dried venom still clung to the dead-fang, as it plunged into his foot. He died, screaming in agony, a few days later. The Wizard's prophecy had been fulfilled.

The smaller kind of gwiber seems to have lingered on in Wales, well into the 'Age of Enlightenment'. Indeed, in one area they were so common, that they were looked on as no more remarkable than foxes. Folklorist Ruth Tongue, interviewed many old people from the Glamorgan area of Wales, at the end of the 19th century. All could remember small, brightly coloured winged-serpents. The creatures had exquisite feathers and were remarkably beautiful, especially during flight. Despite their aesthetic appearance, the snakes were regarded as vermin. One interviewee recalled that they were worse than foxes for killing poultry, and a campaign of eradication was carried out on them. They seem to have died out in the 1850s.

One man recalled how his father and a friend, were attacked by one of these winged snakes that swooped down on them. The pair lashed out at the gwiber with a stick, and eventually succeeded in bringing it down. Another person Tongue spoke with, recalled her father shooting a specimen, and its carcass being hung in their farmhouse for decades. When her father passed on, his possessions were split-up between family members. To the lamentation of cryptozoologists everywhere, the gwiber's body was thrown away like a piece of rubbish!

THE SALAMANDER

Like the basilisk, this tiny-dragon possessed death-dealing powers out of all proportion to its size. It was no more than a foot in length, and shaped like a lizard. Its body was covered in star-shaped markings. The salamander could live in naked-flame without the *slightest* harm to itself. It was also highly poisonous - spitting a foul-foam from its mouth. This caused its victim's hair to fall out, and skin to wither, before death. The only animal immune to its venom was the pig. Pigs could eat salamanders with immunity, but if humans were to then eat the flesh of the pig, they would die - due to the venom accumulated in the swine's fat.

The power of the salamander's toxin was truly immense. Should a salamander enter a pool, the water therein would be poisoned indefinitely. Alexander the Great (356-323 BC) was said to have lost two thousand horses and four thousand soldiers, when they drank from a stream that a salamander had crawled through. It was also believed that if a salamander came into contact with wood used for a baker's fire, then the bread would be contaminated.

Another strange quirk of the salamander was that it was supposed to be able to spin itself a cocoon out of a fireproof wool-like substance. This became known as salamander's wool. This fireproof 'wool' was much sought-after. Pope Alexander III (reigned 1159-1181) was said to posses his own tunic of salamander's wool. The Byzantine Emperor, Manuel Comnenus (1120-1180), was said to have received a letter from the semi-mythical Prester John, a Priest-King who ruled over a mysterious land that some now believed to be Ethiopia. In the letter, Prester John speaks of salamanders, and how their wool is gathered and spun into cloth. When in need of a cleaning, garments made from the wool were cast into flames.

A less deadly - but equally amazing - relative of the salamander was the pyrallis. This was the very smallest of dragonkind, being no larger than a fly. It was bronze in colour, with four legs, insect-like wings, and a reptilian head. The pyrallis was found only in the copper smelting forges and foundries of Cyprus. Whole swarms of them would dance around inside the forges like living-sparks, but should they ever leave the flames, they would cool and die.

Cellini's Salamander

The year was 1505. The five year-old boy - Benvenuto Cellini (1500-1571) - who would later become the famous Renaissance silversmith and artist, was drying clothes beside the fire in his home with his father - Giovanni. Suddenly, the pair saw something moving in the flames. A tiny creature was disporting itself in the midst of the hottest part of the fire. It resembled a small-lizard with queer star-like shapes along its sides. The flames had no effect on the animal at all, and it scurried about on the way that a normal lizard would run up-and-down a wall.

Benvenuto's father called over to his sister, and pointed out the creature to her. Then he smacked his son's ear causing the boy to cry, and said:

"My dear little son, I did not give you that blow on account of anything you have done wrong, but only that you may remember that the lizard you saw in the fire is a salamander, a creature that has never been seen by anyone else of whom we have reliable information".

Unique among the beasts I will study in this book, the salamander has been accepted by mainstream-science and its remarkable-powers explained. Salamanders exist. They belong to a group of tailed-amphibians, (*not* lizards, which are reptiles), of the order *Caudata*. They are distributed worldwide (with the exception of sub-Saharan Africa, and Antarctica). Some are mildly poisonous, and display the fact with bright-colours to deter predators. But none of them have the lethal-venom attributed to them in medieval times. Salamanders often lurk inside damp logs and this may account for their firewalking powers. If such a log were tossed upon a fire the little animals would emerge and try to crawl to safety. As a damp log would not burn quickly most salamanders probably managed to escape the flames. As for the salamander's wool - it sounds very much like asbestos. The symptoms of salamander poisoning - withering of skin and loss of hair - sound very like asbestos poisoning. How this was first linked with the salamander is still unclear.

It hardly needs pointing out that if one type of legendary-dragon can have a basis in fact then so can others. Legends do not suddenly spring into being. Most have a core of truth at their centre.

THE AMPHISBAENA

This freakish-reptile resembled a small snake - with one notable exception; it bore two heads. These twin-heads did not both spring from the neck - side by side - but were rather at opposite ends of the animal. One head was in the regular place, the other sprung from the end of the amphisbaena's tail.

The amphisbaena could move very quickly in either direction, and at any given time at least one of the heads was awake. When one head slept, the other kept vigil over it. Ergo the amphisbaena was almost impossible to surprise. The creature could also hold onto one of its heads with the other to form a hoop-shape and roll at great speed.

The amphisbaena was venomous, and it was said that if a pregnant-woman were to step over one she would miscarry. Its skin was be-lieved to be a cure for chilblains. It dwelt in dry, sandy areas of the Old World. Something startlingly similar is reported to this very day in the militarised zone in the southern part of Mongolia, deep in the heart of the Gobi desert.

Death in the Desert

The sun was beginning to sink, when the family of nomads reached the collection of tents that was the nearest thing that passed for a town in the shifting-sands of the southern Gobi Desert. Already, the temperature was falling, as the mother and father of the family began to erect their tents and tether their camels on the outskirts of the semi-permanent village of Khanbogd. As they unpacked their belongings, they stacked several large-boxes outside their main tent. Exhausted, they fed and watered their animals, and sat down to supper with their young son. Soon they retired and fell asleep.

The boy, however, was not tired. He was excited. Khanbogd was the largest conurbation he had ever seen, and for the first time in months he would have other children to play with. He found getting to sleep hard that night, on account of his excitement.

He rose early, before his parents, and left the tent to explore. As he left the tent he noticed the boxes beside it. The lid of one of them, an ornately carved wooden chest painted bright yellow, was ajar. He wondered if someone had tried to pilfer its contents. The nomads were an honest people and theft was virtually unknown here.

Overcome by curiosity, he pushed the lid off. To his amazement some kind of animal had crawled into the box. It was like none he had seen, blood-red and worm-like in shape. It seemed to have a head at each end of the body. The creature writhed and twitched as the sun's rays fell on it. To interested to be afraid, the boy reached out and touched the creature.

When the boy didn't appear for his breakfast, his parents emerged from the tent to seek him. Their horrified eyes fell on his prostrate corpse straddling the wooden box. Crawling across his back was a grotesque, scarlet, squat, serpent that bore a head at each end of its sausage-like body. Holding his sobbing wife in his arms, the man took up a tent peg and advanced on the monster.

Shrill screams, abruptly cut off, brought several villagers rising out of their homes. They found a whole family; a man, woman, and child, lying dead about a carved yellow box. As their eyes took in the foul-sight, they noticed something worming its way into the dunes on the outskirts of the village. Something blood-red and bloated.

"Maybe it's time this village moved on," one of them muttered.

In the 1930s a group of western geologists were allowed into the Mongolian Gobi - an area that had mostly been closed to outsiders for centuries. The group had set up camp in the rocky, shifting sands. One man was prodding a sand dune with a theodolite. Suddenly he let out a horrified scream. His companions looked up to see the man thrashing and twitching as he hung onto the theodolite. His face was distorted in agony, and an acrid smell filled the air. As his friends ran over, the man collapsed like a puppet whose strings had been cut. To their horror they found that he was dead. Burn marks on his palms looked like those of an electrocution victim. It was as if he had rammed the metal theodolite straight through a power cable. But out here, in the desert, this was a ridiculous idea.

"God Almighty, look at that!" one man shouted.

They turned as one, and saw a sickening sight. A vermiform creature some five feet long, and as thick about as draught-excluder, was wriggling away over the dune. It was a gruesome blood-red in colour and looked like an animated salami. No features were visible on the thing, and it quickly buried itself in the sand. Wisely the men chose not to pursue it.

Amphisbaenas are reported today from the trackless wastes of the Gobi Desert, where the nomads call them 'death-worms' - and with good reason. They are said to spit a yellow, corrosive fluid akin to acid. Even more incredibly, The Death-worm is believed to kill with a massive electrical charge like that of an electric-eel. Many camels and some humans (including at least one Westerner), are said to have been killed in this manner.

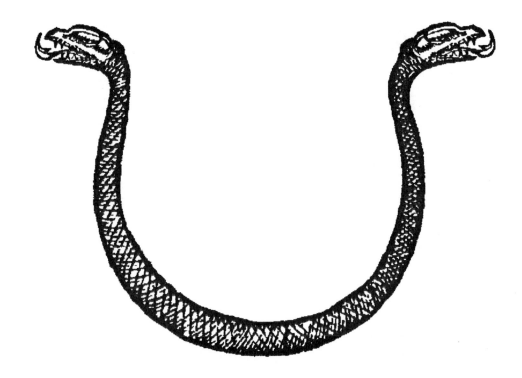

THE EASTERN DRAGON

Asia and the Orient is filled with dragons. From Ancient Persia, across the great continent into Japan in the Far-East. They differ from their western counterparts in several ways. Most importantly, they are thought of as benevolent creatures, friendly to mankind if treated with respect, in stark contrast to their European brethren. Eastern Dragons are associated more with the element of water than with that of fire. They made their lairs in deep pools, lakes, rivers, and seas. The breath of the dragon condensed to form rain. Dragons were believed to control rainfall, and the weather in general. They also controlled the seas and rivers. If offended, they could cause flooding or drought.

In China, the dragon went through a complex staged life cycle taking three-thousand years to complete. Interestingly, at various stages of their changing morphology, they resemble different kinds of western-dragon. Dragon eggs were said to resemble jewels, and when the dragons hatched from them, they looked like diminutive and unimpressive water-snakes (much like the deadly basilisk). After five hundred years, the tiny reptile would grow into a gargantuan snake with a carp-like head. In this phase the dragon was known as a *kiao* and resembled the huge lindorms of Europe. It stays like this for a further thousand years, until it develops a reptilian head and four legs. In this form it is called a *lung.* This guise lasts a further five-hundred years until the dragon grows branching-horns and becomes a *khoi-lung* - the best-known form of the Chinese dragon. Another millennium brings forth fan-like wings in the dragon's adult stage. Then it is known as a *ying-lung* or true-dragon, and resembles an ornate, elongate form of the western firedrake *also* known as the true-dragon.

The Chinese dragon's appearance was detailed by the scholar Wang Fu, (c. A.D. 78-163), of The Eastern Han Dynasty (BC206-AD220). According to his writings, the dragon possessed the head of a camel, the eyes of a daemon, the ears of a cow, the neck of a snake, the antlers of a deer, the feet of a tiger, and the claws of an eagle. Dragons generally had four claws on each foot. The exception was the imperial dragon who had five claws. Only the Emperor of China was allowed to use the iconography of *this* dragon. Anyone else who dared to use it could be put to death.

The male dragon was said to have a magickal pearl imbedded in the skin under its chin. Many serpents and dragons were believed to bear such gems in their skulls - much like the pearls in oysters.

Japanese dragons are called *tatsu.* They are similar to Chinese dragons in their looks, but bear only three claws on each foot. In Japan, dragons are not as closely linked to rainfall as their Chinese relatives. They dwell in mountains, lakes, rivers, and most importantly the sea. Dragons can control the abundance of fish and the catches of fishermen. Angry dragons can cause earthquakes, and those that live in the sea can send tsunami – giant-waves that can destroy whole towns.

Like Chinese dragons, Japanese dragon-Eggs resemble huge jewels. But unlike the lengthy life-cycle of the Chinese dragon, Japanese dragons reach adult size very quickly. They hatch from small holes in the top of the eggs and emerge as little snakes. But upon wriggling free, they grow almost instantly into gigantic dragons. One story told of a peasant boy who brought home some gems he had found near a river. They were, in fact, dragon eggs that hatched out into massive flying reptiles that smashed the roof off his house.

Later in life Japanese dragons may grow wings. These tend to be bird-like as opposed to the bat-like wings of western dragons or the fan-like wings of Chinese dragons. In this form they are called *hai riyo*.

In Indo-China, dragons tend to be identical to those in China, but are called *long* rather than lung. The exception is in Thailand that seems to share its dragonlore with India. In both countries the dragon is known as the *naga*. Nagas tend to be limbless but have the distinct eastern dragon's head. Like other Oriental dragons, they lair in water - and have control over this element. Nagas can take human form but usually retained the serpent-tail whilst in this guise. Nagas can be either good or evil.

In the Middle-East, we see a meeting of the traditions of east and west. In ancient Persia (now Iran), the dragons resembled those of China, with the exception of having feathery-wings. In their nature however, they were closer to western dragons - being savage maneaters. Old persian texts are full of dragon-slaying heroes, whose stories closely resemble the tales of their European counterparts.

The Dragon Pearl

In the province of Szechuan, central China, there was a great drought. Vegetation withered under the relentless beat of the sun. Rivers dried up, crops failed, and there was no indication that the rains would arrive.

Nie Lang was a young peasant boy - employed in the stables of the cruel and greedy Lord Zhou. Each day he was sent out with a huge wicker basket and a scythe, to cut grass for His Master's horses. Each day it became harder to find fresh-grass, and Nie Lang had to search further afield. At last, in desperation, he decided to climb Dragon Mountain, and see if there was any browse to be found on the other side.

After an arduous climb, he reached the summit and descended through the mists to the other side. Sadly, it seemed that the drought was just as severe here as it was on his side of the mountain. Suddenly, a movement caught his eye. A large, snow-white hare had emerged from behind some rocks, and sat watching him. Softly, the boy approached the animal. It seemed plump and well fed. Suddenly, it leapt to its feet, and bounded off a few paces before looking back at Nie Lang as if it wanted him to follow it.

Nie Lang followed the hare for a while until it came to a narrow valley. Here beside a ruined temple, was a luxuriant carpet of long, thick, juicy grass. The hare sat down to eat, and the boy gave the animal his thanks and cut a basket full of grass. Then he set off home, having memorized the way to the secret valley.

Next day, he returned for more grass and was amazed at what he saw. The patch of grass that he had cut on the previous day, had miraculously grown back overnight. He refilled his basket and returned home. So it was, day after day, Nie Lang trekked to the valley and cut more grass from the never-ending source.

One day Nie Lang hit upon an idea. Instead of climbing all the way up the mountain to the valley each day, he would uproot some of the grass, and plant it outside his house. That way the undwindling supply would be in easy reach. Congratulating himself on his cleverness, he did just that. But as he pulled up the turf he found a jar buried beneath it. Opening the jar he found it was full of water, and at the bottom was a large and beautiful pearl. He put the pearl in his pocket and set off home.

Later, he planted the grass beside his house, and showed the pearl to his mother. The pearl lit up the whole house with a silvery-glow. His mother hid the fabulous gem in their biggest rice-jar for safekeeping.

The next day they found that the grass had withered and died, but upon entering the kitchen they found their rice-jar overflowing with rice. The pair quickly realised that the pearl was magick.

There was far more rice than Nie Lang and his mother could eat, so the kindly boy shared his bounty with his poor neighbours. News of the pearl and its powers soon reached the ears of the evil Lord Zhou, who instantly craved it. His soldiers rode out to the boy's house and began to ransack it. They smashed crockery, and destroyed what little furniture the boy and his mother possessed. Nie Lang swallowed the pearl and ran from the men.

He was hidden by a grateful neighbour, but in the night the pearl began to burn in his stomach. He drank bowl after bowl of water. In the morning he was awakened by the sound of men approaching. This time it was not only sol-diers, but Lord Zhou himself, who came to find the pearl. As they burst into the peasant's hovel, he fled through the back-door towards the river, with the evil-lord and his men in hot pursuit.

Stumbling down the steep dry banks, he began to drink what little water there was that still feebly trickled at the bottom. As Lord Zhou and his soldiers reached the banks, they skidded to a halt, horrified at what they saw. Where Nie Lang once stood there was a gigantic-dragon. Its serpentine, electric-blue body, coiled like a river on the dusty-bed. It raised a huge head with a flowing cobalt mane, and branching antlers to gaze at the mortals with opalescent eyes the size of watermelons. Great wings like patterned-fans opened, and the huge reptile rose up in flight. Its immense mouth opened, and bolts of blue-lightning flashed from between the razor teeth.

As the dragon rose, there came a distant rumbling that grew louder with every second. Thundering down the im-poverished watercourse, there came a great torrent of water filling the river. With a casual flick of his mighty tail the dragon sent a magickal wave that swept the tyrant and his underlings down-river, and drowned them.

The skies darkened with massive thunder-heads, and lightning danced from the clouds as rain began to lash the parched-land. As the dragon that was once Nie Lang ascended to heaven, the pearl glittering beneath his scaly chin, his mother called out twenty-four times to him, and he responded to each call with a nod of his head. From then on he watched over the province of Szechuan.

The Kofuku Dragon

At the Kofuku temple in Nara, Japan, there dwelt a most un-monklike monk. His name was Kurodo and a deep resentment festered within him. He was jealous of his fellow priest's achievements, but instead of applying himself to meditation and study he plotted to discredit his peers. Beside a large pond next to the temple, he erected a plac-ard that read; "On the 3rd of March, a dragon shall ascend from this pond".

News of the coming of a dragon spread like wildfire. People thought that it must be true because the monks would never lie. By March 3rd, thousands of people from all over Japan had congregated at the pond to see the dragon. The monks were worried, but they could not admit that there was no dragon, it would make them seem like liars. By noon they were next to themselves with worry, as no dragon had appeared. Kurodo, conversely, was rubbing his hands in delight at his fellow monks' dilemma.

Suddenly, the bright-skies became overcast. As if from nowhere, inky-clouds blotted out the sun. Soon, sheets of rain began streaming down upon the crowd. The spectators held fast however, excited by the prospect of beholding a dragon. Lightning arced down from the clouds, and the waters began to foam. Suddenly a great ebony head broke the surface. Red eyed and ivory-fanged, it supported branching-horns. A long neck followed, and then a twisting, snaky, body with four legs, and black, feathered wings. The monster rose up, lashing its spiny tail, and disappeared into the storm-clouds. Kurodo's plot had backfired, and a real dragon had come to punish his misdeeds and save face for the monks.

The Emperor's Gift.

Once a huge and valuable pearl was sent from China to the Japanese court. During the journey, a terrible storm was whipped up by a great sea-dragon. The pearl was lost overboard, and claimed by the monster. The official held responsible for the pearl - Lord Kamatari - was disgraced, and banished to the small fishing-village of Fukazaki. Kamatari lived quietly there, until he fell in love with a young girl who made a living diving for shell fish.

Though he loved the girl deeply, he was still haunted by melancholy. Once, he told her of his past, and how he had failed the Emperor. The girl persuaded him to take her out in a boat to the exact spot where the pearl had been lost. She then dived overboard.

The girl swam down until she came upon a huge, coral cave. There, coiled sleeping inside, was a huge blue dragon. About him were strewn all manner of treasures collected from sunken ships. She spotted the huge-pearl, the size of an egg. It was barely a foot from the dragon's nose. Swiftly she snatched it up and swam for her life. The dragon's huge yellow eyes flashed open, and he bared his murderous fangs in rage.

Like a shot he was after her - coil after coil of his scaly body whipping out of the cave. He summoned up his slaves; the giant octopus, the giant squid, fierce sharks, and *onis* – flaming-haired daemons. In desperation, she slit open one of her breasts and pushed the pearl inside to keep it safe.

Kamatari pulled her onboard just before the hordes closed in on her. She pulled the bloody pearl from her breast and gave it to him. But her self-inflicted wound proved fatal and she died.

Modern day reports of dragons are more common in Asia than anywhere else on earth. In late July of 2002, an astounding report of what must be the greatest dragon mass-sighting ever filtered out of China.

Lake Tianchi, (or Celestial Lake), lies in Jinlin Province, on the border of north-east China and North Korea. It is the bowl of an extinct volcano, and covers 9.8 square kilometres, and is 373 metres deep. It has a long tradition of being the lair of a dragon, and before the Cultural Revolution it was known as Dragon Lake.

On the 25th of July, a black, elongate creature, with a horse-like head broke the surface only ten metres from the shore. The thirty-foot animal was visible for ten minutes, and leaped from the water on several occasions. Five-hundred people witnessed the dragon's appearance, (including a party of 200 tourists who were climbing the Changbai mountains). One of the latter apparently caught the beast on film.

The sightings spawned a 40 minute documentary on the Huichin TV channel. The programme showed film and photographs of the creature taken over the years, and recounted some of the thousands of eyewitness accounts, mainly from mountaineers reaching back to the 1900s.

MULTI-HEADS AND MUTANTS

Some dragons seem not to belong to a particular species but to be freaks or one-offs. They often display unique features and have singular powers.

In Greek legend, the great dragon 'Typhon' swept up the daemon 'Echidna' in his stormwinds, and mated with her. Together they spawned a family of monsters. Lardon was the ever watchful dragon who guarded the golden apples of Hesperides. The Chimera was a monster with a lion's head a goat's body and a serpent's tail. Cerberus was the infamous triple-headed hound, who stood watch over the gateway to Hades. Orthos was a double-headed dog of enormous size. Strangest of all was The Hydra. This was a seven-headed serpent with poison breath, that terrorized Lerna in Southern Greece. Its most fearful power was that it could sprout two new heads for any one head severed. This made it almost impossible to kill. Finally the Greek hero Heracles had his nephew Iolaus burn the stump of each neck that Heracles hacked off, thus preventing the endless regeneration.

France seems to have had a particular attraction for draconic mutants, as many have appeared in this country alone. The Pedula, (or shaggy beast), haunted the River Huisne. It looked like a normal dragon, save for its lack of wings, and the fact that in lieu of scales, it sported thousands of porcupine-like quills. These were deadly poisonous, and could be fired at victims. It was finally killed by a hero who cut its tail in two. The tail was the only part of its body not protected by spines.

In 520 AD Rouen, The Capital of Normandy, was besieged by a dragon, known as 'the gargouille'. Its breath was not flame, but great torrents of water that flooded the countryside and drowned its victims. The monster was eventually tamed by Saint Romaine, and burned to death by angry villagers.

An almost identical fate befell the tarasque - that laired in the River Rhone. It had a dragon-like tail, but the resemblance stopped there. Its body was shielded by a massive carapace like that of a tortoise. This was studded with spines. It bore six scaly, clawed-legs, and strangest of all was its head that recalled an outsized lion. Saint Martha tamed the monster and it was destroyed by a mob who had lived under its tyranny.

The Dragon Trap

Susa-no-wo - The Japanese God of Storms - frequently walked amidst the world of men in the guise of a mortal. One day, he was travelling along the River Hi-no-kka-mi in the Province of Izumo, when he came upon a beautiful maiden and her elderly parents - all of whom were weeping bitterly. On enquiring the cause of their sorrow, the old man informed the disguised god, that the girl - Kush-inada-hime - was their only remaining daughter. The other seven of her sisters had been devoured by an eight-headed dragon that came down from the mountains. Now the time was drawing near for the dragon to return and claim Kush-inada-hime.

Susa-no-wo offered to destroy the monster, if the girl's parents promised that he could marry her. They quickly agreed and travelled back to their home with Susa-no-wo in tow. The beast would be a terrible opponent - even for a god - and it would have to be defeated using guile. Looking around the old couple's house, he notice a fine stock of home brewed *sake* or rice wine. Soon a plan came to him. He enquired whereabouts in the house the monster gained entry, and then told the family to keep well away. He collected some wooden-boards and divided the large room - that the dragon invariably used as an entrance - into eight partitions. In each partition he placed an open barrel of the aromatic *sake*.

As night drew on he waited by candle-light until finally he heard a repulsive, dragging sound, as if something huge and heavy was pulling itself across the courtyard. The vile sound approached closer, until the wooden shutters at the window were thrown back, and a nest of sickening necks forced their way through the gap. They looked like the vermilion tentacles of some gargantuan octopus - save that, at the end of each, was a slavering, mad-eyed head. Twitching horribly, the heads moved about the room independently, each seeking prey. Then they came upon the partitions. One by one they oozed through and came upon the *sake* barrels. Their nostrils flared as their drooling mouths hovered over the wine. Then, as one, they greedily plunged into the barrels, slurping up the wine.

Susa-no-wo waited patiently until every barrel was empty. Slowly the heads rose up in jerky, slothful movements. The powerful wine had intoxicated the un-natural beast. Leaping from the shadows as he unsheathed his sword, Susa-no-wo hacked at the befuddled heads. As the first one fell to the ground, leaving a thrashing bloody stumped

neck, the others rose in defence. But their drunken state and the wooden partitions made them easy prey for the God's flashing-blade. Soon, eight gore-smeared heads lay on the floor, and the necks jerked and twitched in their death-throes.

Walking outside, the hero saw for the first time, the huge, limbless, slug-like body of the monster. Its tail still writhed, so he hacked it off. There inside, was a miraculous blade - perhaps lodged there by some less fortunate warrior in an earlier battle. Susa-no-wo named the sword Kusa-nagi-no-tachi, and claimed it as his own. The God settled in Izumo with his new-bride and her grateful mother and father.

Ireland has more than its share of latter-day dragon reports. Most are of the lindorm/wyrm kind. Giant, snaky creatures, that haunt the peat-stained waters of many Irish Loughs. But one could hardly ask for a better one-off mutant than the monster that attacked Galway school master, Alphonsus Mullaney and his son, one day in March 1962.

Mr Mullaney and his offspring, (also called Alphonsus), had gone fishing for pike and perch in Lough Dubh.

"We were working on the bog after school and I promised to take young Alphonsus fishing. We carried a twelve foot rod with a strong line and spoon bait for perch or pike, of which there are plenty in Lough Dubh.

For a while I let the boy fish with the long rod and used a shorter rod with worm bait. I got no "answer". After five minutes I decided that the fish were not there that evening, but I took the long rod and walked up and down the bank.

Suddenly there was a tugging on the line. I thought it might be a root, so I took it gently. It did not give. I hauled it slowly ashore, and the line snapped. I was examining the line when the lad screamed.

Then I saw the animal. It was not a seal or anything I had ever seen. It had, for instance, short thick legs, and a hippo face. It was as big as a cow or an ass, square face, with small ears and a white pointed horn on its snout. It was dark grey in colour, and covered with bristles or short hair, like a pig."

The weird creature had apparently taken the bait, and was now angered by the hook and the frantic barking of a nearby spaniel. The boy ran to his father as the thing heaved itself out of the water, and made to charge. The schoolmaster and his son ran for their lives. Later, Alphonsus junior, picked a rhinoceros out of a book of animals, as the closest thing to the monster.

An aquatic, Irish rhino that takes bait meant for fish? The Lough Dubh monster is unlike any other beast save for, perhaps, the *Emela-ntouka* of the jungles of central Africa, but more of that later.

I hope that I have shown you that there is more to the dragon-legends than whimsy and fairytale. I hope too, that I have given you some idea of what a dazzling variety of forms the dragon can take around the world.

Today, someone, somewhere in the world, will encounter a living-dragon. But just *what* is it that they are encountering? This is what I will try to answer in part two of this book.

PART TWO

BEHIND THE MASK

It is well said that at the core of every legend there is a grain of truth. Strip away the folklore - like the layers of an onion - and you will find something very real at the centre.

A legend may have come down to us over hundreds or thousands of years. Along the way it will have picked up much baggage. Religious allegory foisted on it by the church to underline dubious morals, exaggeration or distortion to make local landowners or noblemen into heroes. But the dragon legend does not spring from nowhere. In this part of the book we go in search of its genesis.

Were the great bones of antediluvian titans unearthed by our ancestors? Who, ignorant of their true nature, conceived them to be from fire-spouting monsters? Perhaps our dragons were a little more lively. What of the reptiles that crawl upon the Earth today? The snake with its steely coils and venom dripping fangs has always been a mystical beast. The shedding of its skin was looked on as a form of rebirth. Hence the *snake* is a symbol of everlasting life. Is the crocodile, the world's most lethal predator, the original dragon - the all devouring beast of the ancient waters?

If today's reptiles are spectacular and frightening to mankind, what of the giant saurians of the Earth's dim past. Could dinosaurs have lingered into historic times, and, even more fantastically, could they - or something descended from them - still be alive today? One could not ask for a better dragon.

Finally, are dragons creatures that inhabit other realities? Do they prowl the depths of humanity's collective mind or soar through the skies of alternate dimensions?

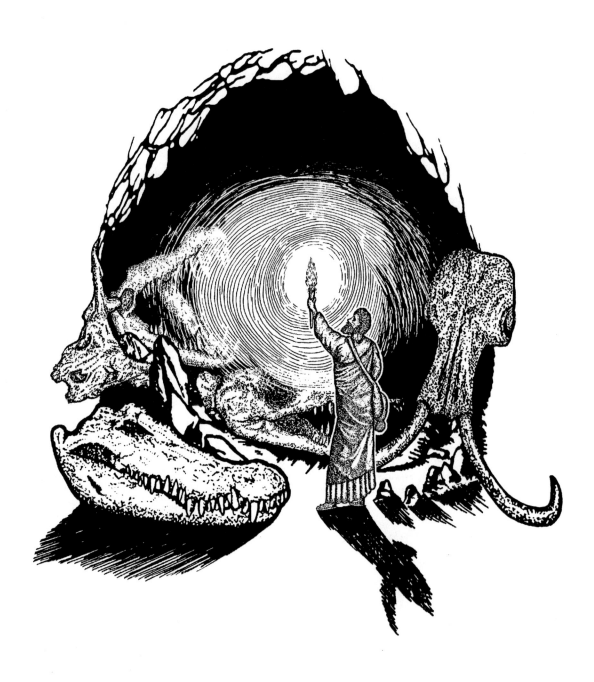

CHAPTER TWO

Dragon Bones

When all those large and monstrous amphibia since regarded as fabulous still in reality existed, when the confines of the water and the land teemed with gigantic saurians, with lizards of dimensions much exceeding those of the largest crocodiles of the present day: who to the scaly bodies of fish, added the claws of beasts, and the neck and wings of birds: who to the faculty of swimming in water added not only that of moving on the earth but that of sailing in air: and who had all the characteristics of what we now call chimeras and dragons, and perhaps of such monsters the remains, found among the bones and skeletons of other animals more resembling those that still exist and propagate, in the grottos and caverns in which they sought shelter during the deluges that effected the infancy of the globe, gave rise to the idea that these dens and caves were once retreats whence such monsters watched and in which they devoured other animals.

Thomas Hope, *'On the Origins and Prospects of Man'*. (1831)

 In the 1670s, natural historian Robert Plot unearthed a massive bone. He believed it to be the thigh bone of a giant. Ninety years later, Richard Brookes - a rural doctor who devoted much of his life to natural history, and the rest of it to fishing - examined the knee joint and came to the conclusion that it was the fossilized scrotum of a giant! Accordingly, he named the bone *'Scrotum humanum'*. It was, in fact, the leg-bone of the carnosaur *Megalosaurus bucklandi* - a nine metre (30 foot) predator that stalked England in the Jurassic and early Cretaceous eras.

There are many cases where the bones of dinosaurs and other prehistoric animals have been mistaken for the remains of legendary creatures. One can readily imagine the impact of finding the massive bones of a dinosaur would have had on early peoples with no knowledge of such creatures. Some believe that this is where we can trace the genesis of the dragon legends.

Beginning in the British Isles, we can find that even the most mundane and common fossil can elicit legends, and they do not have to be of a great size. The common fossilized shells of the extinct cephalopods known as ammonites were often believed to be the remains of serpents. These marine relatives of the modern nautilus lived in spiralled shells. They ranged in size from less than a centimetre to two metres in diameter - females dwarfing males. They became extinct at the end of the Cretaceous epoch some 65 million years ago. It seems that the closely related nautilus survived because it lived in deep waters less effected by whatever global events destroyed much life at the end of this epoch.

Ammonites take their name from the Latin; *Cornu Ammonis* - the 'horns' of Zeus Ammon, (Zeus with a ram's head). Zeus was said to have disguised himself as a ram in Egypt whilst fleeing the dragon Typhon. (Yet another dragon link!).

In Ireland it was believed that ammonites were the victims of Saint Patrick (in the 5th Century AD), who was said to have driven all snakes out of the 'Emerald Isle'. The fossils confirmed this legend, as those snakes that did not leave Ireland were petrified, beheaded and left in the rocks for all to see as a demonstration of God's power.

These fossils were often called 'snakestones', and legends akin to that of Saint Patrick are found in other areas rich in ammonite fossils. One such area is Whitby in north Yorkshire. Here the cliffs date from the Jurassic, when ammonites reached their zenith in both species and number. They are preserved in great numbers and are associated with Saint Hilda. Hilda was a Saxon abbess who founded Whitby Abby in the 4th Century. According to legend, the cliffs were over-run with serpents until Saint Hilda turned them to stone. Her prayers caused them to fall headless from the cliff tops.

Similar legends are woven around Saint Kenya at Keynsham in Avon. The same Jurassic rock that composes the cliffs at Whitby is found here.

The craft of re-carving snakes heads on ammonites and selling them off as relics to religious travellers was popular in Whitby. Michael G. Bassett notes in his book *Formed Stones, Folklore and Fossils* that the type specimen for the ammonite species *Dactylioceras commune* is actually a snake-stone with a carved head. Most of the Whitby ammonites are of this species. Such was the popularity of this kind of fakery that the snakestone became one of the town's emblems during the 16th and 17th centuries. They featured on coins, and on the council's coat of arms, where three of them still appear today.

Snakestones were believed to be potent charms against the bite of venomous creatures. The stones were soaked in water, then the bitten person or animal was given the water to drink. They were also worn like amulets to ward-off snakes, and as cures for blindness and impotence. We can see here the link back to the accounts of dragons such as the Greek *drackon* and the South East Asian *naga,* being sharp eyed, and also the belief in these dragons as fertility symbols.

Many British dragons - such as the infamous Lambton wyrm - were known for their love of milk. Lesser serpents were also supposed to be addicted to milk, and there are tales of farmers having to pluck suckling snakes from the udders of sleeping cows. Fossil sea-urchins were often thought to be magickal 'serpent eggs', and were placed on shelves in dairies to prevent the milk from turning sour.

These magick eggs were known as *ovum anguinum* - stony snake's eggs - and were first recorded in Pliny the Elder's (AD 23-79) *Natural History.* They were supposedly formed by the froth that emanated from a mass of entwined (mating?) snakes at midsummer. The snakes would toss the stone egg into the air. If caught on a cloth before it hit the ground it would have great magickal powers.

The village of Kilve in Somerset has a legend about a dragon called 'Blue Ben' who was supposed to be Satan's steed. His skull was discovered and placed in Taunton Museum. The relic was actually the skull of an *Ichthyosaur* - a group of marine reptiles contemporary with the dinosaurs. These fish eating reptiles superficially resembled dolphins, and ranged in size from 1.5 metres (5 feet) to 12 metres (40 feet). Doubtless, to those who discovered the skull, with its massive eyes and long tooth studded jaw, it was truly horrific and unlike any animal they knew of - *save* for a dragon.

Moving on to Europe we find similar beliefs. In the central German Harz Mountains, ammonites were placed in the milk-pails of cows who had ceased to give milk. Also in Germanic lore, appears a creature known as the *Milchdracken* - a serpent that exclusively sucked from cows. Snakestones were used as a deterrent against it.

In nearby Austria, we find one of the most spectacular cases of a "fossil dragon". The land that is now Klagenfurt (ford of lament) - the capital of the province of Carinthia - was said to have been haunted by an aquatic dragon. The wyrm laired in the River Glan. The name had been given with good reason. The dragon was said to send great floods, destroying all the crossings and drowning countless travellers in its magickally created maelstroms. Shrouded by eternal mists, the villagers could hear its awesome roars during thunderstorms. The Duke of Carinthia built a great tower by the edge of the swamps that surrounded the river. Here a band of knights lay in wait after tethering a bull to a thick iron chain studded with barbs. The dragon duly emerged and swallowed the bull whole. With the barbs fastened in his gut the huge reptile writhed like a fish on a hook. Whilst in this helpless state, the knights rushed forward and slew the monster. The marshes were drained and the town of Klagenfurt was founded, and a castle was built where the Duke's tower once stood.

Spectacular evidence for the existence of the glan dragon was unearthed in 1353, when a huge skull, some 75 cm (two and a half feet) long, was discovered in a gravel pit. The relic was preserved in the Town-Hall. A statue of the dragon was erected in 1590. It was sculpted by Ulrich Vogelsang and its head based on the 1353 skull. The statue still stands today, and spouts water from its mouth - doubtless in reference to the flood-bringing powers of the original dragon.

In 1840 palaeontologist Franz Unger identified the Klagenfurt skull as being the cranium of *Coelodonta antiquitatis* the woolly rhinoceros. This spectacular mammal roamed Eurasia in the Pleistocene epoch (two million to ten thousand years ago), and was one of the most formidable of the ice-age beasts. Nine years after its identification it became one of the first exhibits at a new natural history museum.

For the largest example of fossil bones being passed off as a dragon skeleton, we must cross the Atlantic and move forward several centuries. In 1845 Dr Albert Koch exhibited a remarkable beast at the Apollo Saloon on New York's Broadway. His specimen was a fossilized sea dragon fully 35 metres (117 feet) long. The exhibit consisted of a long, toothy skull raised high on a snake-like neck that continued into an sinuous, elongate vertebral-column, gigantic ribs and the remains of paddles.

Dr. Albert Koch's Sea Serpent

Koch called his monster *Hydragos sillmanii* in honour of the wonderfully named Benjamin Silliman, a scientist who had recognised the existence of sea serpents in 1827. The good doctor happily charged 25 cents per visitor, for the privilege of seeing the dragon. His charge was immensely popular and he did a roaring trade - until one unfortuitous day when a member of the public with zoological knowledge happened into the Apollo.

Professor Jeffries Wyman - who was a competent anatomist - instantly saw Dr Koch's chicanery. He noted that the "dragon" had teeth with double roots, which is a characteristic found only in mammals. He also exposed the fact that the specimen was made up of several different skeletons, giving it an artificially long body. He published a damning account, concluding that the monster was nothing more than the skeletons of several fossil whales strung together.

Koch had indeed made a spectacular hoax. The bones belonged to several specimens of the extinct, archaic whale, *Basilosaurus* (so termed because its *original* discoverer, Dr Richard Harlan, wrongly thought it to be a reptile). Ironically, hypothetical descendents of this cetacean are mooted by some to be the explanation for modern sea-serpents, which we will examine more closely in a later chapter.

Koch was nothing if not resourceful. Having been exposed as a sham-artiste in the States, he merely packed up his serpent and crossed the Atlantic. Re-naming his brute *Hydragos harlani* (after Dr Richard Harlan as Professor Silliman now refused to have any thing to do with it), he exhibited it in Dresden.

However the jig was up. The eminent English palaeontologist Gideon Mantell (the discoverer of the dinosaur *Iguanodon mantelli*), wrote to the editor of the *Illustrated London News* with a damning letter. He pointed out that as well as his current scam, some years earlier he had collected the bones of mastodons and mammoths, and reconstructed them into a species of his own invention called *Missourium*. This fake-monster had been displayed in the Egyptian Hall, Piccadilly. The British Museum actually brought Koch's collection and reconstructed a fine *Mastodon* out of them.

Mantell goes on to say:

"Not content with the interest which the fossils which he collected in various parts of the United States really posses, Mr Koch, with the view of exciting the curiosity of the ignorant multitude, strung together all the vertebrae he could obtain of the Basilosaurus, arranged them in a serpentine form; manufactured a skull and claws, and exhibited the monster as a fossil sea serpent, under the name above mentioned Hydragos."

Amazingly, there were those who *still* believed Koch. In Dresden the chimera was examined by Carl Gustave Carus, a student of comparative anatomy. He attempted to restore the cranium. Only a portion of this had been found by Koch, forcing him to fake the rest. Carus restored it as the skull of a giant reptile, completely in error.

Across the Atlantic *more* fossils were being linked with aquatic dragons but this time no con-artist was behind the affair. Lake Champlain is located on the US/Canadian border and encompasses Vermont, New York State, and Quebec. For over 150 years a dragon like water monster known as '*Champ*' has been reported in this immense body of water. In 1881 a vast elongate skeleton was unearthed by a Mr H H Burge. This was believed to have been the remains of a *Champ* creature. The *Middlebury Register* of May 27th 1881 wrote:

"The proprietors of the Champlain Granite Works, located near Barn Rock on Lake Champlain claim to have discovered a petrified sea serpent of mammoth proportions, being a bout 8 inches in diameter and nearly fifty feet long. The surface of the stone bears evidence of the outer skin of a large serpent while the inner surface shows the entrails. The proprietors are intending soon to begin excavations along the place where it lies embedded in the dirt and granite, to ascertain its size."

More details were printed the following year in the June 8th edition of the *Elizabeth Town Post & Gazette:*

The report of finding a monster in the limestone deposit of the "North Shore" I heard many times and considered it a story originating with some one who was anxious to be the author of a sensation.

Last summer, a party, part of whom were scientific gentlemen by education and profession called at the cottage and almost demanded admission to the apartments of the monster. The Superintendent at the time was extremely busy superintending his many labourers engaged in the quarry, and told the gentlemen he could not leave his busi-

ness to go down to the house, and furthermore, he was not prepared to exhibit what he had found, as there was so little of it, but at some future time he would be glad to show to all his serpent. I had heard the above from one of the party, and made my mind up to say nothing of the serpent when I went there. Just as I was about to bid the good folks good day, the Superintendent said: "I am not in the show business, as many have thought, neither am I showing snakes, but I have something to show you."

On the carpet in an upper room lay six or seven feet in length, pieces of an enormous petrified snake. Some portions were six inches long and some fifteen or more. The pieces were placed together and fitted so nicely that there was no room to doubt of their having been broken apart. The largest end was eight or nine inches in diameter, and only three or four feet from the terminal of the entrails, and two or three feet beyond. The entrails were petrified, but much darker and quite open or porous, showing a wasted condition and differing from the fresh part, and containing many bright and glistening crystals. The vertebra was visible at each broken end, and the flesh part showed traces of what at one time were veins.. The skin was readily distinguished from the flesh as would have been had the monster been cut in two whilst living. After an examination of each piece, and comparing the gradual enlargement of the cavity, thickness of flesh and skin on the belly, and the gradual thickening towards the back, left no room in my mind to entertain the thought that it was an accident or freak of nature with molten rock. During this hour of examination at the south side window with a bright sunlight, the Superintendent had sat quietly and said nothing but answer a very few questions. I said I did not want to be inquisitive, but would like to know in what kind of rock he was found, and his general position.. He said he was not in the rock but was merely attached to the limestone, and his position was as if he had placed himself for rest or sleep, and he had traced his body by actual measurement over sixty feet, and his weight would amount to several tons when all removed. The portions the Superintendent has removed he has secured alone, but will be obliged to have help in getting the remainder or leave the monster to rest in his slumber of death. When the proper time comes the scientific men of different localities will be called upon to make minute examination and publish to the world their verdict.

The remains are next mentioned in the *Burlington Free Press* of November 4th 1886 and was apparently on show at a bank-sponsored exhibition held in Vergennes, Vermont. It was also recorded on page 39 of the exhibition's catalogue. It was subsequently purchased by the notorious P.T Barnum (1810-1891) for his museum. From then on the specimen seems to have vanished. Searches of Barnum's records have so far been fruitless, but America's greatest showman had many collections of such oddities, and it is hoped that the remains reside in some dusty forgotten cellar awaiting rediscovery.

Just what was the Champlain skeleton? It is unlikely to have been a *Basilosaur* like Koch's monster. The surrounding strata is way too young (around 10,000 years). Fossil whales which *have* been found in the area, have been of modern species such as the beluga or white whale (*Delphinapterus leucas*). The presence of skin and entrails is odd. The soft parts of a carcass only fossilize under very-rare circumstances where their decay is impeded, usually by anaerobic conditions. This raises the question of the specimen being sub-fossil, or in other words very recent. Was the carcass of an aquatic dragon discovered in 1881? Sadly, as in many other cryptozoological cases, our evidence has disappeared - and it seems that we shall never know. As for Champ - we will be returning to that in chapter seven.

It is back to the east we must look for the richest lore on dragon bones. Apollonius of Tyana was a traveller in the first century AD, who journeyed from Asia Minor to the foothills of the Himalayas. He records that the countryside was full of dragons, and that no mountain ridge was without one. The locals told fantastic tales of luring the dragons to earth with magick, and prying out the gem-stones that were embedded in their skulls.

The dragons of the high-ridges were said to be larger than the lowland dragons of the marshes. The former had long-necks and prominent crests upon their heads. These were small in young specimens but grew huge in adults. Those from the marshes were said to kill elephants. The dying pachyderm would sometimes fall upon its killer in its death-throes and crush him. Hence, dragon and elephant bones were often found intertwined. The much sought-after gemstones in the dragon's skulls were said to be iridescent and of immense value. The dragons made an awful clashing noise, and shook the earth as they burrowed in the mountains.

Apollonius wrote of seeing many dragon skulls enshrined in an important city he calls 'Paraka'. This may well have been 'Parasha' - the ancient name of the city now called 'Peshawar', which is situated at the eastern-end of the Khyber Pass (in the north of Pakistan), which was already an important settlement by 100AD.

It is interesting to note that some Chinese pilgrims recorded a Buddhist holy-place north of Taxila, (the ancient name for Pakistan). They called this place 'The Shrine of a Thousand Heads'. The pilgrims were writing much later than Apollonius - around 500-640 AD - but it is tempting to speculate that they are reporting the same relics.

So just what were these dragon bones that Apollonius writes of? The Siwalik hills - where these bones were found - are rich in fossils from the Tertiary period, (5 to 2 million years ago). The lowland-dragons seem to have been the fossil remains of the crocodilian *Leptorrhynchus crassidens*. This creature grew to some 7.5 metres, (25 feet) long - a comparable size to some modern crocodiles. Its skulls and bones have been found mixed with those of extinct elephants, such as *Elephas hysudricus,* and *Mastodon silvenisis.* This may have led to the stories of elephant/dragon combat.

Apollonius of Tyana

The mountain-dragons seem to have been based on fossil giraffes which were radically different in appearance to the modern species. *Sivatherium giganteum,* (named in honour of the Hindu god Siva), was an immense, short necked, animal with a skull a metre in length. Its horns - or ossicones to give them their correct name - were quite unlike the small bud-like affairs on present-day giraffes. The two ossicones above its eyes were formed into sharp, devil-like horns. The second pair formed huge, palmate antlers, that lent the animal a moose-like appearance. *Sivatherium* seems to have become extinct relatively recently, and there is some evidence that it persisted into historical times in the middle-east.

The second species of giraffe from the Siwalik was even more bizarre. *Giraffokeryx* had a long neck and four ossicones. One pair were placed above the nostrils, and another above the eyes. All four were sharp and recurved - looking truly draconic despite its smaller skull size of 50cm (20 inches). Just as Apollonius was told, these "crests" would have been much smaller on the skulls of juveniles in both species.

But what of the splendid gems held within the skulls? Often bone material can be replaced with calcite and selenite crystals that bare a strong resemblance to diamond. Both kinds of crystal are commonly found in fossils from the Siwalik Hills. The legendary jewels would seem to allude to these crystals.

The sheer number of such fossils from this area, makes it plain why locals believed that every single hill contained a dragon. Between 1834 and 1842 palaentologist Hugh Falconer (1809-1865), excavated the Siwalik deposits, after reading the ancient traveller's-tales of dragons. In his first six hours of digging he unearthed three-hundred large bones. The bones were of striking quality - black with crystal filling the crevasses where bone-marrow had once been. He collected over 250 fossil elephant and giraffe skulls, and in 1848, shipped five tons of fossils back to London.

Even further back, we can find accounts of what seem to be fossil-bones taken to be from dragons. Hetrodontus, a Greek philosopher who lived around 484 BC, wrote of seeing such things whilst on a trip to the city of Buto in Arabia:

I went once to a certain place in Arabia, almost exactly opposite the city of Buto, to make inquiries concerning the winged serpents. On my arrival I saw the back bones and ribs in such numbers as it is imposable to describe: of the ribs there were a multitude of heaps, some great, some small, some middle sized. The place were the bones lie is at the entrance of a narrow gorge between steep mountains, which there open upon a spacious plain communicating with the great plains of Egypt.

It sounds very probable that what Herodotus saw were in fact the fossil remains of *Pterosaurs*, a group of flying reptiles contemporary with dinosaurs. It is interesting to note that Buto was the Greek name for Ua Zit - the serpent-mother in Egyptian mythology.

The spiritual homeland of the dragon - the Orient - is awash with folklore about dragon bones. Little wonder, as China is one of the World's greatest producers of dinosaur bones. Writing in *The Scientific American* in 1916 Irwin J.O'Malley recorded his discovery of dragon-bones in a Chinese cave.

During the latter part of a holiday trip to the Yangtze Gorges undertaken by my wife and self in November, 1915, we met Mr M.Hewlett, British Consul at Ichang, and his wife, and in their company spent a day in the Ichang Gorge, landing at various points to climb the cliffs and explore some of the numerous caves.

While exploring a large cave on the right bank of the river, and about one mile above the Customs Station at Ping Shan Pa, we discovered the fossils about to be described. The cave is reputed by the Chinese to extend some 20 miles to a point near Ichang.

It is reported that a party from H.M.S "Snipe" spent three days in the cave some years ago and that they failed to reach the end. Evidence that the party penetrated beyond the point where the discovery was made exists in the name of their ship painted on the cave walls at a point considerably further in.

The Chinese name of the cave is Shen K'an Tzu, which means "The Holy Shrine", and one of the characters forming the word K'an is the Chinese character for "dragon". A large rock is seen at the entrance, and some eight ten yards behind this there is a peculiar piece of curved rock bearing some slight resemblance to a portion of a dragon's body; the resemblance is possibly suggestive enough to impress the Chinese mind, but altogether fails to impress the foreigner. After proceeding some hundred yards inside the cave we found ourselves walking on a peculiar ridge in order to avoid the surrounding pools of water. The ridge curved backward and forward across the width of the cave like the curves of a large serpent, the suggestion being so strong we lowered our lamps in order to examine the ridge more closely. To our astonishment and delight, we found that we were in very truth walking along a perfect fossil of some huge reptile. Further inspection revealed the presence of six or eight of these enormous monsters.. Having taken a few small specimens of loose portions of scale for examination in a better light , we left, planning to return the following morning for the purpose of measurement.

*On our return the following morning we selected one of the largest fossils lying for a great part of its length isolated from the others...the coils of the remainder being rather entangled. The isolated portion measured 70 feet, so that it is absolutely certain that the length is at least 70 feet, and as far as we could ascertain, this same specimen extended for another 60 or 70 feet. However, I admit that error is possible here, owing to the interlacing coils of the reptiles. The depth of the body seen in the foreground of the first illustration is two feet. The head is partially buried in the cave wall and appears to be a large, flat head similar to that of **Morosaurus comperi**. About 12 or 14 feet from the head two legs are seen partially uncovered, and again two more about 50 feet from the head. The fact that several persons have penetrated this cave in former years beyond the point were the discovery was made seems to indicate the fossils have been but recently uncovered; by a heavy discharge of water through the cave. It seems probable that these reptiles were trapped by some volcanic disturbance and starved to death; the size of the bodies compared to their length would indicate this. A point of peculiar interest is the resemblance to the Chinese dragon of these fossils. I believe that it has therefore been supposed that the Chinese borrowed their idea of the dragon from Western mythology. The discovery has created a great stir among the local Chinese and foreigners, who are daily flocking to view the fossils. I am attempting to interest the Chinese authorities in Pekin and also the Chinese Monuments Society in order that the specimens may be preserved from damage.*

Morosaurus referred to in the passage above is actually an alternative, long since abandoned, name for *Camarasaurus* - a North American sauropod. This dinosaur bares little resemblance to the fossils described by O'Malley. *Camarasaurus* had a relatively short neck for a sauropod dinosaur (herbivorous, elongate, quadrupeds), with a box like skull and a length of around 18 metres (60 feet).

It seems more likely that O'Mally's dragon bones were the remains of some kind of Euhelophid sauropod such as *Mamenchisaurus*. This Chinese dinosaur had an immense neck some 15 metres (50 feet) long! Its overall length being 27 metres (90 feet). It takes little imagination to realize just how impressive these staggering remains would have been to the first people to stumble across them. You will recall from Chapter One, the Chinese belief that dragons shed their bones along with their skins. Obviously these must have been dinosaur bones.

Dragon bones or *lung ku,* and dragon teeth or *lung chi,* have been used in the cornucopia of Chinese folk-medicine for thousands of years. The *Pan Taso Kang Mu* is a book written in late 16th or early 17th century (Ming Period) China. It collects together fragments of much older works and contains many references to dragon-bones.

The *Pieh luh* is one of these older works. It tells us that different types and parts of dragon bones have differing powers, attributes and efficaciousness. The dragon's spine is the most sought-after part of the skeleton. The dragon's 'brain' is preserved as 'white-earth' which was also of great value. It was believed to cure ailments of the tongue. Charles Gould (1884), speculates that this white-earth or dragon's brain is in fact asbestos. As we have seen, this same substance was known as 'salamander's wool' in the west.

The smaller bones - marked with wider lines - were believed to be female, and the larger bones - with narrower lines - were male. Bones of variegated colour were the most effective and esteemed. Yellow or flesh coloured bones were of medium value, and black bones inferior. If the bones were gathered by a woman, says the book, then they should not be used!

The colours of dragon bones also relate to the internal organs that the bones were thought to effect as medicine:

- Blue = liver and gall
- Red = heart and large intestine
- Yellow = spleen and stomach.

The dragon/water link is also found in the unearthing of dragon bones. J. Needham, in *Science and Civilisation in China* (1954), records the digging of an irrigation-canal between the rivers of Lo and Shang-ye, around 133 BC (Han Period). Many dragon bones were uncovered during the digging. So many in fact, that the canal was named 'Dragon-Head Waterway'. Fifty years after the canal had been dug, the writer Wang Chung, records that dragon-bones had been found after the control of a flood. Doubtless, the large bones of extinct animals would occasionally be washed from their earth-prisons by floodwaters strengthening the belief that dragons controlled waterways, seas, and the weather. A dragon developing into a new stage of life and casting off its old-bones with its old-skin, would naturally cause such a disturbance.

One particular kind of dragon-bone, or rather dragon *tooth,* turned out to be very interesting indeed for it was the tooth of a totally different monster - one that is on the very verge of scientific acceptance. In 1934, a young Dutch palaentologist, Ralph von Koenigswald, was wandering the back streets of Hong Kong, searching curiosity-shops. He stumbled upon an old chemist's shop. Here amongst dried lizards, rhino horn and the bones of tigers and bears, he found a jar of huge teeth, labelled *lung chi.* Von Koenigswald recognised them as being from a primate. Taking one from the jar he identified it as a third lower molar. It resembled a human molar, but was six times as large! The shop's proprietor told him that the 'Dragon's Teeth' sometimes turned-up when the peasants ploughed their fields.

Over the next few years, von Koenigswald collected other teeth, and came to the conclusion that he was dealing with a giant ape. He christened this mighty-beast *Gigantopithecus blackii.* More fossils have be uncovered of this giant in the Kwangsi province of China and in India. *Gigantopithecus* is still only known from its teeth, jaw bones and fragments of skull, but we can learn quite a lot from these. The animal was a true giant. The veritable *King Kong* of fossil apes. The shape of the lower jaw suggests that it was a biped standing over three metres (10 feet) tall. The skull bore a sattigal-crest like that of a mature male gorilla, for the attachment of massive jaw-muscles.

This would have given the head a domed appearance. The large teeth and huge jaw-muscles seem to have been for masticating bamboo - a tough and fibrous food source - and the hard outer shell of the durian fruit.

Gigantopithecus lived relatively recently, around 500,000 years ago in the mid Pleistocene. Animals such as the giant panda (*Ailuropoda melanoleuca),* and the Malayan tapir (*Tapirus indicus),* that lived alongside the giant ape, survive today. This gives rise to an amazing question. Is *Gigantopithecus* still alive? Many believe the giant ape to be one and the same as the yeti - the huge, hairy biped, seen throughout central Asia. The yeti has been reported in areas from which *Gigantopithecus* fossils have been found, in areas unchanged in environment for 500,000 years, in areas incredibly remote. As we will examine in more detail later, biological samples from the yeti - in the form of hair, skin, and bones - have found their way into the hands of scientists, making the case for the yeti's existence a good one. Are the reports of living giant-apes in the areas that giant-ape fossils are found coincidence? I think not. It is ironic that a 'dragons' tooth gave us the first material knowledge of one of the planet's most mysterious and elusive inhabitants!

Skeletons do not have to be fossilised in order for people to believe them to be the remains of dragons. In August 1934, a strange skeleton was found lying in the reeds beside Lake Po Yanghu, near the city of Newchang, in central China. The spinal-column was eighteen feet long, and had twenty-one vertebrae (and the same number of ribs). The skull was domed, long, and jointed, with two horns. The creature had the remains of a rudder-like tail. What the carcass was - and what became of it - seem not to have been recorded. But locals believed it to be a dragon.

In 1996, fishermen off the coast of Malaysia caught what they believed to be a dragon's skeleton in their nets. Furnished with formidable teeth the body consisted of a large skull and a vertebral-column. It was covered in rotting green flesh. The fishermen were terrified, but brought their strange catch back to the market in Kedha, where thousands of people flocked to see it. A local healer called Jefri Ahmed took the body home, cleaned it with bleach, and extracted seven litres of oil from it to use in "magick potions". Fortunately, a photograph of the monster was taken before the mystic took the body away. One look at the snap of the monster, shows it be nothing more than the decaying remains of a killer whale (*Orcinus orca).* The greenish hue was created by the decomposition of the flesh. This story indicates just what a powerful hold the dragon still has over the Orient today.

In October 2000, I visited Thailand to make a documentary for the *Discovery Channel* on the naga - a giant snake from Buddhist and Hindu mythology. In the town of Pom Posi, I was shown what the locals believed to be sacred naga bones. According to local lore, the bone's owner purchased them from a man in Laos after being instructed to do so by a naga that appeared to him in a series of dreams. The man did so, and became the custodian of the bones. He was reluctant to be filmed but sent the bones to the local police-station under lock and key. Myself and the crew waited with baited breath, as the artefact was brought out before us in a silver chalice. Would this be actual evidence of an unknown species of giant snake? In fact the relic was no more than the tooth of an Asian elephant (*Elephas maximus).* Quite how this had fooled the populace in a land with so many elephants I am at a loss to explain.

If one doubts that the dragon has a similar hold here in the west, then a quick look at the events of December 1975 at Durgan Beach near Falmouth in southern Cornwall, will soon dispel them. For years there have been sightings of a sea-monster in the area. The creature was called Morgawr – the ancient Cornish for 'Sea Dragon'. We shall examine these sightings in detail in the final chapter. After a winter storm, a massive carcass was thrown up on Durgan Beach. It was an elongate creature, with a large, domed, wedge shaped head. Locals immediately began to claim that it was physical proof - at last - of what they had known about for years – that Morgawr was a living creature.

Enter Toby Benham - a 13 year old amateur naturalist who unhesitatingly identified the skull as belonging to a pilot whale (*Globicephala macrorhynichus).* The skull was duly cleaned and kept in the art department of Toby's school for several years.

Jonathan Downes, cryptozoologist and director of the Centre for Fortean Zoology (for which I am Zoological Director, and a senior member of the Permanent Directorate) heard of the remarkable item and requested the loan of it for further examination. The skull is sitting in the corner of the CFZ living room as I type this!

Not all remains have been explained so easily. In issue 94 of *Fortean Times*, Pam Thornton wrote to the Letters Page with a remarkable report of a preserved dragon, seen by her daughter outside of Mont St Michel in France. An equally remarkable snapshot of the creature accompanied the letter.

The shrivelled, greyish-green thing has a birdlike head with large eye sockets, supported on a long camel like neck. The body is humped also like a camel, giving rise to the speculation it may be a preserved camel calf. Two limbs sprout from its body terminating in long claws or fingers. A curling tail sweeps up behind it. The body is old and desiccated.

A second letter appeared in *Fortean Times* #97, from Tim Hodkinson who had visited Mont St Michel as a teenager. He recalled seeing the creature inside a museum at the monastery. It was labelled as a 'dragon found near the monastery', and Tim speculated that it may have been a "pterodactyl" that had been preserved in the local quicksands. He goes on to say that the apparent hump is actually one of the monster's two wings held up. The beast was about a metre across.

An examination by a zoologist should be able to solve this mystery, but to my knowledge no qualified person has ever looked at the carcass. This creature sits not in some far flung corner of the globe, but slap bang in the middle of Europe a tantalizing piece of evidence right beneath our noses! It is also interesting that Mont St Michel has a dragon legend of its own - a creature "of the devil" which was supposedly slaughtered by St Michael.

For perhaps the oddest tale involving 'dragon bones' we must move to South America - home to Serpent and Dragon Gods. In 1926 palaentologist Andrew Pride was excavating the silt like deposits of Gran Chaco in Paraguay, (which date back around 10,000 years), when he came upon a remarkable fossil. It appeared to be the fang of a venomous snake, the venom groove clearly visible, but of horrifying dimensions. He presented the fang to Graham Kerr - Regius Professor of Zoology at the University of Glasgow. Kerr examined the fang and found it very similar to that of the African boomslang (*Dispholidus typus*). The giant fang was nine-times longer than a boomslang's fang. As the boomslang is around six feet long, Pride's monster would have been around fifty-four feet in length!

Kerr wrote a paper on this creature in which he named it *Bothrodon pridi* in honour of its discoverer. He also concluded that *Bothrodon* fed on contemporary mega-fauna such as giant ground-sloths. The curved, hook-like, fangs served to hold the prey whilst the venom pumped in. This was a truly terrifying beast - not only the largest snake known to science, but endowed with a lethal-venom that could kill elephant-sized animals. Perhaps *this* was the genesis of the Neo-Tropical Dragon Gods!

The fang of this monarch of ophidians took pride of place in the Hunterian Museum of the University of Glasgow, until it was embarrassingly dethroned in 1939. A cast of the fang was sent to the University of Berlin's Palaentological Museum, where a Dr W. Quenstedt happened to examine it. He instantly recognised it as one of the six curved, groove-bearing, prongs from the shell of a mollusc known as the Chiragra spider conch (*Lambis chiragra*) of the Indopacific. Kerr's venom-dripping, steely-coiled monster was nothing more than a fragment of sea shell. But to this day nobody has explained how an Indopacific shell got to South America!

This woeful-tale has one last twist. Recently the vertebrae of a *real* fossil giant snake has been discovered in South America. The massive animal would have been as thick around as an oil drum and eighteen metres (sixty feet) long. The monster belonged to a primitive group of semi-aquatic giant snakes called *Madtsoids*. These creatures lived up until 10,000 years ago in some areas. Even today, reports emerge from the green-hell of the Latin American rain forests of giant snakes that dwarf even the anaconda. Could there be a surviving form of *Madtsoid*? I address this question in the next chapter.

The bones of dinosaurs and other large animals cannot possibly explain all of the world's dragon legends. So many legends speak of the interaction of humans and dragons, and dragonesque creatures are still reported today. Perhaps it is time we put a little flesh on these bones.

CHAPTER THREE

The Giant Reptiles

"Do not despise the snake because he has no horns. Who is to say he will not, one day become a dragon?"

Ancient Japanese saying quoted in the opening credits of
The Water Margin (Japanese Fantasy TV series 1976-8)

It could be argued that dragons are still among us, and that one only has to go as far as the local zoo to see them. Our ancestors in Africa lived alongside some of the largest and most dangerous reptiles in the world, and their fear has been handed down to us. I find reptiles both beautiful and fascinating, but I am in the minority. Most people's feelings towards reptiles range from mild dislike to outright fear. The human race is appallingly narcissistic and hence finds animals that resemble themselves appealing.

As a one time zookeeper I found the public's ill-founded love of chimpanzees (one of the most disgusting and aggressive animals on Earth) and their xenophobic terror of reptiles insufferable. Could this deep-seated fear be the root of dragon-lore? From The Bible, to Kipling's *Just So stories,* to the Tarzan films, reptiles are cast as villains. And who can forget the ominous ticking of the crocodile in *Peter Pan*? If one follows the thread that, the larger the beast is, the more terrifying it becomes, then some of today's reptiles give anything in legend a run for their money.

Giant Crocodilians

Man has a habit of exaggeration, which is how many "monsters" are created. We have always wanted the animals who share our planet to be larger, and fiercer, and smarter, than they actually are. The more dangerous we perceive the animal to be, then the greater the tales that we weave around it. One only has to look at the world of the cinema. *Jaws* (1975), *Grizzly* (1976), *Alligator* (1980) and more recently *Anaconda* (1997), a tale which bears about as much relationship to reality as do the books of Erik von Daniken! (It is not so much the size of the snake that is a problem, but that it was portrayed as a cheetah-fast animal that eats four or five members of the cast in quick succession.)

Few carnivores are as dangerous to man as many people would like to think. It is, however, fitting that reptiles are one of the few groups of animals with a real tendency towards gigantism, and that the crocodile is one of the few genuine man-eaters.

To be fair, only two of the twenty-three extant species of crocodilian regularly attack humans. These are the Nile crocodile (*Crocodylus niloticus*) and the Indopacific crocodile (*C.porosus*). But these account for five-thousand human deaths a year - far more than all attacks by shark, big cat, or bear combined. Of vertebrates, only humans themselves kill more.

How does one define a 'giant' crocodile? This is debatable, but for now I am classing any animal of seven metres (twenty-three feet), or more, as a giant! As we shall see, there are reports that suggest that twenty-three foot specimens may be dwarfed beside the *true* giants.

There has been a precedent for giant crocodiles in the past. *Deinosuchus hatcheri* was a giant alligator of the late Cretaceous, which flourished in both eastern and western North America. Although it is known only from fragments of its massive skull, estimates of its length are around nine metres (thirty feet).

Even larger was *Sarcosuchus imperator* - a giant gharial of North Africa, from the early Cretaceous. Like modern gharials this species had elongated-jaws, and specialised in feeding on fish. It attained a length of eleven metres (thirty-six feet). The teeth alone were fifteen centimetres (six inches) long, and the armoured dermal scutes that adorned its skin in life, measured thirty-three by fifteen centimetres, (thirteen by six inches) across.

These nightmarish brutes were not confined to the Mesozoic Era. In the Tertiary, a giant caiman - *Purussosaurus brasiliensis* - flourished in The Amazon, and at fifteen metres (fifty feet) dwarfed *Deinosuchus* in size. This specimen of *Purussosaurus* has since been shown to be that of a young one. Many palaentologists believe that an adult male could have reached an amazing twenty-four metres (eighty feet) in length! At this size, its weight would have been in the region of sixty tons. This was only eight million years ago - in the late Miocene - long after the extinction of non-avian dinosaurs.

More recently still - in the Pleistocene epoch - Australia played host to a nine-metre (thirty foot), terrestrial crocodile called *Quinkana fortirostrum*. With teeth as impressive as *Tyrannosaurus rex*, this predator lived on land rather than in the water. Its claws were short and hoof-like, and it is believed that this reptilian giant galloped after its prey!

In the last century or so travellers have brought back tales of monster crocodiles still lingering in ill-explored corners of the tropics. It is my belief that these are not survivors from prehistory, but vast specimens of animals from known species that far exceed the size limits dreamed of by most zoologists.

Herein I will examine the evidence for giant crocodiles, and try to suggest what makes some specimens grow so frighteningly huge.

The Old World seems to have the monopoly on giant crocodilians. Only two New World crocodilians are accorded lengths of seven metres by some authorities. These are The American Crocodile (*C. acutus*), an animal which lives in Central America and the tip of Florida, and the Orinoco Crocodile (*C.intermedius*), of Colombia and Venezuela. However, very few details of such specimens have ever been given. The explorer Alexander von Humboldt, (1769-1859), claimed to have shot at a twenty-two foot (6.7m) Orinoco Crocodile in Venezuela, but we only have his word for it. The maximum length for either species seems to be only about five metres (seventeen feet).

The claims of giant crocodiles from the Old World seem much more believable - if only because of the sheer number of them, and the fact that some were measured by recognised experts.

Officially, the world's largest reptile is the Indopacific crocodile (*Crocodylus porosus*). This animal is also known as the 'saltwater' or 'estuarine' crocodile. However it is confined neither to saltwater, nor to estuaries, hence *my* use of the name Indopacific, which is much more suitable because it defines its geographical distribution.

It is a formidable predator quite capable of tackling such mighty prey as tigers, water buffalo, and sharks. Man is also firmly on the menu of this awesome beast.

An example of just how powerful the Indopacific crocodile is, occurred in the East Alligator River in Northern Australia during March 1987. A Toyota utility-truck was crossing the river in about a metre of water. Halfway across the river the truck met a crocodile. The reptile lashed out with its tail, smashing the truck over onto its side like a toy. The panicked passengers scrambled onto the side of the crippled machine as the crocodile circled it. Finally, some Kakadu National Park rangers came to their rescue in motorboats.

Even more extreme is the case from Princess Charlotte Bay (off the coast of northern Queensland). On the night of

June 2nd 2000, some people on board a trawler in the bay, were awakened by strange sounds. By torchlight they saw a large Indopacific crocodile trying to mate with one of the floats of a seaplane tethered to the trawler. The amorous reptile overturned and sank the aircraft! Needless to say no one was too keen on a salvage operation.

The biting power of a large crocodile has been measured at ten-thousand newtons. This gives it the most powerful bite of any living animal. In the Earth's history, only one creature held a more formidable bite - *Tyrannosaurus rex*!

The largest specimen generally accepted by experts, was an 8.64 m (twenty-eight foot, four inch), male shot on the MacArthur Bank of the Norman River, Queensland, Australia in 1957 by Mrs Kris Pawloski. The mammoth body was too big to move, but was photographed, although, sadly, the photograph was lost in 1968. However, her husband Ron was a recognised expert on crocodiles, and had carefully measured the specimen. He was astounded at its size (having previously measured no less than 10,287 specimens), and having found none larger than 5.5m (eighteen feet).

This giant was never weighed, (because of the impossibility of moving its immense carcass), but conservative estimates put it at a weight of two tons. Other estimates have produced a figure of three tons or more!

There have, however, been some cases of exaggeration with this species. Bellaire, a British herpetologist, worked out that the head:body ratio of a typical crocodile, (as opposed to specialised species like the gharial) at 1:7.5. This had connotations for the remains of some supposed "giants".

The skull from a supposed 8.8m (twenty-nine foot) specimen, killed after a six hour struggle in the Philippines in 1823 by Paul De La Gironiere and George Russell, was measured at twenty-six inches. This gave the true size of the animal as being just under six metres (twenty feet). The original skull measurement was given as thirty six inches. No-one knows whether this is a misprint, an exaggeration, or even if the original skull has been lost and replaced with that from a smaller animal.

Another infamous giant which was cut down to size by Bellaire, was a claimed ten metre (thirty-three foot) crocodile, that had been harpooned in the Bay of Bengal in 1940. The skull was measured at twenty-eight inches, and the total length of the animal was therefore given as only twenty-one feet (6.4 metres). It transpired later that the wrong skull had been measured, and that the skull of the Bay of Bengal crocodile, was much smaller - implying that its owner was not even 6.4 metres in length let alone the 10 metres claimed for it!

Persistent reports, however, argue that - exaggerations aside - Indopacific crocodiles can and do reach massive sizes.

The most famous of these is the creature witnessed in the 1950's by Rubber Plantation owner James Montgomery. Montgomery's plantation was near the Segama River in North Borneo. He claims to have shot twenty specimens between six and eight metres in length (twenty – twenty-six feet), to ensure the safety of workers who washed their laundry at the river.

One particular crocodile dwarfed even these. The local Seluka tribe believed that it was "The Father of the Devil" and threw silver coins into the water to appease it, bringing to mind the dragon-hoards of legend.

Investigating, Montgomery found the beast in question hauled out onto a sandbank. The crocodile filled the whole bank and had the end of its tail in the water. Wisely deciding to leave the monster well alone, Montgomery retreated. Returning later, he found that the sandbank on which the creature had been basking was nine metres (thirty feet) across indicating that the creature must have been in excess of ten metres (thirty-three feet) in length.

Along the Lupar River, (also in Northern Borneo), there once existed a similarly venerated reptile. Bujang Senang or "Happy Bachelor", was the 'King' of crocodiles. He was said to be 7.6m (twenty-five feet) long, and a known man-eater who had accounted for many victims. The Iban tribe worshiped this veritable leviathan - a situation worthy of a story by Edgar Rice-Burroughs or Henry Rider-Haggard!

The late Abang Idris - Chief of Police for the town of Sir Amen - led a ten-year hunt for the huge reptile.

Like *Moby Dick* - the Great White Whale chronicled by Herman Melville - Bujang Senang had outstanding markings - a large white blotch on his tail, and a white back. And like Melville's cetacean, he proved very hard to kill. A Mr. Pit, resident of Sarawak, claimed to have been amongst a group of men who slew Bujang Senang on the third of June 1990. Apparently, a huge crocodile grabbed and ate a woman along the Batang Lupar river - sixty miles east of Kuching. Her five year old child who witnessed this escaped. Mr Pit and his gang solicited the help of a *boto* - or witch-doctor - to help them draw the monster from the river. Once the creature appeared, the men attacked it with parangs - huge machetes similar to samurai swords - and axes. After a thirty-minute battle that hospitalised one of the men, they managed to hack through the iron-wood hard scales, and kill the animal. Its flesh was then sold to some Chinese people for cooking. They reportedly found silver watches, coins, and human hair in the crocodile's gut.

On Mr Pit's web-site, (now defunct), where he recounted this adventure, there was a photograph of the men standing next to the animal's corpse. Unfortunately there is no diagnostic white mark on the tail and the animal looked to be only around five metres (seventeen feet) long - far short of Bujang Senang's reported size.

The 'Happy Bachelor' was finally killed in May 1992. He proved to be somewhat short of the 7.5 metre mark. He was in fact "only" 5.9 metres (nineteen feet, three inches) in length, but he *did* have the trademark white colouration. From the base of his neck to the base of his tail, his dorsal-scutes were worn and bleached. This gave an almost white appearance.

The great naturalist Charles Gould, who wrote the seminal cryptozoological book *"Mythical Monsters"* (some 70 years before the term cryptozoology was coined), was well aware of giant crocodiles. A friend of his, Mr Dennys, a resident of Singapore, told him of a nine metre (thirty-foot) crocodile, that haunted a tidal creek that ran through the city in the 1880s. Another colleague - Mr Gregory, the Surveyor General of Queensland - informed him that Australia's northern rivers were home to crocodiles as long as a whale-boat (twenty-eight feet).

Another giant, still alive at the time of writing in February 2004, lives in the Bhitarkanika Wildlife Sanctuary in Orissa State in eastern India. It is over seven metres (twenty-three feet) in length, and three other animals in the same sanctuary have been reported as having achieved a length of over six metres (twenty feet).

Australia too still harbours giants. Malcolm Douglas, film maker and owner of the Broome Crocodile Park, encountered such a leviathan in a northern Australian river in 1987:

"We call him the "hippo". He dwarfs everything else I've ever seen. Compared with him the 16 foot 4 inch croc we did catch looked like a twelve footer...once we did have him alongside a net. The corks were three feet apart and his length covered eight corks along the net. Maybe a little more."

This would have made "Hippo" at least 7.5 metres (twenty-five feet) long.

In 1929 Claude Le Roy used gelignite to blow up a 7.5 metre (twenty-five foot) crocodile, in a hole just below Hartley's Creek Crocodile Farm, north of Cairns.

Another 7.5 metre (twenty-five foot) monster terrorized the Staaten river for fifty years. Known as 'The Wyabba Monster', the local Aborigines believed that it could never die as it was part of their 'dreaming' - or spiritual existence. Though shot at many times, the croc always shrugged off the bullets and carried on as normal. It was finally put paid to, by hunter Peter Cole in the mid 1950s.

An even larger specimen persists at the time of writing. At over eight metres (around twenty-eight feet), it inhabits the Guider river swamps of northern Arnhem Land.

In former times such a giant would have been more common. Hunting in the first half of the 20th century reduced the number of 'Salties', but since their protection in the early 1970s, the species has made a spectacular comeback in Australia. Soon there may be more reports like these of giant crocs in protected areas.

The largest specimens - of a truly mind boggling size - have been met with not in rivers but in the open sea. The Indopacific is the most pelagic of all crocodiles, having been encountered hundreds of miles from land. Larger than the biggest predatory shark - The Great White at a maximum of six metres (twenty feet) - it has nothing (except man) to fear.

One such sea-going encounter took place in The Gulf of Bengal in 1860. The crew and passengers of the ship *Nemesis* observed a giant crocodile at close range. One of the witnesses was the 'writer W. H. Marshall who described it in his book *Four Years in Burma*:

As The Nemesis was proceeding onwards towards our destination our attention was directed to an alligator of enormous length, which was swimming along against the tide '(here very strong), at a rate which was perfectly astonishing. I never beheld such a monster. It paused within a very short distance from us, it's head and nearly half it's body out of the water. I should think that it could not have been less than five and forty feet long measured from the head to the extremity of the tail, and I am confident that it was travelling at a rate of at least thirty miles an hour.

It should be noted that this animal would have been an Indopacific crocodile and NOT an alligator. Alligators only occur in China and North America. However, early European colonials often used incorrect names for animals, and these have stuck. In Australia, the Indopacific crocodile is often referred to as an alligator, and there is even an Alligator River. In Belize, Jaguars are called 'Tigers' and Spider-Monkeys 'Baboons'. In Australia, monitor lizards are mistakenly known as 'goannas' - a corruption of 'Iguana' - a purely New World animal.

Another man who mistakenly referred to Indopacific crocodiles as 'alligators' was British sea-captain and trader Alexander Hamilton. Whilst in the East Indies in 1705, his men were disturbed by 'alligators' whilst working on a stage, rigged alongside their ship. They fired musket-balls at the creatures, but could not penetrate their armour. One lucky shot finally struck a creature in the eye and entered the brain. The following day they came across the carcass on the shore. They measured it at twenty-seven and a half feet.

The most recent sighting of a giant Indopacific croc comes from the Indonesian island of Ternate. In February of 2002, the seven metre (twenty-three foot) giant had taken up residence in a river close to two villages. It had eaten four people. The headless corpse of its latest victim, a teenaged boy, was found close to the giant's lair.

It is fitting indeed that the other species of crocodile with a claim to having attained monstrous proportions inhabits the dark continent of Africa. The 'Cradle of Man' has a deep hold on our subconscious. If giant reptiles are to exist anywhere it must be here. Despite the depredations of the white-man, and the homespun wars and famines that have plagued its post-colonial history, the heart of the African continent still remains an enigma.

Crocodylus niloticus (The Nile Crocodile), is the world's second largest known species of reptile, and has long been know as a maneater. Worshipped by the Egyptians as 'Sebek' - The God of the Nile - and by innumerable sub-Saharan tribes, this is indeed a frightening animal.

Its prey includes lions, giraffe, buffalo and even black rhino! As with the Indopacific crocodile, it is not adverse to adding humans to its menu.

Some remarkable film illustrating the Nile crocodile's power was taken on the Mara river in Tanzania in 1999. A documentary film crew were recording a group of crocodiles devouring the carcass of a hippo at night. A pride of lions attempted to steal the body and paid dearly. A crocodile sized a lioness, dragged her underwater and killed her with the ease of a bull terrier despatching a rat.

The largest 'official' specimen was shot in 1905 at Mwanza, a hundred km east of Emin Pasha Gulf by the Duke of Mecklenburg. It measured 6.6m (twenty-one feet) in length. This monster, however, pales in comparison to some of the other crocodiles that have been reported by some naturalists and explorers.

The renowned wildlife photographer Cherry Kearton (1871-1940), and his friend James Barns observed an 8.2m (twenty-seven foot) crocodile basking on a sandbank in the Semliki River in Uganda. The size was estimated against other crocodiles and nearby objects. A photograph was published in one of Kearton's books - *In the Land of the Lion,* and apparently the crocodile in question dwarfs its companions. (I found a copy of this book in a second hand book shop in York. The only photo of a crocodile in the book has no other crocodiles for comparison so is of little use. My copy is a sixth edition however, and may not contain the same picture as Kearton's original.)

A 7.93 metres (twenty-six foot) specimen was claimed by a Captain Riddick who is alleged to have shot it at Lake Kioga in Uganda, and another of similar size was killed on the Mbaka River (in what is now Tanzania), in 1903. This was recorded by the experienced field-naturalist Hans Besser. At first he mistook the reptile for a huge canoe half drawn out of the water. It was 7.6 metres (twenty-four feet) long but part of the tail was missing. (Perhaps it had been bitten off by an even bigger crocodile!) The body was ninety-three cm, (three feet, six inches) high, and was 4.6m (14.72 feet) in girth. The skull was 1.4m (4.48 feet) long.

In 1954 Guy de la Ruwiere saw a seven metre (twenty-three foot) crocodile in the Maika marshes in the north east Congo. The animal lifted its massive head out of the water several times. It caused a huge wave when it dived beneath the surface.

One must be careful when estimating size. My colleague Dr Lars Thomas, of the University of Copenhagen, was told by some hunters that they had shot a thirty-five foot crocodile in northern Australia. Dr Thomas had the men show him the carcass and it turned out to be only eighteen feet long. The men had been quite sincere but had not brought a tape measure with them.

World famous explorer Colonel John Blashford-Snell (since 2001, the Hon. Life President of the Centre for Fortean Zoology), heard tales of ten metre (thirty-three foot) crocodiles in Ethiopia's Blue Nile Gorge but personally saw none above six metres (twenty feet)!

One man who is very adept at estimating size is Rupert Bunts. Mr Bunts had been a soldier in Rhodesia, (now Zimbabwe), in the early 1970s, and one of his jobs was to intercept terrorists from neighbouring Zambia. The easiest way to tell if a man was indeed a terrorist was by his boots - Zambian boots being different from Rhodesian ones. On one occasion a suspect ran into the water in the southern end of Lake Kariba in an attempt to swim away from the patrols. The ill-fated fellow was seized and bitten in two by an immense crocodile. Rupert and his companions opened fire on the giant reptile with high-powered SLR rifles. These weapons can send a bullet through a brick wall at the range of a mile. Not even the armour-plate of such a monster could withstand this barrage. Once the titan lay still they drew alongside in a boat. When dragged ashore and cut open, the luckless victim's legs were retrieved. He was indeed a Zambian.

I asked Mr Bunts how large the crocodile was. To my amazement he told me it was between twenty-five and thirty feet long. (I had been interviewing him on a totally unrelated matter when the conversation strayed onto his years in Africa). Mr Bunts was sure of this, as he was used to estimating distance and size as part of his job. Unfortunately, none of the men knew the zoological importance of the specimen and no photos were taken, or samples kept.

More recently a man-eating giant was uncovered by French environmentalist Patrice Faye. The seven metre (twenty-three foot) creature was named 'Gustave' by Faye and his team. His home is on the Burundi side of the Rusizi Delta. Gustave is estimated to be between eighty and a hundred years old, and may have eaten more humans than any other individual crocodile alive. In the past year alone (2002/3) he is *known* to have eaten seventeen people. Locals say he has been dining on man-flesh for over thirty years, so his human victim-tally must be mind boggling.

Patrice and his colleagues are attempting to capture Gustave alive, and put him on display as a tourist attraction. They hope that this will boost the finances of the Rusizi Game Reserve that is currently being regenerated. He is already raking in tourists despite the wars raging in both Burundi and The Democratic Republic of The Congo. Twice before, the French team has attempted to capture Gustave and failed. The third attempt took place between May and December 2003, and was again a failure.

The island of Madagascar has often been touted as a possible lair of giant crocodiles. These were given a name (*Crocodylus robustus*). However the sub-fossil remains were thought to be a giant form of an animal related to the Dwarf Crocodile (*Osteolaemus tetraspis*), which did indeed reach a length of ten metres (thirty-three feet). It is probable that this crocodile grew to such large proportions in order to feed on *Aepyornis maximus*, The Madagascan Elephant Bird. This giant ratite was - in terms of bulk at least - one of the world's largest birds, and was forced into extinction around about the 14th Century by the predations of hunting humans and climatic changes. The Madagascan crocodile also had raised 'horns' above each eye - much like the smaller caimans of South America. Without this large prey species, the giant Madagascan crocodile became extinct, leaving behind only its more modestly-proportioned relatives.

The largest reported crocodiles on the African continent hail from that last great African frontier - the Congo rainforest. They are known to the Lingala and other Congolese people as 'Mahamba'. This lord of the jungle is said to reach a shocking fifteen metres (fifty feet) in length!

In the late 19th Century, Belgian explorer John Reinhardt Werner reported sightings of giant crocodiles that lend some weight to the terrifying folk tales of the native population.

Whilst travelling down the Congo on *The Aja* - a 12.8m (forty-two foot) steam launch - Werner stopped at a sand bank to shoot ducks. He shot one and pursued others over a low ridge when he saw:

...The biggest crocodile I have ever seen. Comparing him to the Aja which lay in deep water some three hundred yards off, I reckoned him to be quite fifty feet long: whilst the centre of the saw-ridged back must have been some four feet off the ground where his belly rested.

Werner stupidly took another shot at the ducks - they had run out of meat on the ship - and alarmed the monster which made off into the water. The creature was also witnessed by a native-boy that Werner had with him.

Around three days later Werner saw another vast specimen. *The Aja* had embedded itself in a sandbank when it was heaved up out of the water by something causing a commotion under the ship:

I saw an enormous crocodile - longer I am certain than the Aja - rush across the bank and tumble into the deep water beyond. I never before saw such a large crocodile move so fast, and I had no time to get a shot at him. He must have heard us coming and was trying to make for the deep water on our side of the bank, when we ran into him and hammed him onto the sand. We struck him, moving at a rate of four miles per hour, but during the short time he was in view I could not see that he bore any marks of the collision!

It would be as well now to pause and reflect on the dimensions of such a huge crocodile. A 7.5 metre (twenty-five foot) creature would be an awesome animal in the two to three ton weight bracket. A fifteen metre (fifty foot) animal would be of a colossal weight. When an animal doubles its size its weight increases eightfold. This is because length, breadth, depth and height have *all* been doubled. If we take the conservative estimate of two tons for the weight of a 7.5 metre specimen, then an animal fifteen metres in length would weigh in the region of fifteen tons - three times the weight of an average elephant! If crocodiles of these dimensions do exist then they are the largest macro-predators on the planet. Most of the Great Whales are plankton feeders, and even the toothed sperm whale feeds mainly on small fish and squid (the giant squid forms only 1% of its diet, and weighs far less than the sperm whale in any case). Such a giant crocodilian would be surpassed only by the giant marine reptiles of the Mesozoic and possibly the largest carnivorous dinosaurs. (Palaeontologist Gregory. S. Paul postulates a maximum weight of twenty tons for the largest Tyrannosaurs, and this seems to have been confirmed by a recently excavated specimen of this dinosaur.). If they do indeed exist, there is no animal on earth that could possibly withstand an attack from one of these giant saurians.

It is obvious that we are not dealing with whole races of gargantuan crocodiles – but rather a few massively large individuals. If they were prehistoric survivors of a giant race then many more specimens would have turned up!

So what is it that causes certain crocodiles to become so large?

I believe that it is a combination of several factors.

Both Nile and Indopacific crocodiles have large distributions. Within their range many sub-species can exist, and these may display large variations in size. A striking example is found along the Aswa River in Northern Uganda. Crocodiles here reach sexual maturity at between 1.5 and 1.8 metres (4.9 to 5.9 feet) and never exceed 2.1m (seven feet). This is less than half the average size. This tiny race has an unusually large head 30.5cm long. This should yield a total length of 2.13 metres, but the Aswa crocodiles fall far short of this. It seems that this is a product of prolonged periods of aestivation; the retarded development being due to this inactivity. It would seem that this is a strategy that has been developed to avoid food shortages.

Other areas such as Lake Malawi, The Congo, parts of Tanzania, (such as the Grumati River) and the Semliki River in Uganda/Zaire produce larger than average specimens.

Where populations of these larger than average animals have remained undisturbed, occasional freaks will be thrown up within the genetic variation that are much larger than the average. The average man is five foot nine inches tall - but a lot of the population exceed this. Most big cities have several seven foot individuals and the record human height is eight foot, 11.9 inches. A large population of "Big Crocodiles" most of whom would reach five metres (seventeen feet) could throw up seven or eight metre (twenty-three – twenty-six foot) specimens occasionally.

Diet is also a factor. Once it was believed that very big crocodilians were immensely old. It was thought that crocodilians grow roughly twelve inches a year until they achieve the length of three metres (ten feet), when the growth rate radically slows down. By this logic to be immensely huge a crocodile must have achieved a great age.

Actually, the greatest authenticated age for a crocodilian is a fifty six year old American Alligator (*Alligator missippipiensis*) at Dresden Zoo.

A crocodile of unknown species died at Yetkatrinaburg in Russia a few years ago, at a reputed age of over seventy years, but this was never - as far as I am aware - properly authenticated.

However, in a paradox - unlike mammals and birds - reptiles seem to live longer in the wild than in captivity.

A female Nile Crocodile called 'Lutemba' lived for many years in a small bay of the Murchison Gulf in Lake Victoria. She was the closest thing to a 'tame' Nile Crocodile ever recorded. Natives fed her fish and she came like a dog when her name was called. In the 1920s she became quite a tourist attraction and a source of revenue. She features in Cherry Kearton's film *Tembi*. At this time she was about 4.25 metres (fourteen feet) long, which is an average size for an adult male, but quite large for an adult female of this species. She was probably at least twenty years old.

Some reports say that she had lived in the area since the 19th Century, and had been used as a Royal Executioner by Ugandan Kings (as, indeed they were used by Idi Amin in the Uganda of the 1970's). This does not – however - seem to fit in with her reportedly placid nature. She disappeared in the mid 1940s at an age of between forty-five and fifty, but possibly considerably older if she had indeed lived in the years of the Ugandan Kings (pre 1894).

Protein intake seems to have more to do with large size than age. In the early 1970s the Louisiana department of Wildlife and Fisheries made some interesting discoveries relating to diet and growth rate in the American Alligator (*Alligator mississippiensis*). Two groups of juveniles were reared on different diets. One was fed coypu (a large South American rodent *Myocastor coypu*) flesh and the other fish.

- Nutritional analyses showed that coypu contained 14.9% crude protein, 2.1% crude fat, 0.1% crude fibre, and 45% moisture.

- Fish, on the other hand, contained 9.9% protein, 4.0% fat, 1.0% fibre, and 60.6% moisture.

Specimens fed on coypu grew 20% larger than their fish-fed peers, over a period of three years. They were also more active and aggressive.

Food with more protein content causes accelerated growth. The Aswa crocodiles were tiny due to aestivation brought on by seasonal food shortages. In other areas where protein-rich food is plentiful all year, the average size of the crocodile population was much greater. So, if we conceive of a population of naturally big crocodiles, feeding on protein-rich prey, that occasionally produces a giant freak whose size is increased still further by its diet, then one can conceive of a truly vast animal.

Tropical seas and teeming rain forests would offer such an abundance of prey. It can be no coincidence that the largest reported crocodiles are seen in these very habitats.

It should be noted that the Indian gharial (*Gavialis gangetius)* has also been credited with huge sizes. Lorenz Hagenbeck - son of Karl Hageback world famous animal dealer - cited one such account. One of his friends was said to have shot a nine metre (thirty foot) gharial whose bloated carcass looked like that of a stranded whale! However reports of such giants in this species seem unknown today.

The crocodile/dragon link goes beyond just giant specimens and offerings of coins. Many crocodiles were displayed as dragons in the past.

The town of Brno in what is now the Czech republic was terrorised by a dragon in the 1600s. The monster devoured townsfolk and livestock until a cunning knight baited the brute with the skin of a calf slaked with lime. The dragon swallowed this whole and was overcome with thirst. Upon drinking, the lime reacted with the water blowing the beast apart. The body was pieced together and hung in Brno's town hall. It is there to this day.

The dragon is in fact a 4 metre crocodile. It was probably given as a gift to a local nobleman by visiting Turkish dignitaries. The animal possibly escaped and killed several locals until the cold of winter put paid to it.

The monster exhibited in Durham in 1568 was almost certainly a crocodile. The event is recorded in the *St Nicholas Register*:

A certain Italian brought into the city of Durham, on the 11th day of the above said, a very great, strange and monstrous serpent, in length sixteen feet, in quantity and dimensions greater than a horse; which was taken by special police in Aethiopia, within The Turk's dominions. But before it was killed it hade devoured (as credibly thought) more than 1,000 persons and destroyed a whole country.

Other stuffed crocodiles purported to be dragons were displayed at the church of Santa Maria delle Grazie, near Mantua in Italy, the cathedral of Abbeville in France, and the churches at Marseilles, Lyon, Chimiers and Ragusta. In the journal *Folk-Lore* in 1898 a writer calling him/herself 'AHS', reported that the skin of a dragon supposedly killed by St Bertrand hanging in the cathedral at Commingues in France was in fact a crocodile skin. At Mons in Belgium, the head of a dragon said to have been slain by the 12th Century knight, Gilles de Chin, was exposed as a crocodile skull some seven-hundred years later.

One of the most celebrated English dragon legends seems to have its beginnings with an escaped crocodile. A translation of a document dating to 1402 runs thus:

Close to the town of Bures, near Sudbury, there has lately appeared, to the great hurt of the countryside, a dragon, vast in body, with a crested head, teeth like a saw, and a tail extending to an enormous length. Having slaughtered the shepherd of a flock it devoured many sheep. There came forth in order to shoot at him with arrows the work men of the lord on whose estate he had concealed himself, being Sir Richard Waldergrave, Knight: but the dragon's body, though struck by the archers, remained unhurt, for the arrows bounced off his back as if it were iron or hard rock. Those arrows that fell upon the spine of his back gave out a sound, as they struck it a ringing or tinkling sound, just as if they had hit a brazen plate, then flew away off by reason of the hide of this great beast being impenetrable. Thereupon, in order to destroy him, all the country people around were summoned. But when the dragon saw that he was again about to be assailed with arrows, he fled into a marsh or mere and there hid himself among the long reeds, and was no more seen.

The neighbouring town of Wormingford claim that this story happened there and not in Bures. In the Wormingford version the dragon was in fact a "crockadrill" brought back by Richard 1st (1157-1199 r. 1183-1199), from The Third Crusade for his menagerie in The Tower of London. The reptile escaped, and made its way through Essex to the River Stour. Its reign of terror was final curbed by Sir George de la Haye, when he slew it after a fearful battle in a field called 'Bloody Meadows'. In the Worminford story the monster is described as having short limbs with great nails or talons and a long curved tail.

The descriptions from both legends do indeed sound remarkably like a crocodile. These creatures were brought back to England and displayed. If one did escape into rural areas it would have caused panic. To folk who were used only to wolves and bears at the worst a six-nine metre (twenty-thirty foot) reptile would have surely seemed like a nightmare from hell!

Crocodilians were known as dragons to the ancient Chinese. The Chinese alligator (*Alligator sinensis*) was known as the earth dragon. Due to its armoured scales it was believed to be a harbinger of war. Zue Qiuming, the author of *The Zuozhaun* (somewhere between 722 and 484 B.C), records that its call was believed to foretell rain and its alternative name was 'The Swine-Woman's Dragon' (for reasons unknown).

These creatures were captive bred as far back as 2600 B.C. The ever enlightening Qiuming mentions that, in the reign of Huangdi (the Yellow Emperor) and Shun there were specialist dragon breeders of great skill. These two emperors were said to have lived around 2600 to 2200 B.C. well before the established dynasties of China.

As recently as 1869 a baby dragon was exhibited in China. English traveller and naturalist Robert Swinhoe (1836-1877) wrote:

In February of 1869, some Chinese were exhibiting, in the native city of Shanghi[sic] what they called a dragon, which they declared had been dug out of a hole in the province of Shense. It was a young crocodile four feet long... They made so much money by showing it that they refused to sell it. I cannot, of course, guess its species.

It was identified as an alligator rather than a crocodile by A. A. Fauvel of the Imperial Chinese Maritime Customs. Also honorary curator of The Shanghai Museum, he was the first to scientifically describe the Chinese alligator. At the time other specimens were being kept in temples at Nanking.

The Indopacific crocodile lived until recently in southern China. If the diminutive Chinese alligator (at two metres) could have such an effect on Chinese culture, what effect would the nine metre, maneating "salty" have? Our old friend Qiuming tells us that this feared creature was known as the "flood dragon". Perhaps this is because it came into contact with man mainly by being swept into inhabited areas by flood waters.

It is only natural that humans associated it with weather control. Marco Polo - centuries later - was told of great, maneating dragons that inhabited the waters of China. Many have taken these to have been Chinese alligators, but it is more likely they were Indopacific crocodiles. Unlike most dragons, the Chinese seemed to have feared and hated the flood-dragon. Indopacific crocodiles were hunted with bow-and-arrow, and waters that they inhabited were poisoned by lime. It may now be extinct in China.

During the reign of Emperor Yuandi, (48-33 B.C), crocodiles in some southern areas had become a particular menace - killing both humans and livestock. A local governor called Han Yu read a proclamation to the creatures directly. It seemed that people were afraid to hunt the reptiles on account of their draconic nature. The proclamation seems to have been some kind of experiment to see if the crocodiles were truly dragons.

After attracting them with goat and cow carcasses. Han Yu addressed them under the Emperor's authority, and gave them seven days to move away from the area and closer to the coast. The Emperor was supposed to have been given the right to rule by none less than the 'Dragon-Emperor' who ruled all dragons. If the crocodiles ignored the demands, then they were either disobeying their own ruler, or were just beasts with the *appearance* of dragons.

Crocodiles appear to have become fair game after this. Crocodile meat was much esteemed and often eaten at marriage feasts. The tail however was believed to be poisonous. This is interesting as the Egyptians symbolised death and darkness as a crocodile's tail. The scaly hide was made into drums that were used in ceremonies to bring forth rain.

Marco Polo (1254-1324), told of dragon-like monsters in the province of Carajan, part of Yunnan in southern China:

Very great serpents are bred in this country, some of which are ten paces in length and in thickness ten spans. They have two little feet before near the head, with three talons or claws like lions, and eyes bigger than a loaf, shining very bright. They have their mouths and jaws so very wide that they are able to swallow a man, great and sharp teeth; nor is their any man or other living creature which can behold these serpents without terror. There are also some less, of eight, six, or five paces long, which are taken after this manner: in the daytime they used to lie hid, by reason of the heat, in holes, out of which they go at night to seek their prey and devour whatsoever they get, lions, wolves, as well as other beasts, and then they go to seek water leaving such a track through their weight in the sands as if a piece of timber had been drawn there; whereupon the hunters fasten under the sands great iron spikes, in their usual tracks, whereby they are wounded and slain. The crows presently proclaim the serpent's fate and by their cries invite the hunters who come and flay him, taking out his gall which is used for divers medicines, amongst other things for the biting of mad dogs, a pennyweight given in wine; and for women in travail; for carbuncles and other distempers, and they sell the flesh dear as being exceedingly delicate.

The description is obvious to any herpetologist worth his salt. Marco Polo is describing Indopacific crocodiles. These animals formally inhabited this part of southern China and might even still stray across the borders from Myanmar, Laos, and Vietnam.

Strangely, there have been reports of crocodiles in another dragon-haunted country; Korea. Korea would seem to be too far north and too cool for such animals. No crocodilians are known in this country today. However, Henry Hamel, the yeoman of a Dutch ship wrecked on the coast of Korea in 1598, wrote:

In Korea the rivers are often pestered with alligators or crocodiles of several sizes; some are 18 to 20 ells long; the eye is small but very sharp; the teeth are placed like those of a comb. When they eat they move only the upper jaw… three children were once found in a crocodile's belly.

In fact, crocodiles move the lower jaw when eating. The upper jaw is at one with the rest of the skull. An ell is an old measurement equivalent to forty-five inches. This yields a maximum length for the Korean crocs of nine-hundred inches or around sixty feet!

One wonders how many early travellers in the orient were shown dragons worshiped in temples, that were in reality crocodiles. German traveller Englebert Kaemfer encountered a dragon worshiped in a Japanese temple in 1690.

He tells us that he saw:

A huge four footed snake, scaly all over the body like a crocodile with sharp prickles along the back; the head beyond the rest monstrous and terrible.

From his description, the creature seemed to be a crocodile. He even refers to a crocodile in his description.

Kaemfer had almost certainly not viewed a living crocodile prior to this. Almost identical stories are told from Polynesia. On Hawaii a monster called *Kihawahine* - who resembled a huge lizard - was said to reside in a pond close to the palace of the hawaiian Royal Family - whom she protected. A similar god - *Moko* - was worshiped in the Cook Islands. Once again, the deity was described as a giant aquatic lizard, and must have been based on a crocodile.

The power and influence of the crocodile should never be underestimated. Even as far afield as New Zealand, where crocodiles have never occurred, there are legends of a giant, savage, water-reptile that sized unwary humans and devoured them. The *Taniwha* seems to have been based on stories about crocodiles handed down by The Maori's Polynesian ancestors and transferred to the rivers and lakes of their new home.

GIANT LIZARDS

In 1884 the great Victorian naturalist Charles Gould wrote a fascinating tome entitled *Mythical Monsters – Fact or Fiction*. This book was published only 25 years after Darwin's *The Origin of Species*, and postulated the zoological existence of supposedly legendary creatures. Herein Gould tackled such absentees from the ark as the unicorn , the phoenix, the sea serpent, and most importantly the dragon. After tracing draconic history for several chapters he comes to the following conclusions on the nature of dragons.

We may infer that it was a long terrestrial lizard, hibernating, and carnivorous, with the power of constricting with it's snake like body and tail; possibly furnished with wing like expansions of it's integument, after the fashion of Draco volans , and capable of occasional progress on its hind legs alone, when excited in attack. It appears to have been protected by armour and projecting spikes, like those of **Moloch horridus** *and* **Megalania prisca**, *and was possibly more nearly allied to this last form than to any other which has yet come to our knowledge. Probably it preferred sandy, open country to forest land, its habitat was the high land of central Asia, and the time of its disappearance about that of the Biblical Deluge discussed in a previous chapter.*

Although, it probably, in common with most reptiles, enjoyed frequent bathing, and when not so engaged, or basking in the sun, secluded itself under some overhanging terrestrial bank or cavern. The idea of its fondness for swallows, and power of attracting them, mentioned in some traditions, may not impossibly have been derived from these birds hawking around and through it's open jaws in pursuit of flies attracted to the viscid humours of it's mouth. We know that at the present day a bird, the trochilus of the ancients, freely enters the open mouth of the crocodile, and rids it of parasites affecting its teeth and jaws.

In a way, Gould came closer to the truth than anyone suspected.

In 1912 the zoological world was rocked by the discovery of a seemingly prehistoric monster on a remote trio of islands in Indonesia. The whole scenario ran like the plot of an outlandish Edgar Rice-Burroughs novel. The most notorious of the group was Komodo - a speck of an island only twenty-five miles long and 240 square miles in area. It had an evil reputation; The Sultan of Sumbawa - a neighbouring island in the chain - used it as a penal colony, marooning wrong-doers, political rivals, and other undesirables upon this formally uninhabited fastness. Occasionally pearl-fishers would happen upon its shores. Those who returned told hair-raising tales.

Stories began to circulate of a crocodilian monster lurking undiscovered on Komodo. It was up to twenty-three feet long, armed with cruel teeth and claws, and with an appetite for human-flesh. It became known as the *ora* or *boeaja darat* (land crocodile), and its infamy soon reached the ears or western scientists.

The director of Java's Botanical Gardens in Jakarta (Djakata), Major P. A. Ouwens took an interest in the riddle. The first report from a westerner had come in when an aviator had made an emergency landing on Komodo, and found his plane surrounded by what he described as "horrible dragons". Ouwens contacted J. K. H van Steyn van Hensbroek, the Governor of Flores, a larger island to the east of Komodo. This gloriously-named gentleman was a keen naturalist. In true Professor Challenger style, he sallied forth on an expedition into the dragon's lair.

Now more sightings by westerners emerged, and Henbroek enlisted the aid of two of these witnesses. A pair of Dutch pearl-fishermen - named Kock and Alderon - claimed to have encountered these brutes, and once on this 'Devil's Island', they led the Governor to the hut of a local man, where he examined the skin of an *ora*. Later on the monster's spoor was discovered, and finally in true colonial style Henbroek "bagged" a specimen.

At seven feet four inches, the creature fell far short of the claimed size. Neither was it a crocodile. Komodo's killer beast was a giant varanid or monitor lizard. Soon after, four live specimens were captured for the Botanical Gardens. The largest was 9. 5 feet long. The giant was named *Varanus komodoensis*; the Komodo Dragon.

With a maximum recorded size of 10 feet 2 inches, the Komodo dragon is the largest known living lizard. A bulky animal, it can rival a lioness in weight, and is *far* more formidably armed. Covered in mail-like scales, it has claws like butcher's meat-hooks, but its teeth are the deadliest weapon in its arsenal. Razor-sharp, these backward-curving ivory daggers are serrated like steak-knives. As well as slicing the prey's flesh, these serrations trap slivers of meat. These soon become rancid, and a breeding ground for virulent bacteria. Dragons are ambush hunters - lurking predators that lunge at victims inflicting deep slashing bites. Even if the initial attack fails to bring the prey down, the unfortunate animal is doomed as the dragon's microscopic allies infect the victim's bloodstream causing death within days. The dragons have an excellent sense of smell, and the patience of Job. Tasting the air with a flickering forked tongue and a Jacobson's organ like that of a snake, (to whom varanid lizards are closely related), in the roof of the mouth, the dragons relentlessly stalk the wounded creature following the pungent stench of the rotting, open wound. These horrid injuries are prevented from healing by the bacteria and will weep pus like an invitation to the predators who doggedly home-in.

There are reports of Komodo dragons reaching far greater lengths than commonly excepted. A pair of Germans were said to have shot a specimen in World War Two that was sixteen feet (nearly five metres) in length. The men lashed their prize to a pole, and carried it back to their boat. As they headed out to sea the dragon revived, the bullets having only stunned it! The irate reptile tore free of its bonds, and sunk the boat, forcing the men to swim for their lives. Another report tells of a seven metre (twenty-three foot) individual sighted on a remote beach.

The dragons feed mainly on deer, wild-swine, and carrion, but thanks to their unique mode of killing by infection, they can tackle animals many times as large as themselves, (such as water-buffalo). It seems that this mode of attack evolved to allow the dragons to predate upon pigmy stegodont elephants that once shared their island home. This puts one in mind of the ancient Greek philosopher's insistence that dragons killed and ate elephants and raises the fascinating conjecture that stegodonts may have lingered longer into historic times than anyone realised. After the extinction of their pachyderm prey, the dragons switched their attentions to smaller animals.

Man has also fallen prey to these magnificent reptiles. In 1975 a Swiss banker holidaying on Komodo unwisely strayed off the designated path. Ambushed by a dragon he was eaten before anyone knew he was missing. More recently a man stupid enough to go jogging in dragon territory was torn to ribbons. One can readily imagine the horror of being attacked by a 10 foot, elephant-killing lizard, exploding from the undergrowth jaws-agape. The rank, pestilent-breath, and constantly flickering yellow tongue dancing like flames about the maw, make this lizard a convincing (if modestly sized) dragon. Now imagine it three times the length and sixteen times the weight - a reptilian nightmare from the worst visions of a mediaeval artist. Surely such a creature could not exist? Well it did, and in all probability still does!

The Pleistocene Epoch (2 million-10 thousand years ago), was typified by the proliferation of megafauna. Animals of huge size lived on all the continents (with the exception of Antarctica). Australia played host to some of the most bizarre and amazing. These included:

- **Diprotodon**   a semi-aquatic hippo sized wombat.
- **Procoptodon**, a 10 foot tall kangaroo.
- **Nototherium**   a marsupial "rhino".
- **Palorchestes**   that sported an elephantine trunk.
- **Genyornis**   a giant flightless, carnivorous duck! It was so massive
                    it even dwarfed the moas of New Zealand and the Madagascan elephant bird.

To prey upon this surreal cavalcade of antipodean herbivores, equally strange carnivores evolved. The mammalian hunters remained modest in size such as *Thylacoleo carnifex* the marsupial "big cat", and *Thylacinus cynocephalus* the thylacine or marsupial "wolf", both of which are rumoured to survive today. The reptiles, however, reached a vast-size; giant pythons such as *Wonambi* - as thick about as oil drums, giant land dwelling crocodiles, (the genuine article this time!) such as *Quinkana* that galloped after prey on hoof like claws and tore it apart with teeth akin to those of *Tyrannosaurs rex*.

The most spectacular reptilian macro-predator must have been the giant varanid *Megalania prisca*. This immense lizard reached lengths of 30 feet - rivalling the largest contemporary crocodiles. Much like a scaled-up Komodo dragon, *Megalania* preyed on the large herbivores of its time, although due to its sheer size and power it probably relied less on viral killing. The projecting armour mentioned by Gould in fact belonged to a giant tortoise, *Meiolania*, whose fossil remains had been jumbled up with *Megalania*'s. The Aborigines arrived about twenty-thousand years ago. Sharing their environment with such a monster was daunting indeed, and *Megalania* – almost certainly a maneater - etched itself onto the Aboriginal culture. The vast beast became *Mungoon-galli* - 'The Goanna Bunyip'. The natives believed that *Mungoon-galli* whipped-up sand-storms with his mighty tail, in much the same way as the Chinese believed that dragons controlled the weather. This is one of the many 'coincidences' to be found when one studies dragonlore world wide.

Around ten thousand years ago, Australia's climate began to change. It became more arid, the rainforests retreated north, and the inland waterways shrunk. At the same time, the humans exploited the new dryness and began to light enormous bush-fires. Bush-fires are a natural part of many tropical areas during the dry season, but sustained fires with climate change and human hunting was too much for many of Australia's megafauna, and the giant marsupials and birds disappeared.

With its prey gone, *Megalania* was presumed to have followed them into extinction. But this may not have been the case. The Komodo dragon survived the extinction of its elephantine prey by hunting smaller creatures. There is no reason that *Megalania* could not have done the same. It should be noted, that as well as the modestly-sized indigenous fauna, there are many introduced species in Australia. These include feral Asian water-buffalo and dromedary camels.

The Aborigines have always told of encountering giant-lizards, but as Australia began to be colonised by white men, they too crossed paths with the lord of the outback. One of the first sightings took place in 1890 at the village of Euroa, Victoria. A thirty-foot lizard came lumbering out of the bush causing panic and leaving a trail of king-sized footprints. A posse of forty men, armed with guns and nets, set out with cattle-dogs to trap the monster. The beast had other ideas, however, and vanished into the scrub to be seen no more.

Many disappearances in the trackless bush-land have been blamed on *Megalania*. Whilst this is unproven it remains a disturbing possibility. In 1955 at Loadstone on the Queensland/New South Wales border, a timber-cutter was working deep in a forest when one of these monsters lunged out of the shadows and bit into his hand. The lizard cleanly severed several of his fingers. His screams alerted a co-worker who - in Saint George style - grabbed a railroad spike and rammed it into the dragon's head before it could complete its kill. The beast measured 20 feet.

Length. When the two returned with colleagues several days later the corpse was gone - presumably eaten by another, larger dragon.

Three other loggers were more fortunate in May 1961. They were in a remote part of the Wauchop forest (New South Wales). Having marked some trees for felling, the trio sat down to brew tea in a previously cleared area. This place was now covered in rotting wood and the loggers heard the crunching of something large approaching them. Looking up they saw a titanic lizard bearing down on them from an embankment. Fleeing in terror the three locked themselves in their truck and watched horrified as the dragon stalked across the dirt track and back into the forest. All agreed that its length was thirty feet, and that it held its body three feet off the ground.

Perhaps the most important sighting happened in 1979 in the Wattagan mountains (New South Wales), as it involved a professional herpetologist - a scientist who specialises in the study of reptiles! Frank Gorden had taken his four-wheel-drive Landrover into the mountains to look for tiny lizards known as water skinks. After several unfruitful hours searching, Gorden returned to his vehicle and noticed a large "log" lying on a 6 foot high bank next to the land-rover. Gorden couldn't recall this log being there before, but thought nothing of it until he turned the ignition, causing the "log" to rear up on four powerful legs and charge off into the woods. Gorden, who was left in a mild state of shock, estimated it to be 28-30 feet long in comparison to his land-rover. It is highly appropriate that after failing to find any tiny lizards he found one very big one! When a recognised expert in the field sees an animal like this - close up and with a frame of reference for size - doubts about its existence are seriously eroded.

These giants are usually described as being a mottled grey-green in colour, and as in the sighting above are often mistaken for fallen trees. Perhaps this is a form of camouflage employed in the ambush hunting employed by *Megalania*. In another case, also from the Wattagans, two farmers stopped their land-rover to move a log that was blocking the road in front of them. Once again, the dead-wood became animate, transforming into monster far longer than the twenty-foot road was wide. Fortunately, (as the men were outside the vehicle and approaching the monster in blissful ignorance), it could not have been hungry as it merely sauntered off into the bushes.

Further north in New South Wales, is one of the largest subtropical rainforests in Australia - the Limpwood Nature Reserve. The reserve is a vast plateau of undisturbed forest. It has sheer escarpments and forms part of the Macpherson Range that runs between New South Wales and Queensland. The northern portion is part of a 20 million year old extinct volcano whose lava-core now stands as Mount Warning.

In 1984, the late Peter Sleeman was walking through the forest. He was in a stand of what had been dry eucalyptus that had been logged and had subsequently been taken over by the imported Central American shrub lantana. As he walked round a bush of lantana, he clearly heard footsteps following him. Cautious as to who might be following him in such a remote area, he side-tracked down a natural pathway to a small clearing, and waited for his stalker to emerge.

To his horror, it was not a person but a giant monitor that lumbered around the corner. It resembled the lace monitor (*Varanus verius)* except for its huge size. The lace monitor has a head around fifteen centimetres (six inches) long. This giant's head was four times this size, and was held around one metre (three feet) from the ground. He only observed the head, front legs and front-portion of the body. The animal flickered out its forked tongue and tasted the air. Sleeman realized - with dread - that he was being hunted.

Luckily, it seemed Sleeman's hiding-place was good, and the monster went upon its way. Sleeman left the area and never returned. Scaling his lizard up four-times from a lace monitor, we can estimate a creature between six and eight metres (twenty to twenty-six feet) long. He passed the story on to the brother of Gary Opit, a respected Australian zoologist with many years field experience, who hosts an environmental programme on 2RN North Coast ABC Radio. Gary and his brother explored the area but found no trace of the dragon.

Another report investigated by Gary was a sighting by a woman near Brunswick Heights at the mouth of The Brunswick River. The lizard was sprawled across the road on Fingle Street, and covered the entire width - some six metres (twenty feet). It rose up and walked off into the bushes of the reserve.

New South Wales does not have the monopoly on dragons. Many other areas seem to be inhabited by them. The Nullarbor plain in South Australia is one such place. The plain is riddled with sinkholes and catacombs like a vast piece of stilton cheese. Like the caverns of ancient Europe these are said to be dragon lairs.

In 1940 an aboriginal family made camp close to the catacombs. They slept outside of their truck – off-road. One of the children wandered off at sunset, and despite a frantic search could not be found. Next morning a trail of out-sized lizard prints and the mark of a long, heavy tail were found leading into one of the caves. It was assumed that a *Mungoon-galli* had emerged during the night and eaten the child. Needless to say the family did not linger long.

In the same region in 1973, two men driving a jeep late one night, found their headlights illuminating a weird pe-destrian - an immense goanna, six feet high, and twice the length of the jeep. Its skin was described as leathery and grey like that of an elephant.

Just how tough this skin *is* was demonstrated in an encounter from the Margret River area of the Kimbley region of north-eastern Australia in 1982. A stockman was mustering his cattle, when to his amazement, he saw a twenty-foot lizard stalking his charges through some long grass. He raised his rifle, and fired two rounds at the dragon from a distance of only 150 feet. The animal seemed totally unharmed and wandered back into the bush.

Megalania has often been blamed for livestock killings. In 1968 some soldiers were on a jungle training exercise in the Normamby range, Queensland, when the came across a dead cow. The cow had been literally torn in two, and was in a remote swamp miles from habitation. One of the privates told Australian researcher Rex Gilroy:

We found reptile tracks and tail marks in the mud around the kill. It now became obvious to us all that the cow had been killed elsewhere, on some pastureland far off, and dragged through the forest to the swamp where it had been devoured.

The normally courageous men now became gripped with fear.

We left the area in some haste, the kill was a fresh one, not even hours old. The 20 inch or so width of the claw marks in the mud, their distance apart, plus the tail marks, suggested to us that the reptile was up to 30 feet long. We also examined the drag-marks for some distance through the forest, and the path trampled through the foliage in the opposite direction by the monster perhaps only half an hour before.

Back in New South Wales - in Keyhole, south of The Lamington Plateau - a farmer and his family were roused one night in 1977 by the sound of something attacking his chicken-coop. Doubtless suspecting marauding dingoes, he released the farm-dogs. Shining his torch into the night he saw that both the intruder and his dogs had vanished. Upon searching the grounds in the morning he found the chicken-coop smashed to matchwood, and no trace what-soever of his dogs or poultry. What he *did* find however, were a trail of dragon-tracks leading across the property and into the surrounding woods. A couple of scientists from Brisbane University are said to have investigated and taken plaster-casts of the prints, but nothing has been heard from them since. Perhaps - like most of academia when faced with something outside of their cosy little world-view - they simply decided to ignore it.

Ignoring *Megalania* is something farmers do at their peril. The next case is unusual in that the beast was observed in the act of killing its prey, but, if the report is to be believed this specimen was a giant even by *Megalania* stan-dard. On a farm in Cassock, (close to the Wattagans) in 1978, the landowner spotted a gargantuan lizard in a far paddock. The dragon was engaged in ripping up a cow with its stiletto like teeth. The terrified farmer rushed to gather his friends. The locals came with dogs, rifles and jeeps, but the monster had gone. Once again the familiar calling-card of tracks led into the surrounding swamps and forests. Measuring the lizard against the fence posts the farmer estimated the brute's length at forty-five feet! Its head reared nine feet above the ground.

The previous year, two teenaged sisters and two teenaged boys saw a similar sized specimen on a jungle path in the mountains outside of Townville, Queensland. Karen and Susan Denman along with Tom Carroll and Alan Johnson, watched the animal emerge out of dense forest whilst they hid behind bushes. Karen said:

It looked like a goanna, only it was far, far too big for that. It had a large goanna like head, long neck, a huge, almost elephant like body, enormous legs and big claws, and a long, thick tail. The creature was covered throughout with large scales of a mottled grey colour. It stood parallel with the swamp, and we estimated it's length from head to tail to be a good 40 feet, and it's height about 6 feet tall standing on all fours. We watched as the monster began moving off, trampling foliage as it moved back into the forest. We then got out of there fast. No one believes us to this day, but we know what we saw.

The Cassock area mentioned earlier seems to be a hot-spot for sightings. In the mid 1970's 'lizard fever' hit the town (and nearby environs), with ten detailed accounts reported. Tony Harris of Newcastle saw a dragon wandering through an orange orchard in Quorrobolong in 1974. The twenty-five foot reptile was apparently supplementing its meat diet with fruit. This is not unknown in Varanids - the smaller specimens of which will scavenge around human habitation eating all manner of unlikely food items.

The following year, a Cessnock farmer saw another dragon emerge from scrub and scuttle past his barn. Measured against the building it was thirty-feet long and three-feet tall.

The dragons were still active in the 1990's. In 1992 a property owner was inspecting fence-posts just outside of Dubbo (New South Wales), when a fifteen-foot lizard leapt over the fence only twenty-feet away from him. He backed up to his land-rover, and jumped in as the reptile ran past.

Dr Lars Thomas - a Danish zoologist, author, and University lecturer - told me of a sighting of a giant lizard made by a colleague of his in 1997. The woman in question was driving north from Ayers Rock, and had seen many goannas on her journey. Then she saw - what at first she took to be a crocodile - running through the desert. She then realised that she was way outside the range of crocodiles in Australia, and that this was something quite different. It ran like a huge monitor-lizard, tail erect. The giant passed quite close to her car, leaving her in no doubt that it was a thirty-foot lizard.

Amazing as it seems, Megalania appears to *still* be stalking the outback of that great southern continent of Oz. Into the new Millennium, a true prehistoric-monster - worthy of Ray Harryhausen - is awaiting discovery. As if this were not enough, Megalania has one last trick up its scaly sleeve. It has been said that "..in China nothing is new". Indeed China is looked on as the cradle of civilised man. As seafarers, the Chinese were second to none, and many believe that *they* discovered America centuries before Columbus. With junks up to 500 feet long by 100 feet wide, and capable of carrying a crew of 1,000 it is little wonder that they were the masters of the ancient seas.

By the 5th Century they were employing paddle-wheels, and by the 12th building massive vessels with twenty-three paddle-wheels apiece. The fifty-foot rudder of one of these, now resides in Beijing Museum. The Chinese traded with the Javanese, and via them gained knowledge of antipodean waters. It seems that they were more interested in trade and mining than establishing permanent colonies, but that they reached Australia and left their mark is beyond doubt.

In 338 B.C, Chinese scholar Shin Tzu, wrote of animals kept at The Imperial Zoo in Peking. One description is that of a kangaroo - obviously this must have come from Australia, either directly, or via-trade in the South Pacific.

Missionaries who travelled to China in the 16th century, were shown a 6th Century map of Australia. Over 1,000 years previously the great philosopher Confucius wrote: 'Spring and Autumn Annals', in which he describes two Solar Eclipses, (believed by The Chinese to be dragons swallowing the sun), observed by oriental astronomers in Arnhem land, Northern Territory - both in the 5th Century B. C.

In an effort to prolong his lifespan, the Emperor Qin Shih Huanhg-ti, (the ruler who began work on The Great Wall of China), despatched a fleet of ships on a special mission in 213 B.C. Their objective was to procure a 'mystical fungus of immortality'. They visited *Pen Lie* (Java), *Fong Zhand* (New Guinea), and the great golden land of *Yink Zhou* (Australia). Sadly, the fleet never returned and the Emperor died aged 49.

That others were more successful, is born out by many ancient Chinese maps showing Australia. One on a vase found in 1961 and dating back 2000 years, another on porcelain and dating to 1477, show the whole Pacific Rim - from the west-coast of America to Australia.

The Asian seafarers left artefacts in the great southern continent as well. At Darwin, Northern Territory, workmen dug up a statuette of *Shou Lao* - the Chinese God of Longevity - from the roots of a banyan tree. The relic dates from the Ming Dynasty, and may have been left by the great admiral Cheng Ho. On orders from the Emperor Yung Lo, The Admiral sailed for Australia in 1405, with sixty-two nine-masted ships - each more than 500 feet long. Accompanying him were 28,000 men and their families.

Cheng possessed a magnetic-compass, (invented in China around the year 1090 AD). His business was trade, diplomacy with the islands of Southeast Asia, and the establishment of a colony in Australia (in a change to earlier oriental travellers). He was also transporting astronomers to study the southern skies and to make offerings to *Shao Lin* - The Taoist Goddess of Mariners.

In 1980, a woman found a carved stone head of *Shao Lin* in a coastal hillside near Milton, New South Wales. Earlier, in Taree, (also in New South Wales), campers stumbled on a weathered carving of Buddha. A jade figure of The Buddha was also unearthed from soil deposits in Cooktown, Queensland 40 years ago.

Any of these may have been left by Cheng's men, or by previous Chinese visitors. Cheng is said to have circumnavigated Australia, and penetrated deep into the interior, (there seems however, little evidence of his planned permanent colony).

It is an attractive thought that the gallant Cheng and his people may well have encountered *Megalania* on their travels. Australia, (still one of the World's most unspoilt continents) was then even less populous than today. Who knows what was then - and maybe still is - roaming the trackless-jungles and the outback. We have already seen that crocodilians were considered to be dragons in China. The Indopacific crocodile is found in northern Australia, but maybe these mariners met *Megalania* as well. Perhaps Cheng was greeted by a creature from his ancient folk-lore, a creature that centuries before, earlier maritime Chinamen had seen and brought home via word of awed mouth. The bejewelled oriental rain-god in the parched southern land; the *original* Chinese Dragon!

At the time of writing, a piece of startling and exciting evidence of recent *Megalania* survival has come to light. Ralph Molnar - an Australian palaeontologist and *Megalania* expert - has revealed that he has an un-fossilised *Megalania* bone! It is part of an ileum or hip bone, and Molnar estimates its age to be between 100 and 200 years old! This puts a whole new light on the subject. An animal believed to have died out 10,000 years ago was possibly still around within living memory. This is the best piece of evidence for the continued existence of *Megalania* yet uncovered.

Australia cannot claim monopoly on giant lizards. Its close neighbour New Guinea also has dragons. In the Second World War, Japanese soldiers caught glimpses of what they described as 'tree climbing crocodiles' deep in the Papuan jungle. Then, in the summer of 1960, panic broke out on the island, as rumours that people had been killed by twenty foot long dragons began to circulate. The monsters were said to breath fire and drink blood. Their victims were left with foot-long claw-marks in the flesh. The scare became so bad that the government authorities moved people in the stricken areas into stockades, and offered substantial rewards for the capture of one of the beasts. The reward went unclaimed, the dragons disappeared and the riddle went unsolved for the next twenty years

In 1960, Lindsay Green and Fred Kleckhan - two administration agricultural officers - found some skin and a jaw bone of one of the dragons held as relics in a village near Kariuku. Today they would have been able to identify these specimens via D.N.A. analysis, but such things were unheard of back then.

In 1969, David M. Davies - an explorer - was shown Papuan cave paintings showing what looked like a giant-lizard standing on its hind legs. His native companions reacted with fear at the picture.

Late in 1978 a specimen was finally filmed in Southern Papua by Jean Becker and Christian Meyer. However even *this* could not determine if this was a new species.

In the mid 1980's, famed British explorer Colonel John Blashford-Snell was told of the 'tree climbing crocodile'. Locals called it *Artrellia* and seemed to go in great fear of it. He was told that it stands upright and breaths fire. From the descriptions given to him by an old chief, he sketched an animal looking much like a dinosaur. One story told of a young warrior – who, many years ago - was hunting deep in the forest. Feeling weary, he sat down on a log. The 'log' in now familiar style revealed itself as a dragon. It towered ten feet tall on its hind-legs, and possessed toothy, crocodile-like jaws. The man fled back to his village in terror.

Intrigued, the Colonel hit the trail. No less a man than the brother of The Premier of the Western Province, told him that an elderly man had died in the Daru hospital after being attacked by a female *Artrellia* protecting her nest. A village elder also said the creatures could grow to over fifteen feet long, and often stood on their hind-legs, lending them a dinosaur-like appearance. They were arboreal, and leapt down onto their prey, which they killed with their huge claws and infectious bite. Even small specimens were feared. A short time before, a small one had been captured and placed in a wooden cage. It swiftly broke free and killed a large dog before escaping back into the jungle.

The Colonel searched for the dragon himself but had no success. He then offered a cash reward for anyone who could bring him a specimen. Eventually, a village priest shot a small *Artrellia*. It was identified as *Varanus salvadori* - the Salvadori Dragon, (a previously known species but one that none suspected could grow so large). The Colonel later saw several twelve foot specimens for himself, and one huge individual with a head as large as a horse was also seen. Such a vast specimen would be in excess of seven metres (twenty-three feet).

At fifteen feet, the Salvadori Dragon is the world's longest lizard that is currently excepted by science. However it is not the largest. This accolade still goes to the Komodo Dragon. Over two-thirds of the Salvadori Dragon's length is taken up by its sinuous tail, whereas the Komodo Dragon's tail takes up only half its entire length and outweighs its elongate cousin by several times. Yet the possibility remains that specimens of this serpentine dragon grow far larger than is currently known, and lurk undiscovered in this huge island's ill-explored interior. This idea is supported by a number of accounts.

Robert Grant and David George were exploring the Strachan Island district in 1961, when they encountered a grey-skinned lizard some eight metres (twenty-six feet) long. The creature's neck alone measured a metre, (three feet).

In 1999 two groups of people spotted a dinosaur like creature at Lake Murry near Boroko. It was six metres (twenty feet) long, with crocodile-like skin. It had thick hind-legs with smaller front-limbs and a long tail.

Both of these sightings seem to refer to gigantic Salvadori Dragons. In March 2004 a new sighting of a Papuan dragon emerged.

Police hunt 'dinosaur' in PNG

March 12, 2004 - 12:38PM

Reports a live dinosaur had been sighted on a volcanic island of Papua New Guinea prompted the deployment of heavily-armed police in search of the mystery creature. Villagers in the superstitious island province of East New Britain this week said they fled in terror after seeing a three-metre tall, grey-coloured creature with a head like a dog and a tail like a crocodile.

They said the creature was living among thick green plants in a mosquito-ridden marsh just outside the provincial capital Kokopo, near the devastated town of Rabaul which was buried by a volcanic eruption in 1994. Kokopo's

Mayor Albert Buanga said the dinosaur would make a great a tourist attraction, if it existed. A government official today confirmed police carrying M-16s and shotguns searched the area but found no trace of the creature.

Eyewitness Christine Samei told reporters she ran for her life after seeing a three-metre tall, grey creature with a head like a dog and a tail like a crocodile which was as fat as a 900-litre water tank. "It's a very huge and ugly looking animal," Samei told local media. A government official said the villagers had identified the creature from books and movies about dinosaurs. "They told us it was a dinosaur," the official told AAP.

Although police found no trace of the creature, Senior Sergeant Leuth Nidung warned villagers to take extra precautions when going about their daily business, amid reports it had eaten three dogs. Villagers were told to report any further sightings immediately to police, who were already organising a more thorough search of the area. Black magic and other superstitions are common in many parts of PNG's predominantly village-based society.

Each year large numbers of foreigners visit the area to see World War II relics as well as the devastated town of Rabaul - the only urban centre in the world built inside the crater of a giant volcano.

Dinosaurs might have roamed the earth millions of years ago, but claims by Kokopo villagers of a sighting of a dinosaur-like creature has got the town buzzing, and the authorities eager to track it down to see if it is for real. Since the alleged sighting of the creature, villagers in Kokopo, East New Britain province, and policemen have formed search parties to go out after this thing. Yesterday, 20 villagers and six policemen armed with rifles and bush knives rushed to Tinganavudu village to hunt down the "dinosaur". The party was led by Senior Sergeant Leuth Nidung and Mayor Albert Buanga. Reporters were also asked to join the search.

But after an hour of search, there was no sign or trace of a creature that was described to have a dog's head and the body similar to that of a crocodile and grey in colour. Christine Samei, who claimed she saw the creature on Wednesday morning, said: "I heard the people talking about it and went there to see for myself. It's very huge and ugly looking animal."

Ward Councillor Michael Tarawana said villagers told him the creature was sighted by women on several times, adding he had heard claims that the creature had eaten three dogs. Although the search party came up with nothing, Sergeant Nidung urged villagers to be alert and take extra precaution when going out to the garden or to sea. Real or imagined, Sgt. Nidung said the next search party would involve more that 30 men and they would sweep the area more thoroughly.

Worth a mention before we continue, is a unique case from Panama. In 1991 a fifteen foot long lizard said to weigh 1,320 lbs and be fifty years old, was captured and shot in dense swamps some twelve-miles west of Panama City. The creature had previously killed a lizard hunter. It was baited with 24lbs of pig's tripe and a huge hook. No one seems to know what became of the carcass. The largest known lizard in Panama is the green or common iguana (*Iguana iguana*), but at six feet in length, it falls far short of this mysterious reptile.

Snakes, giant and otherwise

Snakes hold a special fascination for man, perhaps because of their "alien-ness". Their vermiform-bodies have no limbs, and their eyes no lids. They have no ears and 'hear' by picking-up vibrations - via their bodies - through the ground. Many types are venomous, and the idea of such small, (in the main), animals being so formidably armed is disturbing. Humanity fears that which is different, and this fear has manifest in many different ways from the snake-veneration of the Aztecs, to the disgusting rattlesnake round-ups of the southern United States, where thousands of snakes are captured, and cruelly slaughtered in the name of 'fun' by inbred red-necked scum. It is unsurprising then, that snakes have their part to play in the rich tapestry of dragonlore.

One of the most formidable of dragon kin - the basilisk - may have had its genesis in a very real group of snakes -

The cobras. As you may recall from Chapter One, the basilisk was vulnerable to only two creatures, the rooster and the weasel. Weasels belong to a group of mammals called *Mustelids*. These include stoats, otters, badgers, wolverines, and martens. The group bares a striking similarity to the *Viverrids* or mongooses. This is a case of convergent or parallel evolution, where two distinct groups of animals develop to resemble each other due to fulfilling similar ecological niches. There *are* differences. Mustelids have greater variation in form, and grow larger than Viverrids, but the weasel and the common mongoose are sufficiently alike for confusion to arise between the two. The cobra's hood could also add to the legend by being distorted into the basilisk's crown.

The idea of weasel/mongoose confusion is only one instance of Europeans confounding new animals with familiar ones. As we saw earlier, in the Central American country of Belize (formerly British Honduras) locals still call spider monkeys 'baboons' and jaguars 'tigers'. This is a legacy from British Colonial times, when Englishmen - ignorant of local fauna - named them after creatures they knew back in India. One wonders how many other zoological puzzles began this way.

Another factor in the legend of the basilisk seems to lie with the black mamba (*Dendroaspis polyepis*) - a large and highly-venomous snake of sub-Saharan Africa. This snake can reach four metres (fourteen feet) in length, and is renowned for its aggressiveness. When in a warning display, it can rear up to the height of a man, and unlike most other snakes it will actively pursue and attack anything that it perceives as a threat. Most snakes strike only once. The black mamba strikes repeatedly, and has a potent neurotoxin (nerve paralysing), venom. It has been recorded on many occasions, that black mambas shedding their skin, will sometimes retain a flap of old dead skin upon their head. This strongly resembles the crest of a cockerel, and may well have led to legends of crested-serpents - both in Africa and elsewhere - via visiting foreigners.

An unknown species of African snake, bares an uncanny resemblance to the basilisk. The crested crowing cobra is reported from central and southern Africa. This reptile is said to be six metres (twenty feet) long, and grey or brown in colour. It has a scarlet crest like a rooster's comb on its head, as well as a pair of red wattles. Its cockerel-like attributes do not end there. The creature makes a noise very like a cockerel's crowing, hence its name. It is said to be arboreal and highly venomous. Hyraxes seem to be its favoured prey. It also attacks humans, by lunging from overhanging-branches, and biting their faces. Some natives, when walking through forested areas, are said to carry pots of boiling-water on their heads to scald the attacking creature.

Doctor J. O. Shircore obtained some remains of a crested crowing cobra in 1944. A witch-doctor in Malawi gave him a plate of bone from the crest with skin still attached, and several vertebrae and neck bones from at least two specimens. He describes the plate thus:

Its skeleton consists of a thin lanceolate plate of bone (1 ½ ins by ½ in wide, at its broadest part) with a markedly rounded smooth ridge 1/8 of an inch wide, slightly overhanging both sides of the upper border, with a distinct voluted curve to the left. The lower border is sharp-edged and faintly ridged. The lateral surfaces are concave, throughout the long diameter. The whole fragment is eminently constructed for the insertion and attachment of muscles-much the same as the structure of the breast-bone of a bird. Some skin, part of which spread smoothly above the plate, on one side, is red in colour: and attached to the lower angle is a dark wrinkled bit, which appears to be a remnant of head skin- all of which should be valuable for purposes of identification. A small portion of bone, tapering towards both ends, ½ inch long by 1/8 inch wide, is missing from the lower anterior border, including the tip-it was broken off for use in medicine by the witch-doctor, from whom the specimens were obtained.

Shircore, it should be noted, was a medical doctor. His note appeared in the magazine *African Affairs*. The remains have never been identified and to my knowledge nobody knows of their current whereabouts.

In a 1962 letter to the publication *African Wild Life,* John Knott recounts his brush with an individual of what may be the same species. Whilst driving home from Binga in the Kariba area of Zimbabwe, (*then* Southern Rhodesia), in May 1959, he ran over a two metre long black snake. Upon investigation he discovered that the reptile had a symmetrical-crest on its head. The crest could be erected by way of five internal prop like structures.

The crested crowing cobra seems to have a smaller counterpart in The Caribbean. The eminent Victorian naturalist Phillip H Gosse records it in *The Romance of Natural History, Second Series*. In 1845-46 Gosse visited Jamaica where he first heard of the creature from a respected medical man.

...he had seen, in 1829, a serpent about four feet in length, but of unwonted thickness, dull ochre in colour with well-defined dark spots, having on its head a sort of pyramidal helmet, somewhat lobed at the summit, of a pale red hue. The animal, however, was dead, and decomposition was already setting in. He informed me that the Negroes of the district were well acquainted with it; and that they represented it as making a noise, not unlike the crowing of a cock, and being addicted to preying on poultry.

Gosse's friend Richard Hill had heard of the snake from a Spanish acquaintance on Hispaniola. It was said to inhabit the eastern regions of the island, in what is now the Dominican Republic.

My friend's Spanish informant had seen the serpent with mandibles like a bird, with a cock's crest, with scarlet lobes or wattles; and he described its habits – perhaps from common fame rather than personal observation - as a frequenter of hen-roosts, into which it would thrust its head, and deceive the young chickens by its imitative physiognomy, and its attempts to crow.

Jamaican resident Jasper Cargill offered a sovereign for any specimen of the snake, but was not successful in obtaining one. Cargill himself had seen the elusive snake some years before as Gosse records.

...when visiting Skibo, in St George', an estate of his father's, in descending the mountain-road, his attention was drawn to a snake of dark hue, that erected itself from some fragments of limestone rock that lay about. It was about four feet long and unusually thick bodied. His surprise was greatly increased on perceiving that it was crested, and that from the far side of its cheeks depended some red coloured flaps, like gills or wattles. After gazing at him intently for some time, with its head well erect, it drew itself in , and disappeared among the fragmentary rocks.

Cargill's son shot a specimen some years later.

...some youngsters of the town came running to tell me of a curious snake, unlike any snake they had ever seen before, which young Cargill had shot, when out for a day's sport in the woodlands of a neighbouring penn. They described it as a serpent in all respects, but with a very curious shaped head, with wattles on each side of its jaws. After taking it in hand and looking at it, they placed it in a hollow tree, intending to return for it when they should be coming home, but they had strolled from the place so far that it was inconvenient to retrace their steps when wearied with rambling.

When the youths returned the next day, the corpse was missing - presumably taken by some scavenger. When the tale was recounted to Richard Hill, his godson Ulick Ramsay, told him that he *too* had seen such a snake shortly before:

... not long previously, he had seen in the hand of the barrack-master-sergeant at the barracks of a Spanish town, a curious snake, which he, too, had shot among the rocks of a little line of eminences near the railway, about two miles out, called Craigallechie. It was a serpent with a curious shaped head, and projections on each side, which he likened to the fins of a eel, but said were close up to the jaws.

The legendary basilisk has lent its name to another deadly snake. One of the first venomous snakes met by European settlers in North America was the Mexican west-coast rattlesnake. Due to its potent poison its scientific name is *Crotalus basiliscus*.

Often it seems the fear of snakes leads them to be blamed for all sorts of baleful happenings. In Rome, during the reign of Pope Leo X (1475-1521 Pope: 1513-21), a basilisk was captured, and blamed for an outbreak of plague. Another was said to lurk in a well in Vienna, and killed people with its pestilent breath. It was discovered in 1202. In 1587 a specimen was killed in a cellar in Warsaw after causing the death of several locals. It turned out to be a disappointingly small snake. The others were also probably harmless snakes found in areas were sulphur or methane fumes had built up to dangerous levels, or where natural diseases had broken out. (Remember the wyvern's propensity for spreading disease).

But what of the other factors in the basilisk legend? It seems that these also have explanations within the realm of the natural rather than the supernatural. The miraculous egg-laying cockerel is not so fantastic as it at first sounds. There is a disease in fowl that causes a hen's ovaries to become infected. This prevents the production of the female hormone oestrogen. Oestrogen controls feminine characteristics, and when these are prevented from developing, masculine traits appear. These include developing a comb and wattle, crowing, and attempting to mount hens. If the victim recovers, it returns to it's former feminine self and may lay once more; ergo a cock that lays eggs.

How about the snakes that sometimes slithered out of hens eggs, to the mortification and horror of medieval cooks? Snake eggs are leathery-shelled and not at all like birds-eggs, so confusion between the two - or deliberate mischief (a jester switching hen eggs for snake eggs for example) - is unlikely. The explanation is almost as grim as the original legend! Chickens often suffer from round-worms (*Ascaris*); endoparasitic, internal creatures that are mainly passed out in the bird's droppings but they can on occasion enter the reproductive-tract and be incorporated into an egg. In times past - when there were no stringent hygiene laws - this would have occurred far more often than today. Round worms can measure up to forty centimetres (sixteen inches) and one could readily imagine the terror evoked by cracking open an egg to find a writhing "basilisk" within!

The basilisk has not entirely been banished into limbo; it had one last trick up its scaly sleeve. When the Spanish conquistadors first began to explore South America, they discovered a large lizard. It was bright green and bore a rooster-like crest on its head. They naturally called it a basilisk. *Basiliscus basiliscus* - to give it its Latin name, (there are in fact several related species) - lacks its legendary counterpart's baleful stare, but it has a power almost as incredible. When alarmed, this sixty centimetre (two foot) lizard rears onto its hind legs, and runs across the surface of rivers. Its elongate toes splay-out spreading its body weight. As long as it runs quickly it does not break the surface-tension of the water. Hence it is sometimes known as the Jesus Christ lizard.

The Basilisk's cousin - the salamander - has a very similar story to tell. As we have seen, it has passed on its name to a group of harmless amphibians - most notably the European fire salamander (*Salamandra salamandra*), a striking black and yellow species. The lethal poison that could find its way into bread if the baker used wood that a salamander had crawled across may have its genesis in rye-ergot - a form of fungus that could grow in flour in less hygienic days. Rye-ergot - if ingested in bread - could cause hallucinations and be lethally poisonous. In France in 922 40,000 people died of rye-ergot poisoning, and in 1128, 14,000 died in Paris alone.

An exotic snake may explain the legend of the dragon of Saint Leonard's Forest in Sussex. In 1614 a bizarre creature appeared in the forest, much to the alarm of the locals. John Trundle published a broadsheet describing the phenomenon in full:

In Sussex there is a pretty market towne called Horsham, near which is a forest called St. Leonards Forrest, and there is a vast and unfrequented place, heahie, vaultie, full of unwholsome shades and overgrown hollows were this serpent is thought to be bred, certaie and too true, that there it yet lives, within 3 or 4 miles compass are its usual haunts, oftentimes at a place called Fay-Gate, and it hath been seene within half a mile of Horsham, a wonder no doubt, most, terrible and noisome to the inhabitants thereabouts.

There is always in his track or path left a glutinous and slimie matter (as by a small simailitude we may percive in a snail) which is very courpt and offensive to the scent, insomuch they percive the air to be putrified withal which must needs be very dangerous; for though the corruption of it cannot strike the outward parts of a man, unless heated into the blood, yet by receiving it into any part of our breathing organs (the nose or mouth) it is by authoritie of all authors, writing in that kinde, mortall and deadlie; as one thus saith: "Nosia Serpentane est admits sangine Pestis (Lucan).

The Serpent or Dragon as some call it, is reputed to be nine feete or rather more in length, and shaped almost in the form of the axle-tree of a cart, a quantitie of thickness in the middest, and somewhat smaller at both ends. The former part which he shoots forth as a necke is supposed to be an ell long, with a white ring as it were of scales about it. The scales along his back seem to be blackish and so much as as is descovered under his bellie apereth to be red; for I speak of no nearer a description than a reasonable ocular distance; for coming too neare it hath already been too dearlie pay'd for as you shall hear herafter.

It is likewise descovered to have large feete, but the eye may be there deceived, for some suppose that serpents have no feet but glide along upon certain ribbes and scales, which both defend them, from the upper part of the throat, unto the lower part of their bellie, and also cause them to move much faster, for so this doth and rids away, as we call it, as fast as a man can run. He is of counterence very proud, at the sight or hearing of man or cattle, he will raise his neck upright, and seem to listen and looke about him with great arrogance. There are likewise on either side of him discovered two great bunches, so big as a large foote ball, and as some think will grow into wings, but God I hope will so defend the poor people of the neighbourhood, that he shall be destroyed before he grow so fledge. He will cast venom about 4 roddes from him, so by woefull experience, it was proved on the bodies of a man and a woman coming that way, who aferwards were found dead, being poysoned and very much swelled, but not preyed upon; likewise a man going to chase it and as he imagined to destroy it with great mastiff dogs were both killed and he himself had to return with haste to preserve his own life. Yet this is to be noted that the dogs were not preyed upon, but slaine and left whole-for his food is thought to be for the most part in a conie warren which he most frequents, and it is found to be much scanted and impaired in the increase it had wont to afford. These persons whose names are hear under-printed have seen this serpent, besides divers others, as the carrier at Horsham, who lieth at the White Horse in Southwark, and who can certifie the truth of all that hath herein been related.

John Steele,
Christopher Holder,
And a widow woman dwelling at Fay-Gate.

The description of the serpent 'raising up his head' sounds very like a cobra rearing up in a threat posture. The fact that its victims remained uneaten, whilst the serpent fed on smaller animals such as rabbits (conies) also points to a venomous snake. The 'bunches' in the creature's middle may have been reference to a sighting just after the snake had fed, lending it a fatter appearance about the middle. As for the slime and fouled-air, some snakes will spout foul-smelling excreta from their cloaca if alarmed. The snake was indeed probably a cobra that had its genesis in one of the animal collections at the time, and escaped into the area. The reports began in August and only lasted a few months before the cold winter would have killed any tropical reptile at large.

It is not the venomous snakes that cause the most awe in us however, but the giant constrictors. Constricting snakes - the boas and pythons - are the largest snakes alive, although not all reach excessive lengths (some are barely two feet long). Five species are known to exceed twenty feet in length. These are:

- *Python reticulatus*, the reticulated python at 33 feet
- *Eunectes murinus*, the anaconda at 29 feet
- *Moreli amethistina*, the amethystine python at 28 feet
- *Python sabae*, the African rock python at 25 feet
- *Python molurus*, the Indian python (including the subspecies *P.m.bivittatus*, the Burmese python) at 26.5 feet.

Charles Gould, in his magnum opus *Mythical Monsters*, tells us of his belief that constricting snakes once grew far beyond their modern dimensions:

I fancy that at the present day the numbers, magnitude, and terrifying nature of serpents but feebly represents the power which they asserted in the early days of man's existence, or the terror which they then inspired.

These snakes kill by suffocating - not crushing - victims in their muscular coils, and make good analogues for the 'wyrm' type dragon. This is even more so, when one considers the amazing lengths reported for some specimens. These lengths far exceed the accepted maximums given above. Our search for giant snakes will take us all around the tropics, but we will start in the cradle of mankind - Africa.

In the swamps of the Sudan is said to live a giant python known as the *lau*. Natives describe the beast as twelve-thirty metres (forty to a hundred feet) long, thick about as a donkey and yellow in colour. Some descriptions furnish it with a crest or mane, (a curious appendage for a snake but one seen in several areas). Strangely, it is also said to possess facial-tentacles with which it grabs its prey. Another reoccurring motif is horns or tentacles on the head.

The folklore attached to this monster is singularly bizarre. If the *lau* sees a human before he sees it, the man will die. Conversely if the man sees the *lau* first it will be the serpent that expires.

The 1920's explorer and naturalist J. G. Millans interviewed a westerner who firmly believed in the monster. Sergeant Stephens, (who was never identified with a first name), told him, "*One Abriahim Mohamed, in the employ of the company (a telegraph company), saw a lau killed near Raub , at a village called Bogga. The man I knew and closely questioned. He always repeated the same description of the monstrous reptile. More recently one was killed by some Shilluks at Koro-a-ta beyond Jebel-Zeraf (Addar Swamps). I obtained some of the neck bones of this example from a Shilluk who was wearing them as a charm. These I sent to Deputy-Governor Jackson (now of Dongola province), who in turn sent them to the British Museum for identification, but no satisfactory explanation was given, nor was it suggested what species of snake they could belong to*".

Abrahim's story of the size and shape of the great reptile was corroborated by one Rabha Ringbi, a Nian-Niam from the neighbourhood of Wau in the Bahr-el-Ghazal, who had seen a similar monster killed in swamps near that place: "*Dinkas living at Kilo (a telegraph station on the Zeraf) told me that the lau frequents the great swamp in the neighbourhood of that station and they occasionally hear it's loud booming cry at night.*

"*A short time ago I met a Belgian administrator at Rejaf. He had just come back from the Congo, and said he was convinced of the existence of the lau as he had seen one of these great serpents in a swamp and fired at it several times, but his bullets had no effect. He also stated that the monster made a huge trail in the swamp as it moved into deeper water.*"

Another intriguing piece of evidence was photographed by Captain William Hutchins and published in the magazine *Discovery*. This was a wooden ritual-mask of the beast. When Hitchins questioned Meshengu she Gunda, the native singer and sculptor who made the mask, as to the beast's existence the African replied philosophically: "*I might have said, as a young man, when I was ignorant, that there was no such there is no such thing as a motor car. I had never seen or even heard of one then. But there is your motor car in the sight of my eyes and I have sat on it's chairs and heard it's bowels digest inside it. It is thus of the lau*".

As far as I know, there have been no recent reports of the *lau*. Perhaps this is unsurprising given Sudan's recent troubled times. The facial tentacles mentioned recall an aquatic Asian species *Epeton tentaculaatum*, the fishing snake. Could the *lau* be a giant African analogue? No-one will know until the trackless-swamps of the Sudan are once again penetrated.

Captain C. R. S. Pitman - a British naturalist and expert on African snakes - was told of a titanic serpent that had inhabited a pool in the Bwamba escarpment in Uganda. It was said to be of venerable age and was worshiped by the locals. In a strange turnabout, Pitman (or his source), never explained why the snake was killed and eaten. Perhaps the animal died of natural causes and the tribesmen took advantage of the flesh, or maybe it had killed livestock or people. In any case Pitman was told of the creature's massive size:

His informant said, "*I have no reason to disbelieve what the head man says: he is a reliable man and he measured it with a linear tape measure... every single soul who was present when the snake was measured states that it much exceeded the tape measure... I was shown the place where they stretched it out... This was certainly approximately 130 feet."*

Pitman's informant obtained the jaws, teeth, and two of the vertebra. Pitman himself never saw these relics and they were never examined by a zoologist. The informant may have been telling a tall - or in this case long - tale. His "certainly, approximately" statement does not inspire confidence. I would be inclined to dismiss this story if it were not for the other sightings of giant snakes in Africa.

Further west, something very like the *lau* may have been photographed by a Belgian military helicopter-pilot in the Katanga region of Zaire in 1959. According to William Corliss, the photographs were apparently taken at a low altitude, and purport to show an unbelievably colossal snake entering a hole by some termite mounds. The reptile is pictured so clearly that even the scales on its hide are visible. The photographer was one Colonel Remy van Lierde, who claimed that the snake reared up at his helicopter. The original pictures were submitted to the Eighth Reconnaissance Technical Squadron U.S Air Force experts in Massachusetts for analysis. The vegetation surrounding the snake may have been unassuming shrubs or giant trees, (I assume no botanists have ever examined these shots), but also in the picture are several termite mounds. These colonial insects build concrete hard nests six metres (twenty feet) tall as par for the course. But are these old, huge, nests or small new colonies? The termites build their nests so that the largest face receives the most sunlight in early morning and afternoon. Judging by the intensely cast shadows, the Air Force technicians estimated the termite mounds to be around six metres tall. This meant that the surrounding trees were twelve to fifteen metres (forty to fifty feet) tall. This would make the serpent a full sixty metres (two-hundred feet) long!

However, having examined the photographs I can see no signs of termite mounds and nothing else that gives any sense of scale. Remy van Lierde is an unusual name, and as he had risen to the rank of Colonel by 1959, one can assume that he may well have been the same man who as a Flight Lieutenant flew a Hawker Tempest fighter-plane out of Newchurch in 1944. If we assume that he *was* a fighter pilot – and we *know* he was flying a helicopter over Katanga – then we can deduce that he was flying an anti-terrorist mission, probably accompanied by a colleague with a machine gun. If this is so then he would have been flying at a relatively low altitude of 50-100 feet, and the aforesaid photograph becomes even less impressive – most probably only a large African rock python.

An African rock python of thirty-two feet was supposedly shot near Bingerville, in the Ivory Coast. Though unconfirmed, it beats the official record by seven feet. The Ivory Coast seems a haven for large pythons, because another of the same species was killed in Adiopodume that was twenty-four feet long.

In August 2000, an oil-worker from Egbema-Ogba, Nigeria, was swallowed by a seven and a half metre (twenty five foot) rock python. George Otoh, (33), was relieving himself in bushes when the massive snake attacked. His body was later discovered inside the reptile.

One remarkable woman who had experience with giant snakes in Africa was Mary Kingsley - niece of author Charles Kingsley. She had led a sheltered life until the age of thirty, then suddenly decided that she wanted to explore Africa, and study its religions and superstitions. In a time were women were *meant* to stay at home, she explored the then *truly* wild areas of west and central Africa collecting specimens for the British Museum. She recorded her remarkable adventures in a book *Travels in West Africa*. Therein she tells of outsized specimens of several species:

The largest crocodile I ever measured was twenty-two feet three inches, the largest gorilla five feet seven inches. I am assured by the missionaries at Calabar that there was a python brought into Creek Town in the Rev. Mr Goldie's time that extended the whole length of the Creek Town mission-house veranda and to spare. The python must have been over forty feet. I have not a shadow of doubt it was. Stay-at-home people will always discredit great measurements, but experienced bushmen do not, and after all, if it amuses stay-at-homes to do so, by all means let them; they will have dull lives of it and it don't hurt you, for you know how exceedingly difficult it is to preserve really big things to bring home, and how, half the time, they fall into the hands of people who would not bother their heads to preserve them in a rotting climate like West Africa. The largest python skin I ever measured was a damaged one, which was twenty-six feet.

Modern day "experts" would do well to take a leaf from Miss Kingsley's book. Time and again, armchair zoologists will proclaim that 'this' or 'that' cannot exist, without ever leaving the ivory-towers of their lecture halls.

The deserts of northern Africa would not seem a likely place for a gigantic snake to exist but there are reports, both ancient and modern of vast, crested, naga-like snakes in both Algeria and Tunisia.

Around 250 BC at the time of the first Punic War (264-241 BC), Rome was embroiled in a prolonged struggle with the city of Carthage (where modern day Tunis stands) over the control of Sicily. General Marcus Atilius Regulus led his army towards the city when he came to the River Baradas. A titanic serpent rose up from the reed beds. The men fell back in horror, and after some consultation decided to cross the river further up stream. But as the soldiers began to ford the waters, the monster reappeared and seized a man. As each of the warriors tried to cross he was snatched by the beast's massive jaws, encircled in its coils and dragged under.

After many men were lost in this way - and it seemed as if the serpent would defeat the entire army - Regulus ordered that the giant snake should be bombarded with ballistae - giant, rock-hurling catapults. Ballistae were trained on the creature, and it gradually began to retreat under the bombardment. One boulder struck the giant's skull with fatal force and the monster snake collapsed onto the bank.

The soldiers dragged the vast corpse onto the bank and measured it. It was an astounding thirty-six metres (120 feet)! The jaws and skin were sent back to Rome as a trophy, where it was on public display in a temple on Capitol Hill until 133 BC, when it was lost during the Numantine war with the Iberian Celts. Regulus himself was granted an ovation.

Time and again the priceless cadavers of cryptids are lost to science. In the case of the giant snakes of the Sahara this has happened several times.

Africanus Leo (Hasan ibn Muhhammad al Wazzan al Fasi), was a traveller and writer born in Granada in 1485. He was enslaved by European pirates but freed by Pope Leo X. He travelled widely in Africa and visited Timbuktu twice. His were the first descriptions of the city to find their way to Europe. He wrote of huge, venomous dragons inhabiting the Atlas Mountains in North Africa. Events in the 20th century may support his claims.

In 1958, Belkhouriss Abd el-Khader - an Algerian who served in the French army at Beni Ounif, Algeria - was attacked and bitten by a thirteen metre (forty-three foot) snake. The snake was killed and its skin preserved although it has since been lost.

The following year an fantastical story - a sequel to Regulus's adventure - occurred near a garrison in Ain Sefra, Algeria. A monster-snake that had just swallowed a whole camel was captured in a trench that had been filled with branches by nomads. A French battalion - the Twenty-sixth Dragoons - were brought in to kill it. Their carbine rifles did little damage and they had to finish the monster with machine guns. The beast was thirty-six metres (120 feet), the same size as Regulus's reptile, and bore a metre long (three foot) crest on its head. No-one seems to know what became of the body.

In early January 1967, a nine metre (thirty foot) snake was seen on the construction site of the Djorf-Torba dam, east of Bechar, Algeria. A worker called Hamaza Rhamani wedged it against some rocks with his bulldozer. He reported that the beast's fangs were some 2.5 inches long. Later that year, in the same area Rhamani saw another specimen. He followed its trail to some barrels of oil from which – bizarrely - it seemed to have been drinking. He saw the snake coiled in the shadow of a pile of crushed rocks and estimated the length to be five-seven metres (eighteen-twenty-three feet).

Asia too has its tales of giant serpents. In 1976 *The Times* carried a story of a python in India that was captured in the act of swallowing a man. Retelling the story afterwards, the local villagers referred to the snake as a dragon. In fact it is here in Asia, on the island of Celebes, (now Sulawesi), that the *official* longest snake in the world was captured – an eleven metre (thirty-three) foot reticulated python taken in 1912. Of course, larger specimens *have* been reported. 18th century explorer, Francis Legaut, claimed to have encountered one fifteen metres (fifty feet) long on Java. A brute of similar size was reported in *The North China Daily News* of November 10th 1880. The story tells of a western hunter (whose name is never revealed), who came across a remote hut in the dense jungle between Buddoh and Sirangoon on the Malay peninsula. Upon the roof was the skin of a gigantic python. Inquiring as to it's origin with the hut's owner he was told this story:

The Malay was awakened one night by his wife's screams. Investigating he found to his horror an immense snake that had drawn the poor woman's whole arm into it's maw and was in the processes of swallowing her. The plucky fellow seized two bags and stuffed them into the corners of the giant reptile's mouth thus forcing them to open wider. The snake released the woman and turned upon the man whipping it's coils about him. Fortunately for the Malay his arms were free and he grabbed his parang and hacked at the vasty serpent. The snake unwound and slithered through an opening beneath the hut. Both the man and the hut were covered in blood.

Come morning he followed the python's trail to a patch of plantain palms. In it's death throws the beast had smashed the trees and uprooted them. In the midst of the destruction lay the offending creature, dead. He had been offered 60 dollars from some Chinese who had travelled long distances to buy pieces of the monster's flesh due to it's medicinal properties (the reader will remember the magickal attributes of dragons blood from a previous chapter). They also offered him 6 dollars for the skin, this he kept however, as a trophy of the ordeal. The skin was between 7 and 8 fathoms (50-56 feet) long.

Unfortunately, skins can be stretched when removed from the corpse of a snake - giving an unnaturally long appearance. Even so, this snake - if the estimates were right - must have been a colossal animal, so big in fact that one doubts that it could have been killed anything like so easily as it is claimed.

An even more dramatic story is recounted in the Victorian natural history tome *Pictorial Museum of Animated Nature*:

The captain of a country ship, while passing the Sunderbunds, sent a boat into one of the creeks to obtain some fresh fruits, which are cultivated by the few miserable inhabitants of this inhospitable region. Having reached the shore the crew moored the boat under a bank, and left one of their party to take care of her.

During their absence, the lascar who remained in charge of the boat, overcome by the heat, lay down under the seats and fell asleep. Whilst he was in this happy state of unconsciousness an enormous boa (python) emerged from the jungle, reached the boat and had already coiled it's huge body round the sleeper, and was in the very act of crushing him to death, when his companions fortunately returned at this auspicious moment, and attacking the monster severed a portion of its tail, which so disabled it that it no longer retained the power of doing any mischief. The snake was then easily dispatched, and was found to measure, as stated 62 feet and some inches in length.

If this event actually occurred, then the creature would have been an outsized reticulated python, not a boa. Once again the ease of its death raises suspicion.

Pythons have been captured far out to sea, and it seems that on occasion the giant Asian snakes swim to sea and are mistaken for true sea-serpents, (a subject we shall be dealing with – in detail - in the final chapter). Such a creature was observed from the deck of the China Navigation Company's ship *Taiyuan* between Yokohama and Melbourne in 1907. The witness was one S. Clayton a third officer. Clayton was on the bridge when he saw what he thought was a large tree trunk floating ahead of the ship. He altered course slightly as to avoid hitting the debris. He looked at the object through binoculars and was alarmed to see a mouth open at one end:

Almost abreast now and no longer foreshortened, was stretched an enormous writhing serpent of fabulous size. Yet monstrous as it was, its proportions were as fine as our English grass snake, though the head may have been more angular and boldly outlined.

The creature so far as I could see, appeared to be a perfect replica of a land snake. It was at least 70 feet long, having a girth corresponding in size to its length for a snake. It was a rather dark cane colour, (of course I saw none of the underside), having uneven dark brown patches of figuring such as one might expect to find joined by concatenation on closer inspection. Its convolutions were not vertical as many illustrations depict them, but horizontal in the plane of the surface of the water: the serpent being just submerged only. Apart from its writhing motion I could gather nothing about its propulsion...It did not seem to panic at the very close proximity of the ship; but continued steadily along our side, its course being exactly opposite to ours.

I have wondered if it could have been a python of staggering dimensions, something on the lines of the S. American Anaconda, but far larger, crossing between the islands.

Indeed my private opinion of the serpent's length has always been eighty feet, but I state it here as seventy purposely to err on the side opposed to exaggeration.

True sea-serpents move with a vertical flexation - that is up and down. Snakes, conversely, move in a horizontal plane. Clearly, what the good seaman observed was a massive snake of some kind.

In the mid 1970s a pair of pythons each twenty-seven metres (ninety feet) long, were said to have attacked a road-mining bulldozer in Indonesia. After an hour-long struggle, one was killed. Nothing more was ever heard of this, nor of the whereabouts of the body. The whole story seems very much like third-hand newspaper tat.

In 1998, British poet and rap "artist" Robert Twigger explored several Indonesian islands in search of giant pythons for the Channel 4 television series *To the Ends of the Earth*. The largest he found was a seven metre (twenty three foot six inch) reticulated python. With a 19th century attitude, Twigger allowed his native guides to slowly and cruelly slaughter the beautiful snake as he looked on impassively, and he even joined in the eating of the poor animal afterwards.

The official record for the reticulated python stands at ten metres (thirty-three feet) for a specimen killed near a mining camp in the Celebes. Animal dealer Henry Trefflich is said to have obtained a thirty-two foot specimen from an unspecified source but this has never been proven. Other claimed giants include a thirty-three footer killed on Java and a thirty foot python killed near Penang, Malaysia in 1844.

One verified titan was "Colossus" - a 28.5 feet reticulated python held at Pittsburgh's Highland Zoo. At the time of his death (from old age) in 1966 he was estimated to weigh 300lbs.

In the dying days of 2003, the zoological world was rocked by the fantastic claim that a reticulated python 14.85 metres (forty-nine feet) long and 992lbs in weight had been captured in Sumatra. The story was that the monster snake had been venerated by the Kubu tribe as a tribal elder. A snake handler called Imam Darmanto had heard about the creature and after a year of negotiation with the tribe was allowed to take it to a zoo in the village of Curugswue in Java. It took sixty-five men and tribal blessings to capture the giant reptile.

The *Guardian* sent reporter John Aglionby to check out the story. Sadly when he measured "Fragrant Flower" (as the snake had been named), it turned out to be only seven metres (twenty-three feet) long. Either Damarow was lying to attract more people to the zoo (attendances were up 60%) or the Kubu had given him another snake whilst their sacred giant remained in its jungle fastness. Sadly the former is the more likely to be true.

On my quest for the naga in Thailand mentioned earlier, I interviewed many witnesses to giant snakes in and around the Mekong river. Officer Suphat - the chief of police at Pom Posi in north east Thailand - was one such witness. In October 1996, he was one of thirty people who saw a naga swimming in the Mekong from some riverside cliffs. He saw what at first he took to be debris floating in the river. He soon realised as it drew closer that it was swimming against the flow. It was a vast, black, snake-like animal which he estimated to be a staggering seventy metres (230 feet) long! It moved with horizontal-flexations indicating that it was reptilian in nature.

The crowd watched as it passed, and then - as if a mesmeric spell was broken - fled in terror. The chief later told a Buddhist monk about his encounter, and the monk confirmed that he had seen a naga. He went on to state that a statue of Buddha had sunk in the river whilst being transported some years ago, and the nagas still guard it.

The excessive length given in this case, can I think be explained by a sighting of several creatures swimming in line (perhaps a female being pursued by males), or a long wake being mistaken for a vastly elongate body.

The naga has reared its head in other parts of Asia as well. In 1966 a peasant digging in the mud on the bank of the Mekong, close to the Lan Xang hotel in Vientiane, the capital of Laos, uncovered some huge white eggs. Subsequently he claimed that the naga appeared to him in a dream, demanding the return of its eggs, and threatening to flood the river if they were not given back. He took the eggs to General Kong Le, leader of the Neutralist army. The general showed them to Premier Prince Souvana Phouma, and warned him of the impending peril. Le was to lead the people in a ceremony of atonement but the Prince was unimpressed by the peasant fairy tales. The ceremony was never carried out, and the monsoon rains brought a huge flood to the city. Tragically, no-one knows what happened to the naga eggs.

Back in Thailand, a strikingly similar event was recorded in May 1980. Fisherman Prancha Pongpaew found seventeen eggs in the River Ping, north Thailand. The eggs were the size of water-melons and seemed to be linked together in a chain like toadspawn. He brought five of them to the surface and took them back to Songhtam village. The eggs were broken but they smelled so bad that they were thrown to dogs who ran away in fear.

That night, the villagers were awoken by an odd wailing sound and were horrified to see two black serpents - the size of palm trees - with crested heads, rearing up out of the river. The following night, a religious ceremony was preformed on the banks of the river but the Nagas did not reappear.

It should be noted that snakes either lay eggs on land or give birth to live young. The strand of linked eggs in water is very odd and distinctly un-reptilian. They sound like outsized toad spawn. Perhaps the nagas and the eggs were two unconnected events.

The year previously, a naga had caused a stir in Malaysia when it turned up in a disused mining pool in Semenyih. Fisherman Lebai Ramli saw it rise up from the water, and fled in terror. The incident caused a local stir as crowds of people, some armed, swarmed to the pool to try and see the monster. Sign-boards were put up telling people the way to the pool, and there was even an ice cream man on hand! Amazingly the naga obliged. It surfaced at about 12.30 when many witnesses saw a creature with a head the size of a scooter-wheel. Farmer Enick Arshad described seeing a log-like creature swimming 12-20 feet from the bank.

Enick Jaafar's 12-year-old son claimed to have seen a snake-like animal with a head - the size of an oil drum - held two-feet above the water. Enick himself saw the creature shortly after World War 2. He described it as a snake the size of a tree trunk.

The monster was held responsible for the disappearance of two buffaloes and other local livestock.

Australia unsurprisingly has also produced giant snake stories. Charles Gould was told by his acquaintance, G. R. Moffat, that the aborigines on the Lower Murray river between Swan Hill and the Darling junction, knew of a giant black serpent that lived in the Mallee scrub. It was twelve metres (forty feet) long, of huge girth, but very swift. Fortunately it produced a vile stench that warned of its approach. A white man - the son of Mr Peter Beveridge of Swan Hill - station had seen the beast. This was around 1857.

Mr Henry Liddell, a resident on the Darling River, was told identical stories by stock-riders and ration-carriers. The ebony monsters were considered not uncommon between Wentworth and Pooncaria in the 1870s.

The mother of all down-under giants, was reported back in 1822, by two men in front of a bench of magistrates in

Liverpool near Sydney. The men told them that just four km outside of town, they had come across a snake fourteen metres (forty-seven feet) long. and three times as thick as a human. Thinking it was dead, one of the pair unwisely threw a rock at it. To their horror, it was very much still alive, and rose a metre and a half off the ground. The magistrates seemed to believe them, as a posse of armed townsfolk ventured to the location of the encounter but found only a large track bearing the impression of scales.

The longest snake actually measured in Australia was a twenty-eight foot amethystine python killed at Greenhill near Cairns in 1948

It is in South America that we meet with the most numerous reports of outsized ophidians. This is unsurprising, as the neo-tropics is the lair of the giant snake *el supremo* - the anaconda. In terms of bulk, this snake is by far the largest in the world. Its girth is far greater than that of the reticulated python. Ever since the white man first ventured tentatively into the 'green hell', he has brought back tales that are the very stuff of nightmares - snakes whose size defies belief.

The earliest man to return with such bone chilling yarns was one Charles Waterton (1782-1865) - better known as Squire Waterton - a great British eccentric and adventurer. A Yorkshireman from a wealthy Roman Catholic family, The Squire insisted on sleeping on bare-boards with a block of wood as his pillow. Almost unique in his age, he was a teetotaller and violently opposed to hunting for sport. He was a passionate naturalist, and collector of animals, and with true intrepid Yorkshire spirit, he made four expeditions to South America between 1812 and 1824 - travelling in Brazil, Venezuela, and Guiana.

In typical Waterton style, he exposed as much of his skin as he could in the jungle at night, hoping to be bitten by a vampire bat. He was most disappointed when he was not bitten - but one of his companions was. The ungrateful man ran and hid in a latrine. Waterton's books are full of such shenanigans, and it is obvious he enjoyed himself immensely. The Squire lived to the ripe old age of 83, a miracle when one reads of some of the risks he took!

Of the anaconda he writes:

The camoudi snake (as it was called in British Guiana) has been killed from thirty to forty feet long; though not venomous, his size renders him destructive to the passing animals. The Spaniards in the Oroonoque positively affirm that he grows to the length of seventy or eighty feet and that he will destroy the strongest and largest bull. His name seems to confirm this; there he is called "matatoro" which means literally "bull killer". Thus he must be ranked among the deadly snakes, for it comes to the same thing in the end whether the victim dies by poison from the fangs, which corrupts his blood and makes it stink horribly, or whether his body be crushed to a mummy and swallowed by this hideous beast.

A missionary Father de Vernazza wrote in the 19th century surely what is the most fatuous description of the anaconda:

The sight alone of this monster confounds, intimidates and infuses respect into the heart of the boldest man. He never seeks or follows the victim upon whom he feeds, but so great is the force of his inspiration, that he draws in with his breath whatever quadruped or bird may pass him within twenty to fifty yards of distance, according to its size. That which I killed from my canoe upon the Pastaza (with five shots from a fowling piece) had two yards of thickness and fifteen yards of lengths; but the Indians have assured me there are animals of this kind here of three or four yards in diameter, and from thirty to forty long. These swallow entire hogs, stags, tigers, and men, with the greatest facility.

The good father was confusing diameter with circumference methinks, else his snakes would be extremely stout. Alternatively, he may have shot one that had just eaten a large prey-item such as a tapir. The super snake suction he speaks of is total fantasy, but the supposed mystic effects of anaconda breath is a stubborn myth - as we shall see in a moment.

Another 19th century yarn that stretches the imagination, was told by a botanist called (appropriately) Dr Gardner. Whilst travelling in the province of Goias - near the head waters of the Araguaia River - his host's favourite horse disappeared from its pasture, and could not be found despite an intensive search. Finally they came upon the bloated body of a giant snake in a tree. It was dragged out into the open by two horses and found to measure eleven metres (thirty-seven feet) in length. When slit open, it was found to contain the broken half-digested bones of the missing horse. The unfortunate animal's head was intact.

In fact, the anaconda is an aquatic rather than an arboreal snake. Its great weight makes it a poor climber when adult. This would have been compounded by such a heavy meal. making its treetop siesta an impossibility. Also, a full grown horse would be exceptionally hard to swallow even for a thirty-seven foot snake. As well as having a large body, a horse possesses very long legs that cannot be readily folded back against its trunk. It would seem that thirty-seven feet would be the bare minimum length that a snake would need to be, to achieve such a feat.

In 1944 another specimen of this size was encountered in Columbia by a team of prospecting geologists led by Roberto Lamon. The men shot the snake and measured it at 11.4 metres (37 feet 6 inches). The group left the creature to eat their lunch, intending to come back and photograph their trophy and skin it. Upon their return they were amazed to find it gone. The bullets had merely stunned the animal which had recovered and absconded in their absence.

Fredrico Medem - a Columbian herpetologist - saw an anaconda that he estimated to be between nine and twelve metres (thirty-forty feet), and obtained a report of another thirty-four feet long.

General Candido Mariano de Silva Rondon - who lent his name to the Rondonia area of Brazil - saw a specimen killed by Indians, some 11.6 metres (thirty-eight feet) long. There are several records of snakes in this size bracket that cannot easily be dismissed, as some have involved reputable scientists. A 10.4 metre (thirty-four foot) anaconda was shot by Vincent Roth, director of The National Museum, in British Guiana (now Guyana). Mr R. Mole - a naturalist who made many important contributions to the knowledge of the wildlife of Trinidad - reported a ten metre (thirty-three foot) example there in 1924. Dr F. Medem of the Colombia University, saw a 10.26 metre (33 foot 8 inch) snake killed on the Guaviare River.

In 1909 war was on the verge of exploding in South America. A "rubber rush" to rival the gold-rushes of the oldwest was happening, and a dispute was occurring in the Rio Abuna rubber plantations on the western borders of Brazil. Peru and Bolivia also meet at this point, and a bitter wrangle between the three countries over the valuable resource was growing to dangerous levels. Into this drama, The Royal Geographical Society sent a mediator to defuse the situation. Major Percy Fawcett - a 39 year old artillery officer - was to make the first intensive study of the area.

It was whilst engaged in this task that he initially herd of giant snakes. The manager of a remote hamlet called Yorongas, told him that he had killed a fifty-eight foot anaconda in the lower Amazon. Fawcett disregarded the story at first, but subsequently claimed to have shot an even bigger specimen.

Several months after the conversation at Yorongas he was on the Rio Abuna, upstream from its junction with the Rio Rapirrao when:

....almost under the bow of the igarite there appeared a triangular head and several feet of undulating body. It was a giant anaconda. I sprang for my rifle as the creature began to make it's way up the bank, and hardly waiting to aim smashed a .44 soft-nosed bullet into it's spine 10 feet below the wicked head. At once there was a flurry of foam, and several heavy thumps against the boat's keel, shaking us as though we had run on a snag. With great difficulty I persuaded the Indian crew to turn in shoreward. They were so frightened that the whites showed all round their popping eyes, and in the moment of firing I had heard their terrified voices begging me not to shoot lest the monster destroy the boat and kill everyone on board, for not only do these creatures attack boats when injured, but there is also a great danger from their mates.

We stepped ashore and approached the reptile with caution. It was out of action, but shivers ran up and down the body like puffs of wind on a mountain tarn.. As far as it was possible to measure, a length of 45 feet lay out of the water, and 17 feet in it, making a total length of 62 feet. It's body was not thick for such a colossal length-not more than 12 inches in diameter- but it had probably been long without food. I tried to cut a piece out of the skin, but the beast was by no means dead and it's sudden upheavals rather scared us. A penetrating foetid odour emanated from the snake, probably it's breath, which is believed to have a stupefying effect, first attracting then paralysing it's prey. Everything about this snake was repulsive.

Such large specimens as this may not be common, but trails in the swamps reach a width of 6 feet and support the statements of Indians and rubber pickers that the anaconda sometimes reaches an incredible size, altogether dwarfing that shot by me. The Brazilian Boundary Commission told me of one killed in the Rio Paraguay exceeding 80 feet in length.

This is the most celebrated and oft repeated encounter with a giant anaconda, but it is also one of the most questionable.

- Firstly, the width given for this snake is absurdly small. The anaconda is a massively built snake. A specimen *half* this length would have a width twice as wide or more. Fawcett's snake would have had to be an emaciated near-skeleton!

- Secondly his assertion that "there is a great danger from their mates", implies that anacondas mate for life and their partners will seek revenge for the killing of a mate. This is nonsense, no snakes are life-maters, and anacondas breed in huge "mating balls". These consist of dozens of males competing to mate with one larger female.

- Finally no snakes have "stupefying breath". This idea of breath that draws in and paralyses prey can be traced back to dragonlore, as mentioned earlier. The breath of a giant anaconda may well be foul but it possesses none of these attributes.

For these reasons, I am inclined to reject Fawcett's story as a traveller's tale. The man himself disappeared several years later whilst looking for a lost city in the jungle.

There are other accounts however, which are not so easily dismissed, and the anaconda has one huge advantage over the python that may well allow it to attain a greater size. All pythons are oviparous - that is they lay eggs. This must be done on land. Anacondas are ovo-viviparous - they retain the eggs *inside* their bodies until the young hatch, then give birth to them live. This means they do not have to leave the water - their final link with the land is broken. Living in water almost all of the time, means anacondas are buoyed up - they do not have to support their own body weight on land very often, and hence can grow to a very large size.

The Marquis de Wavrin was another explorer of South America, and was active in the years before the Second World War. He told the great Belgian cryptozoologist Bernard Heuvelmans, that he had seen anacondas over thirty feet long, and that the natives told of far larger ones. He once shot an eight metre (twenty-six foot), individual that had been coiled around a branch. When he expressed a desire to retrieve the cadaver, his canoe-men told him that it was a waste of powder to shoot such a small snake and a waste of time picking it up.

They went on to say, *"On the Rio Guaviare, during floods, chiefly in certain lagoons in the neighbourhood, and even near the confluence of this stream, we often see snakes that are more than double the size of the one you have just shot. They are often thicker than our canoe."*

F.W. Up de Graff - an explorer of seven years experience - spotted a giant anaconda as it lay in shallow water under his canoe. He said:

It measured fifty feet for certainty, and probably nearer sixty. I know this from the position in which it lay. Our canoe was a twenty-four footer; the snake's head was ten or twelve feet beyond the bow; it's tail a good four feet beyond the stern; its body was looped into a huge 'S', whose length was the length of our dugout and whose breadth was a good five feet.

Algot Lange claims to have shot a seventeen metre (fifty-seven foot) anaconda, and skinned it. Willard Price, the author of the wild life "Adventure" series (wherein youthful heroes travel the world capturing wild animals for zoos in unlikely adventures, that in zoological terms, are about as accurate as a lobotomised chimp with Parkinson's disease attempting to forge a Rembrandt!), says he then took the hide to New York. He also claims the snake "mesmerised" his men (snake's hypnotic powers are a myth). Of course he - as the white man - had enough mentalpower to resist the snake's trance inducing gaze and save the day by machine-gunning the offending reptile. Nothing more was heard of the hide and given Price's love of bullshit, it is perhaps best to write this off as a hoax.

Another tall tale that involved a hypnotic anaconda was related by Harold. T. Wilkins in his 1952 book *Secret Cities of Old South America*. Wilkins heard the tale from one Alfred.G. Hales, who had - in turn - gleaned it from Indians far up the Brazilian Amazon. An Indian was fishing one night in his canoe, when two moon-like lights on the bank, attracted him, and drew him to the shore. The lights were - in fact - the eyes of an anaconda. Just as he was about to reach the shore, another giant reptile (hinted at as being a dinosaur), lunged up from the river and snatched the giant snake from the branches.

The natives had also told Hales that anacondas lurked near temples, luring parrots from the trees with their hypnotic eyes that changed colour from green to red!

When witnesses are cross examined - face to face - by a renowned zoologist, we have to give them a little more credence. One of the witnesses of the next case was interviewed over several days by no less an authority than Heuvelmans himself.

It was in 1947, when many wild and sometimes fierce tribes were still commonplace in the South America. A particularly warlike group were the Chavantes - who had recently killed a number of Brazilian officials. Francisco Meirelles of the Service for the Protection of the Indians, organised an expedition to try to establish peaceful relations with this tribe. The five month endeavour included in its twenty-man line up. Serge Bonacase - a French painter whom Heuvelmans later interviewed.

By the second month, the company had reached a large island between the two branches of the Araguaya river, and made base-camp there. The men spent several days in preparation for the big push into the wilderness (or the *sertao* as the 'green hell' was known). They spent long reconnaissance and hunting trips away from the island. On one such trip, eight of them were hunting capybaras in a swamp between the Rio Manso, (charmingly known as the *Rio das Mortes* - 'The River of Death', as the Chavantes butchered any one who dared to cross it), and the Rio Cristalino. The Chavantes did not put in an appearance, but the group encountered something far more frightening:

The guide pointed out an anaconda on a rise in the ground half hidden among the grass. We approached to within 20 metres of it and fired our rifles at it several times. It tried to make off, all in convolutions, but we caught up with it after 20 or 30 metres and finished it off. Only then did we realise how enormous it was; when we walked the along the whole length of it's body it seemed as if it would never end. What struck me most was it's enormous head.

As we had no measuring instruments, one of us took a piece of string and held it between the ends of the fingers of one hand and the other shoulder to mark of a length of one metre. Actually it could have been a little less. We measured the snake several times with this piece and always made it 24 or 25 times as long as the string. The reptile must therefore have been nearly 23 metres long.

Unfortunately, none of the men were zoologists, and none realised the importance of the find. Bonacase himself had heard so many stories of giant anacondas he believed them to be commonplace. The carcass, and even the skin, would have weighed the men down too much for them to have brought it back. So, sadly, this invaluable specimen was left to the jungle scavengers. (This seems to be the bane of cryptozoologists. Specimens always seem to fall into the hands of those who do not know their importance, and hence seldom find their way to civilisation.)

The late 1950s brought perhaps the most dramatic encounter with an anaconda. The political climate, with its up-surgence in communism in Latin America, was such that the U.S government placed C.I.A agents in sensitive areas. One agent - called "Lee" - was told by a cattle-rancher of a giant-snake lairing in a cave in Bolivia. The reptile was said to be over ten metres (thirty-three feet) long. It was said to have eaten ten Indians and many cattle over the years. Every three months, or so the serpent emerged, seized a steer, dragged it into the river, killed it, then ate it. Then it would return to its cave.

The rancher wanted Lee to capture the animal and take it too a zoo as it was "probably the largest snake in the world". The problem was discussed at the embassy many times until someone came up with an audacious plot to catch it. The plan was to flush the monster from its lair with tear-gas whilst a long sack (complete with zip fasteners), was held over the *caves* mouth. There would be two "zip-men" - one at each end of the sack - to hasten the operation. For added security Lee carried (ironically) a .357 python pistol.

It was just as well Lee was "packing heat", as things did go spectacularly wrong. The tear-gas was shot into the cave, and the anaconda - thrashing madly - shot out of the cave, and into the sack. Once its entire length was inside, both ends were zipped up. The agents had not reckoned with the snake's vast strength however. Its violent writhing split the sack - end to end - and the brute was free.

The livid animal came rushing at Lee who whipped out his pistol, and managed to put a bullet in its head. The snake threw itself into a huge loop, smashing into a small hardwood tree about as big as a telephone pole. The tree was shattered like matchwood and the snake fell back into the jungle. Lee pumped another two bullets into its head. When it had expired they measured it Its length proved to be thirty-four feet three inches. Lee skinned the snake and took the hide back to the United States where he kept it in his garage. Its current whereabouts are unknown. As noted earlier, this size would seem very small for a snake which was able to swallow such large livestock.

Lee's colleague David Atlee Phillips, understandably doubted his friend's outlandish story. Sometime later he was attending a party at Washington, and mentioned the saga to Darwin Bell, then Deputy Assistant Secretary for International Labour Affairs. Bell claimed not only to have known Lee but to have taken part in the capture attempt.

"I was the tail zipper man," he told an amazed Phillips.

More recently, a giant anaconda was reported near Sao Paulo, Brazil. Farmer-come-hunter Joao Menezes was fishing with his three year old son Daniel, and turned his back on the boy to store some fish in a wooden shack. Suddenly his son's screams rent the air, and the horrified Menezes, turned to see a forty-five foot anaconda had risen from the waters and sized his boy by the neck. He tried in vain to prise the snake's jaws apart then ran home for his rifle. By the time he got back, however, the boy had been crushed and was in the process of being swallowed.

More recently still, Colonel John Blashford-Snell was told a most intriguing story whilst travelling across the Andes by river from Bolivia to Bunenos. It seems that a thirteen metre (forty-three foot) anaconda was captured by a farmer after it had eaten a cow. He apparently encited it with a pig on a rope. Subsequently he tried to sell his story, unsuccessfully, to the press. The creature is now said to be residing in a pond on a farm in north west Brazil. This occurred in late 1999.

If the creature is being fed by the farmers it may well remain in the pool. This is a cryptozoological "sitting duck". If the story is true is should be child's play to find and film this giant. The author hopes to find financial backing to do just that!

Even 45-66 footers seem like runts in comparison to some of the claimed monsters. There is a school of thought that there are two separate species of giant constrictor in the Neo-tropics, the giant anaconda and the markedly different and far larger *sucuriju gigante* or giant boa.

The Marquis de Wavrin - whom we met earlier - was told of such behemoths by his canoe-men who seemed to think them different to anacondas. Once, when the Rio Uva was in flood, some Piapoco Indians tried to take a short cut to the Rio Guaviare via some marshes and lagoons. Having just crossed a small lake, the Indians heard a sound akin to thunder behind them - even though the rains had ceased and the skies were clear. Looking back, they saw the waters in turmoil, as a massive animal thrashed about in mid-water. Then a gigantic snake's head broke the surface, and the animal disported itself momentarily, before diving again. (We should note here the interesting parallels with oriental dragons, and their association with rain and storms). The Indians believed that had the monster surfaced whilst they where crossing, they would have been devoured. Not unreasonably, they vowed never to take that particular short cut again.

The Marquis himself only narrowly missed seeing a *sucuriju gigante*. He reached the Rio Putumayo the day after a giant boa had dragged off an ox. The people were still in a state of shock. He writes of these giants:

Around the upper Paraguay they give the name minocao to a more or less fabulous snake: the natives say it can reach the size of a canoe. They suppose that it is a sucurijiu or a boa-constrictor that has grown very old and turned into a water snake. On the upper Rio Parana, in Brazilian territory, I have also been told of these enormous snakes, capable of dragging a canoe to the bottom. These monsters frequent deserted places, and never leave a river. The fear they arouse is quite superstitious. This idea of a giant serpent growing from as small snake, is also seen in Asian dragon legends. The concept of a snake becoming too large to live on land and hence taking up an aquatic lifestyle, echoes the Scandinavian lindorm stories.

One man who was convinced of the giant boa's existence, was Lorenz Hagenbeck .

The Hagenbecks were a dynasty of animal collectors who had supplied zoos worldwide with animals for over a century. In the days when captive breeding programmes were only a twinkle in zoo curator's eyes, the Hagenbecks provided rare and exotic beasts from all around the globe. It was one of Hagenbeck's explorers who first discovered the pigmy hippopotamus, (*Choeropisis liberiensis),* in Liberia on 28th February 1913. Lorenz himself discovered the skin of the Andean wolf, (*Dasycon haganbecki)* in a Buenos Aires market in 1927. As far as we know, no westerner has ever seen this animal alive and only one skull from this rare animal has fallen into the hands of zoologists.

The Hagenbeck family papers include several reports and transcripts pertaining to the "mother of all snakes".

Two of Hagenbeck's confidantes were Roman Catholic priests, Father Victor Heinz and Father Protesius Frickel. Father Heinz was lucky enough to see the giant boa on more than one occasion:

During the great floods of 1922 on May 22 - at about three o'clock to be exact - I was being taken home by canoe on the Amazon from Obidos; suddenly I noticed something surprising in midstream. I distinctly recognised a giant water snake at a distance of some thirty yards. To distinguish it from the sucurijiu, the natives who accompanied me named the reptile, because of its enormous size, sucurijiu gigante (giant boa).

Coiled up in two rings the monster drifted quietly and gently downstream. My quaking crew had stopped paddling. Thunderstruck, we all stared at the frightful beast. I reckoned that its body was as thick as an oil drum and that its visible length was some eighty feet. When we where far enough away and my boatmen dared to speak again they said the monster would have crushed us like a box of matches if it had not previously consumed several large capybaras.

Spurred on by such a dramatic encounter, the priest began to study the phenomenon seriously. He discovered that another specimen had been killed, a day's march from Obidos, as it was in the act of swallowing a capybara (*Hydrochoerus hydrochaeris)*, the world's largest rodent. This semi-aquatic species resembles a giant guinea pig and grows to the size of a large dog and are one of the principle prey-species of the anaconda. This particular snake had been on the shore of Lago Grande do Salea. Its stomach contained four adult capybaras. Elsewhere, two huge round scats were discovered and attributed to the giant boa. They contained animal hair. One had an oxen's hoof bone protruding out of it. The snake itself was far from finished with Father Heinz.

My second encounter with a giant water snake took place on 29 October 1929. To escape the great heat I had decided to go down river at about 7 p.m. in the direction of Alemquer. At about midnight, we found ourselves above the mouth of the Piaba when my crew, sized with a sudden fear, began to row hard towards the shore. "What is it?" I cried, sitting up. "There is a big animal", they muttered very excited. At the same moment I heard the water move as if a steamboat had passed. I immediately noticed several metres above the surface of the water two bluish-green lights like the navigation lights on the bridge of a riverboat, and shouted: "No, look, it's the steamer! Row to the side so that it doesn't upset us." "Que vapor que nada", they replied. "Una cobra grande!" Petrified, we all watched the monster approach; it avoided us and recrossed the river in less than a minute a crossing that would have taken us ten to fifteen times as long. On the safety of dry land we took courage and shouted to attract the attention of the snake. At this very moment a human figure began to wave an oil-lamp on the other shore, thinking no doubt, that someone was in danger. Almost at once the snake rose on the surface and we were able to appreciate clearly the difference between the light of the lamp and the phosphorescent light of the monster's eyes. Later, on my return, the inhabitants of this place assured me that above the mouth of the Piaba there dwelt a sucuriju gigante.

This account is interesting from a zoological point of view, because it contains a detail unknown to Father Heinz. The priest and his friends tried to attract the snake by shouting, to no avail. However the animal responded to the light stimulus. This is because snakes are deaf - a fact of which, Heinz and co. were clearly unaware of. This lends the report some weight and as far as I know has not been commented on before.

Heinz began to interview other witnesses. One of these was Reymondo Zima, a Portuguese merchant who had lived for nine years opposite the town of Faro on the Rio Jamunda

On 6th July 1930 I was going up the Jamunda in company with my wife and the boy who looks after my motorboat. Night was falling when we saw a light on the river bank In the belief it was the house I was looking for I steered towards the light and switched on my searchlight. But then we noticed that the light was charging towards us at an incredible speed. A huge wave lifted the bow of the boat and almost made it capsize. My wife screamed in terror. At the same moment we made out the shape of a giant snake rising out of the water and performing a St Vitus's dance around the boat. After which the monster crossed this tributary of the Amazon about half a kilometre wide at fabulous speed, leaving a huge wake, larger than any of the steamboats make at full speed. The waves hit our 13 metre boat with such force that at every moment we were in danger of capsizing. I opened my motor flat out and made for dry land. Owing to the understandable excitement at the time it was not possible for me to reckon the monster's length. I presume that as a result of a wound the animal lost one eye, since I saw only one light. I think the giant snake must have mistaken our searchlight for the eye of one of his fellow snakes.

In the same area, in 1948, an old pupil of Father Heinz - Paul Tarvalho - had a sighting of his own. He observed - from a distance of some 900 feet - a gargantuan snake emerge from the water. Tarvalho estimated it to be fully fifty metres (167 feet) long! This mammoth serpent followed his boat for a moment, and needless to say Tarvalho made off a top speed.

Father Frickel was brave (or foolish) enough to approach one of these titans on land. Whilst on an expedition on the upper reaches of the Rio Trombetas, he saw the head of a giant boa lying in water by the bank. The foolhardy father approached to within six paces of it, and noted its eyes were as large as dinner plates. This is another difference to the true anaconda whose eyes are comparatively small and beady.

As a one time zookeeper specialising in reptiles, I can vouch for the astounding strength of constricting snakes. Once, a young Indian python no more than three feet long, lifted the perspex lid of its tank, and escaped for several days. The lid had been weighed down with several large rocks, but these had proved no obstacle to the snake. One can imagine the titanic strength wielded by a *sucuriju gigante* that - if reports are to be believed - can exceed 150 feet in length! Father Heinz had a story related to him demonstrating just how powerful the giant boa is.

On 27 September 1930, on an arm of water that leads from Lake Maruricana to the Rio Iguarape, a Brazilian named Joao Penha was engaged in clearing the bank to make it easier for turtles to come up and lay their eggs. At a certain moment, behind one of those floating barriers made of plants, tree trunks, and tangled branches, against which steamers of 500 tons often have to battle to force a passage, he saw two green lights.

Penha thought at first that it was some fisherman who was looking for eggs. But the whole barrier shook for 100 metres. He had to retreat hurriedly from a foaming wave 2 metres high struck the bank. Then he called his two sons, and all three of them saw a snake rising out of the water pushing the barrier in front of it for a distance of some 300 metres until the narrow arm of the water was finally freed of it.

During all this time they could observe at leisure its phosphorescent eyes and the huge teeth of its lower jaw.

Three photographs exist - apparently showing specimens of the giant boas killed in 1933, 1948 and 1949. The first two were published in Rio de Janeiro newspapers. All of these had been developed by the same man - Miguel Gastao, the proprietor of a bazaar at Manaus. Father Heinz interviewed him, and was assured that none of the photos had been tampered with.

The first had been brought in by the Brazilian-Colombian Boundary Commission, who said the snake been killed on the banks of the Rio Negro. The thirty metre (100 foot) creature had been machine-gunned, and in its death-throes had reared up nine metres (thirty feet) crushing bushes and small trees under its two ton bulk. Four men had been unable to lift its head.

The second was captured alive whilst swallowing a steer (the bull's horns were still protruding from the snake's mouth). A rope was affixed about its neck and it was towed into Manaus (this begs the question why such a large and powerful animal behaved in such a placid way). There it was finally killed by machine-gun fire. It was alleged to be forty metres (131 feet) long and to weigh five tons!

Tim Dinsdale, the late monster hunter and world-renowned cryptozoologist, examined the photo published in the *Diario de Pernambuco* on January 24 1948. He said:

One of the first things that struck me looking at this photograph, was that although the beast appeared to have an enormous blunt snouted head of a giant snake type it was altogether different from the anaconda, boa constrictor, and python. For one thing it had eyes that were much too large, and a great bag of a mouth, the mottled white markings on which where unlike those on the anaconda, which in old age sometimes develops jowls beneath the lower jaw......

....Another thing: in the photograph at the sixth convolution the body is at its visible greatest. Whereas on the largest of known snakes, the reticulate python, skeletal rib-structure is clearly greatest at the fourth convolution.

I have never actually seen a copy of this picture, but Dinsdale's observations seem to be born out by his detailed sketch taken from the original.

The second 1949 photograph was taken after a dramatic encounter in the ruins of Fort Tabatinga on the River Oiapoc in Guapore territory. The thirty-five metre (117 foot) snake crawled ashore and made its lair in the fort, (just like a medieval dragon). It took an amazing five-hundred rounds of machine gun fire to kill it. The titanic cadaver was photographed as it floated down river. The picture shows a large snake floating belly up in water. The far bank is visible with buildings on it, but without knowing the width of the river and how far the body is from the bank, we cannot estimate its size. The extremities are below the water and the body seems distended with gas. I have only seen black and white prints of this, but Dinsdale - who saw a colour copy - said its belly was a mottled-white, a description that does not fit the anaconda.

Naturalist Peter Matthiessen, was told by Fausto Lopez - a hotelier from Pucallapa, Peru - that in the 1950s he saw an old and harmless "anaconda" thirty metres (100 feet) long, that had been killed by Indians on the Huallaga river. How any snake measuring 100 feet can be considered harmless is quite beyond the comprehension of this author.

So far, all the sightings of the giant boa have been in South America, but there is one report that suggests they might range further north. Francois Poli was a French explorer who studied shark fishing in Lake Nicaragua. In his book *Sharks are Caught at Night*, he recounts how he met a German called Brennecker, who encountered a giant boa on the borderlands of Nicaragua and Honduras:

I was driving a jeep along a sort of natural track winding between two lines of trees when I saw, about 50 yards ahead, a huge fallen tree trunk which barred the way. I told the boy who was with me to find some way of shifting it. He came back at a run. It wasn't a tree-trunk at all, but a snake. It stirred and began moving slowly towards us...

I've seen the most incredible snakes in this country during the past twenty years - and I can assure you I know how to handle a gun. But that day I left the revolver where it was; I just stepped on the gas and drove off.

Jeremy Wade interviewed several Amazonian fishermen whilst he was exploring the area in 1995. His first informant was Dorgival Sabino, who saw a giant boa on the Rio Negro (seemingly the place for them):

It was a gigantic animal, like a monster. A snake, but of a size much bigger than normal with the difference that its head was like some kind of dinosaur, with, I don't know whether they were teeth or horns, just that it was grotesque.

Sabino put its length at twenty metres (sixty-five feet), and its width at a metre (three feet). The horns are more problematical. The only horn-bearing snakes are all vipers (such as the rhinoceros viper and the horned viper). It has been suggested that the horns, that have been reported on giant snakes several times, are in fact the horns of bulls that the snake is swallowing protruding from the corners of its mouth.

On a tributary called the *Rio Purus*, Wade met another witness - Amarilho Vincent de Oliveira. Whilst navigating the backwaters one night some twenty years before, Oliveira and a companion came upon what looked like a floating-tree in his torch light. As they passed it, he looked back. and saw the "tree" had turned ninety degrees to face them despite there being no current. They doubled back and crossed the ninety-metre channel paddling stealthily up the other side. The "tree" again turned to face them. This time they got a look at it, and it became apparent that this was no fallen tree.

Its head had horns like the roots of a tree, and could see these greenish eyes as well. We just left the canoe on the bank and got out of there. Afterwards, people saw movements in the water there, many times. With no wind, there would be waves that covered the beach.

Again, I think that a prosaic explanation for the horns can be found. You will recall Joao Penha's description of a giant boa pushing its way through a tangled mass of vegetation that was blocking the river. Could not this specimen have done the same and still retained some branches caught on its head? By torch-light these could have been mistaken for horns.

In 1996 Wade returned to continue his inquires. This time he travelled to an even more remote area. One 76 year old man described how as a boy he saw a rib cut from a giant snake that had been shot, but which was too large to drag ashore. The rib was a metre (three feet) long. The snake was killed by an engineer who had spotted a strange light on the river just before a large wave washed his boat onto a bank.

Botanist Grace Rebelo dos Santos, told Wade that in June 1995, she saw two lights appear in the middle of the river. The lights emanated from a place that earlier that evening, a dragnet had become caught on something very heavy, that had then escaped.

She said, *"It came right in close to the bank then disappeared. The lights were like torches, about 30 cm apart.. I'm not going to say it was a cobra-grande but I remember clearly how blue the lights were, which I thought very strange."*

What are we to make of these claims? Do snakes in access of 150 feet actually exist? The answer is that currently no one knows for sure. Such monsters seem fantastic, but so did the giant squid, the gorilla, and the okapi before they fell into the hands of western science. We have seen in the previous chapter, that there is a fossil precedent for giant snakes in South America. Perhaps these antediluvian constrictors are not extinct at all, but still linger in the dim, steamy, interior of the Amazonias.

Could these gigantic serpents be of a prehistoric lineage thought long extinct? One group of fossil snakes that I have mentioned before - the *Madtsoids* - did reach huge sizes. A fossil rib from South America suggests a snake of eighteen metres (sixty feet). The *Madtsoids* were at first thought to be giant boas or pythons, but we now know they belong to a more primitive basal group of snakes. Despite their primitive nature, they were highly successful, and spread across the world. Evolving in the *Cretaceous* period - over 100 million years ago - some, such as the Australian *Wonambi,* lingered until only 10,000 years ago. Could some species have survived and grown to even more titanic proportions in remote jungle areas of the world?

Giant reptiles are still alive today. Even at the start of the 21st century there are dragons on Earth. Monstrous crocodiles, lizards, and snakes, can *all* make effective dragons; but they cannot explain all dragonlore. Their major stumbling block is that they are ectothermic - relying on the environment to provide their body heat. Hence all large reptiles are found in the tropics. This cannot explain the abundance of dragon legends from temperate or even cold climates. It could be argued that early explorers brought back distorted traveller's tales of them, but most dragon legends pre-date travel to the tropics. We have to look elsewhere for the genesis of European dragons.

CHAPTER FOUR

Dinosaur Survival and Dinosaur Descendents

"No; a reptile - a dinosaur. Nothing else could have made such a track."

Professor George Edward Challenger, cited in
The Lost World by Sir Arthur Conan-Doyle (1912)

o group of animals that have ever lived, hold us in such a thrall as dinosaurs. They rampage through our childhood imaginings, and stalk across the silver screen from the jerky black and white silent, *The Ghost of Slumber Mountain* (1918), to the hi-tech realism of *Jurassic Park* (1993). There are dinosaur theme parks, dinosaur toys, dinosaur sweets, dinosaur clothes, and more books have been written about dinosaurs than any other creatures.

The fascination is understandable. Humanity has been dominant on earth for less than one million years; dinosaurs were the unchallenged rulers of this sphere for more than one hundred and twenty million years! The cause of dinosaur extinction has still to be established. Palaeontologists are divided into two camps over this. The first are the 'smoking gun theories' - these evoke great global catastrophes to explain the terrible lizards fall from supremacy. These include massive volcanic activity in Asia, radioactivity from exploding stars and the ever-popular asteroid. The second camp point out that dinosaur decline was gradual and look to much more reasonable ideas such as climate change, and new diseases crossing newly formed land-bridges as sea-levels fell with global cooling.

The idea of total dinosaur extinction is totally false. Dinosaurs are around us all the time, and in some ways they are just as successful now as they ever were - for birds are dinosaurs. As far back as 1860 when *Archaeopteryx* (then thought to be the first bird), was discovered in the Solenhofen shale of Bavaria, the link between dinosaurs and birds has been known. The specimen bore tail-bones, teeth and claws like any small carnivorous dinosaur, but beautifully preserved about it were unmistakeable feathers. Since then, many feathered dinosaurs have been discovered - some pre-dating *Archaeopteryx* by several million years. All modern birds can literally be considered dinosaurs. Pneumatic bones, erect stance, and skull fenestrations, are among their many shared features, and - strange as it may seem - *Tyrannosaurs rex*, the largest and savagest predatory dinosaur, has more in common with your pet budgie than it does with *Triceratops*. When feeding ducks in the park you are feeding dinosaurs. Your local pet shop sells dinosaurs for your home and if you watch your uncle Ted eating chicken you can boast to your friends you have seen a "man eating dinosaur". However, small feathery things that go 'tweet' are not what the word 'dinosaur' summons up for most people. Are there any non-avian dinosaurs surviving today? If so, they would truly make excellent dragons. Are there any giant sauropods or razor toothed coelurosaurs slinking through the jungles or lurking on remote mesas awaiting formal discovery by incredulous scientists? There are those who think the answer is 'yes'!

We begin our dinosaur safari in the cradle of mankind; darkest Africa.

Anyone boarding the Southampton train from Waterloo station on 23 of December 1919 at 11.30 a.m, may well have been startled by two outlandish figures. One was a fierce-looking hound that seemed more wolf than dog. The other was a tall, weather-beaten man carrying a rifle. The man was Captain Leicester Stevens, and his dog was

'Laddie' - a wolf/dog hybrid; a barrage-dog who had bravely carried messages under heavy fire in the First World War. His quest was to travel to central Africa to hunt a surviving "*brontosaurus*". His intentions had made national news, and ironically - given what we now know about dinosaurs - an old lady from the Wild Birds Protection Association, had written to him asking him not to shoot the dinosaur. Sportsmen, hunters, and demobbed soldiers had written too, asking to accompany him. Perhaps unwisely, he elected to go alone - save for his dog.

The pair made it to the jungle but were never seen again. No-one knows what became of them. Without the adequate backup that a team expedition would have provided, they probably fell victim to tropical illness and died alone - thousands of miles from home. Sadly, it seems the report that had inspired their endeavour was a hoax. It appeared on the 17th of November 1919 in *The Times*.

A TALE FROM AFRICA
Semper aliqud novi

The Central News Port Elizabeth correspondent sends the following;

The head of the local museum here has received information from a M. Lepage, who was in charge of railway construction in the Belgian Congo, of an exciting adventure last month. While Lepage was hunting one day in October he came upon an extraordinary monster, which charged at him. Lepage fired but was forced to flee, with the monster in chase. The animal before long gave up the chase, and Lepage was able to examine it through his binoculars. The animal ,he says, was about 24 feet in length, with a long pointed snout adorned with tusks like horns, and a short horn above the nostrils.

The front feet were like those of a horse, and the hind hooves were cloven. There was a scaly hump on the monster's shoulders.

The animal later charged through the native village of Fungurume, destroying the huts and killing some native dwellers. A hunt was organised but the government has forbidden the molestation of the animal ,on the ground that it is probably a relic of antiquity. There is a wild trackless region in the neighbourhood which contains many swamps and marshes, where, says the head of the museum, it is possible a few primeval monsters may survive.

Firstly, the animal described does not resemble a "*brontosaurus*". This creature - more properly known as *Apatasaurus* (the name *brontosaurus* came about due to a mix up in fossil skulls) - was a sauropod dinosaur, a long necked herbivore. The creature Lepage reported more closely tallies with a ceratopsian dinosaur - the group that contained such horned dinosaurs as *Triceratops*, *Styracosaurus*, and *Monoclonius*. Any dino-buff cannot fail to have noticed the glaring errors that make even this identification a non-starter. Ceratopsians had rounded elephantine feet, not hooves. They also possessed a bony frill about the neck that an observer could not have failed to notice. Horned dinosaurs lacked this odd animal's scaly shoulder hump. Lepage's animal is a complete chimera, and the story sounds like a fabrication.

The unlikely saurian was back in the news on December 4th:

News apparently corroborating the report of the existence in the Congo of a monster known as a Brontosaurus (the thundering saurian) comes from Elizabethville.

A Belgian prospector and big game hunter named M. Gapelle, who has returned from the interior of the Congo, states that he followed up a strange spoor for 12 miles and at length sighted a beast certainly of the rhinoceros order with large scales reaching far down its body. The animal, he says has a very thick kangaroo- like tail, a horn on its snout, and a hump on its back. M.Gapelle fired some shots at the beast, which threw up its head and disappeared back into a swamp.

The American Smithsonian expedition was in search of the monster referred to above when it met with a serious railway accident, in which several persons were killed...

Needless to say, the Smithsonian Institute did not find this amusing, especially as several of its members had been killed in a railway accident in Africa. This only confirmed the tall tales in the eyes of both the popular press and the general public. The Smithsonian Institute felt that it had to quash such outrageous nonsense, and wrote a letter to *The Times* which was published on the 21st of February:

Sir,

I am authorised to contradict the statement that the members of the Smithsonian African Expedition who proceeded to this territory came here to hunt the brontosaurus. There is no foundation for this statement. I may also state that the report of the brontosaurus arose from a piece of practical joking in the first instance, and, as regards the prospector "Gapelle", this gentleman dose not exist except in the imagination of a second practical joker, who ingeniously coined the name from that of Mr L. Le Page.

Yours faithfully

WENTWORTH. D. GREY
Acting Representative of the Smithsonian African expedition in the Katanga
Elizabethville, Jan 21

Another bogus report was printed in *The Rhodesia Herald* on July 15 1932, in which a Mr. F. Grobler claimed to have knowledge of the existence of a giant lizard known as the *Chepekwe*. Grobler stated that it had been discovered six months earlier by a German scientist in the swamps of Angola. The reptile fed on hippos and rhinos, and Grobler claimed to have seen a photograph of the monster squatting on a hippo it had just killed. Grobler's gravitas seemed supported, as he claimed to have acted as a guide to the renowned explorer Hans Schomburgk in his expedition into the Dilolo swamps. The Major had stated in a lecture the previous year that a tradition of giant reptiles was prevalent in central Africa.

Shortly after this, a Swedish man, J. C. Johnson - an overseer on a Belgian rubber plantation - wrote to the *Cologne Gazette* enclosing claimed photographs of the creature. These - together with his story - found their way into *The Rhodesia Herald*. The lurid tale runs thus:

On February 16 last I went on a shooting trip, accompanied by my gun-bearer. I only had a Winchester for small game, not expecting anything big. At 2 p.m. I reached the Kassai valley.

No game was in sight. As we were going down to the water, the boy suddenly called out "elephants". It appeared that two giant bulls were almost hidden by the jungle. About 50 yards away from them I saw something incredible- a monster, about 16 yards in length, with a lizard's head and tail. I closed my eyes and reopened them. There could be no doubt about it, the animal was still there. My boy cowered in the grass whimpering.

I was shaken by hunting-fever. My teeth rattled with fear. Three times I snapped; only one attempt came out well. Suddenly the monster vanished, with a remarkably rapid movement. It took me some time to recover. Alongside me the boy prayed and cried. I lifted him up, pushed him along and made him follow me home. On the way home we had to traverse a big swamp. Progress was slow, for my limbs were still half- paralysed with fear. There in the swamp, the huge lizard appeared once more, tearing lumps from a dead rhino. It was covered in ooze. I was only 25 yards away

It was simply terrifying The boy had taken French leave, carrying the rifle with him. At first I was careful not to stir, then I thought of my camera. I could plainly hear the crunching of rhino bones in the lizard's mouth. Just as I clicked, it jumped into deep water.

The experience was too much for my nervous system. Completely exhausted, I sank down behind the bush that had given me shelter. Blackness reigned before my eyes. The animal's phenomenally rapid motion was the most awe-inspiring thing I had ever seen.

I must have looked like one demented, when I at last regained camp. Metcalf, who is boss there, said I approached him, waving the camera about in a silly way and emitting unintelligible sounds. I dare say I did. For eight days I lay in a fever, unconscious nearly all the time.

It seems the herbivorous *Triceratops/Brontosaurus* had been transformed into the savage, carnivorous *Tyrannosaurus rex*. All the more challenging to the intrepid. Unfortunately, Johnson's picture did not live up to his story. It is a tawdry fake showing a Komodo dragon inexpertly superimposed on a dead rhino. So poor is the quality that it would not frighten anyone over the age of five, let alone send a supposedly seasoned-hunter into a fear-crazed fever for over a week.

The reader might feel a little disheartened at this point, as *all* the African stories so far have turned out to be hoaxes. There are, however, two points to note.

Firstly, we have sorted the chaff from the wheat and can now proceed to genuine reports; and secondly, the hybrid animal reported seems to have characteristics of *both* dinosaur-like creatures reported in Central Africa, as there are two distinct kinds. Moreover one kind is indeed referred to as *Chepekwe* in some areas.

Let us take a look at this beast first.

A dishevelled tramp peddling gridirons, wandered up the garden path of Etherlreda Lewis's Johannesburg home one day in 1925. Most folk would have shooed such an unwholesome fellow off their property, but Ms Lewis was a kindly soul and invited him in for refreshments. As it turned out, this was a stroke of luck for both the vagrant, and for Lewis - who was a novelist. The old man began to reminisce about his past, and the literary immortality of both himself and his host was assured.

The tatty old gent of the road was one Alfred Aloysius Smith - or 'Trader Horn' as he had been better known. The novelist soon realised she had a veritable gold mine in her living room, and transcribed his stories into a series of best selling books.

Horn's tale was the stuff of pulp fiction. He was born in Lancashire, and educated in a strict Roman-Catholic school, (St. Edwards' College, Liverpool). Here he was taught French, Portuguese, and Spanish. This did not suit the young tearaway at all, and he was soon expelled for excessive wildness and for "always being on the roof"!

He took a ship to the West African country of Gabon, and there - aged seventeen - started work for a British Trading Company - Hatton and Cooksons - buying ivory and rubber and selling various trade goods. This is where his story really takes off. Horn claimed all kinds of fantastic adventures, hunting every known jungle beast, canoeing up unexplored rivers, and generally behaving in a manner fitting of a character in a Tarzan novel. After five years of these shenanigans, he came home to Lancashire and married his childhood sweetheart. Soon after, they moved to London and in an attempt to settle down, Horn became a reporter, then a policeman. These - not exactly sedate - jobs failed to excite him enough, so he joined Buffalo Bill's Wild West Show, and moved to Pittsburgh, U.S.A. Here his wife died, and he was gripped by wanderlust once more, and glibly shipped his two children back to relatives in England.

What he lacked as a father he made up for as a traveller. He roamed the world like 'The Wandering Jew', visiting Mexico, Australia, Madagascar, and of course his beloved Africa. Eventually, poverty caught up with him and he became a drop-out, ending up in a Johannesburg doss-house. Shortly after, he met Lewis, and 'Dame Fate' smiled on him again. So popular was his life-story that it was made into a Hollywood film in 1930, (one wonders if Horn ever saw it, and if so what he thought.) Horn died, and was buried in Whitstable, Kent, in 1931.

The obvious question is how much - if any - of Horn's narrative can be trusted. We must remember that he was an old man recalling events of half a century or more before. Also a warm meal, and roof over his head, would have been incentive enough for him to spin the wildest yarns for his host's entertainment. Finally, Lewis herself probably spiced up the stories with a novelist's style.

Perhaps we should not be so quick to reject all of Horn's adventures - some quite reputable persons have held stock in what he said. One such was Dr Albert Schweizer, who commented: *"apart from a few unimportant slips the statements made by Trader Horn about the country are generally accurate."*

It would be surprising if Horn had not heard of "dinosaurs" in Africa, and true to his reputation he does not disappoint us. Once, by some lakes in the Cameroons, he came across a three-toed footprint as large as a frying pan. This he linked to a creature known as the *Amali* which was spoken of by pigmy bushmen. He also claimed to have seen carvings of it in their caves. This curious track turns up again in the saga of the Africa monsters.

Carl Hagenbeck believed in a giant saurian haunting the swamps of Africa, but appears to have only known of a "brontosaurus" type creature. Some of his informants, however, also knew of a short-necked, horned beast. Hans Schomburgk, for example, had heard tell of a dangerous animal lurking in Lake Bangweulu in East Africa. The animal was said to kill hippos, but malaria prevented Schomburgk investigating further.

It was another English ex-pat that gathered more information on the horned giant of Lake Bangweulu. J.E. Hughes was born in Derbyshire in 1876 and attended Cambridge University. After this his family apparently expected him to except a career in The Church of England. This apparently repulsed him so much that - much like Trader Horn before him - he rebelled. The British South Africa Company offered him a job as Assistant Native Commissioner in the newly formed Civil Service of north-east Rhodesia. After seven years of service, Hughes resigned and became a hunter/trader. He lived for the next eighteen years on the Mbawala islands on Lake Bangweulu. He recorded his life in a book, *Eighteen years on Lake Bangweulu*, in which he writes of the monster:

For many years now there has been a persistent rumour that a huge prehistoric animal was to be found in the waters of our Lake Bangweulu. Certainly the natives talk about such a beast and "Chipekwe" or "Chimpekwe", is the name by which they call it.

I find it is a fact that Herr Hagenbeck sent up an expedition in search of this animal, but none of them ever reached the Luapula or the lake, owing to fever, etc.; they had come at the wrong time of year for newcomers.

Mr. H. Croad, the retired magistrate, is inclined to think there is something to the legend. He told me one night, camped at the edge of a very deep small lake, he heard a tremendous splashing during the night, and in the morning found a spoor on the bank not that of any animal he knew, and he knows them all.

Another bit of evidence about it is the story Kanyeshia, son of Mieri-Mieri, the Waushi Paramount Chief, told me. His grandfather had said that he could remember one of these animals being killed in the Luapula in deep water below the Lubwe.

A good description of the hunt has been handed down by tradition. It took many of their best hunters the whole day spearing it with their "Viwingo" harpoons - the same as they use for the hippo. It is described as having a smooth dark body, without bristles, and armed with a single smooth white horn fixed like the horn of a rhinoceros, but composed of smooth white ivory, very highly polished. It is a pity they did not keep it, as I would have given them anything they liked for it.

I noticed in Carl Hagenbeck's book "Beasts and Men", (abridged edition, 1909, p.96,) that the Chipekwe has been illustrated in bushman paintings. This is a very interesting point, which seems to confirm the native legend of the existence of such a beast.

Lake Young is named on the map after its discoverer, Mr Robert Young, formerly [Native Commissioner] in charge of Chinsali. The native name of the lake is "Shiwangandu". When exploring this part in the earliest days of the Administration, he took a shot at an object in some floating sudd[sic] that looked like a duck ; it dived and went away, leaving a wake like a screw steamer. This lake is drained by the Manshya river, which runs into the Chambezi. The lake itself is just half-way between Mipka and Chinsale Station.

Mr Young told me that the natives once pulled their canoes up the Manshya into this lake. There were a party of men, women, and children out on a hippo-harpooning expedition. The natives claimed that the Guardian Spirit of the lake objected to this and showed his anger by upsetting and destroying all the men and canoes. The women and children who had remained on the shore all saw this take place. Not a single man returned and the women and children returned alone to the Chambezie. He further said that never since has a canoe been seen on Lake Young.. It is true I never saw one there myself. Young thinks the Chipekwe is still surviving there.

Another bit of hearsay evidence was given me by Mr Croad. This was told to him by Mr. R. M. Green, who many years ago built his lonely hermitage on our Lulimala in the Ilala country about 1906. Green said that the natives reported a hippo killed by a Chipekwe in the Lukula - the next river. The throat was torn out.

I have been to the Lukulu many times and explored it from its source via the Lavusi Mountain to where it loses its self in the reeds of the big swamp, without finding the slightest sign of any such survival of prehistoric ages.

When I first heard about this animal, I circulated the news that I would give a reward of either £5 or a bale of cloth in return for any evidence, such as a bone, a horn, a scrap of hide, or a spoor, that such an animal might possibly exist. For about fifteen years I had native buyers traversing every waterway and picking up other skins for me. No trace of the Chipekwe was ever produced; the reward is still unclaimed.

My own theory is that such an animal did really exist, but is now extinct. Probably disappearing when the Luapula cut its way to a lower level- thus reducing the level of the previously existing big lake, which is shown by the pebbled foothills of the far distant mountains.

Perhaps, if we are to believe Mr Young's tale, the creature's ferocity kept it from being hunted very often. A picture is emerging of a huge, dangerous, semi-aquatic animal with a single horn and an antipathy towards hippos. Many have come to the conclusion that these are Ceratopsian dinosaurs. These were a sub-order of Ornithischia (bird-hipped dinosaurs) and contained such well-known horned dinosaurs as *Triceratops* and *Styracosaurus*. They were all herbivores, and were typified by bearing horns and a bony frill - like an Elizabethan ruff - that grew from the rear of the skull to protect the animal's neck. The number of horns varied between the species - some such as *Monoclonius* bore only one horn on the snout.

There are two main stumbling blocks with the dinosaur theory. First and foremost there is no fossil evidence for any species of non-avian dinosaur surviving beyond the Cretaceous period (which ended 65 million years ago). Secondly, there is no indication of any species of dinosaur being aquatic, let alone Ceratopsians. So we need to look elsewhere for this beast's identity. Let us examine some more evidence.

The *Daily Mail's* dinosaur fiasco did produce at least one seemingly genuine piece of evidence in what seems to be an honest letter from C. G. James - a gentleman who had resided in Africa for 18 years. His letter was published on December 26, 1919.

Sir, I should like to record a common native belief in the existence of a creature supposed to inhabit huge swamps on the borders of the Katanga district of the Belgian Congo - the Bangweulu, Mweru, the Kafue swamps. The detailed descriptions of this creature vary, possibly through exaggerations, but they all agree on the following points:

It is named the Chipekwe; it is of enormous size; it kills hippopotami (there is no evidence to show it eats them, rather the contrary); it inhabits the deep swamps; its spoor (trail) is similar to a hippo's in shape; it is armed with one huge tusk of ivory.

It is useful at this point to realise that Lakes Bangweulu and Mweru are connected via the Luapula river-system, (where supposedly a specimen was killed).

Identical reports have come in from elsewhere in the 'dark continent'. Lucien Blancou, chief game inspector in French Equatorial Africa: collected stories of unknown animals between 1949 and 1953. Some of these seem to refer to an animal like the *Chipekwe.*

The Africans in the north of the Kelle district, especially the pygmies, know of a forest animal larger than a buffalo, almost as large as an elephant, but which is not a hippopotamus. Its tracks are only seen at long intervals, but they fear it more than any other dangerous animal. The sketch of its footprint which they drew for M. Millet is that of a rhinoceros. On the other hand they do not seem to have said that it has a horn, though they certainly not said that it has not. While M. Millet was at Kelle, in 1950 if I am not mistaken, one of the best known African chiefs in the district came several days march to inform him that "the beast had reappeared". Unfortunately, this is all I can say, for M. Millet left the district in 1951, and I have not been able to go there myself. The rewards in kind which this official offered the pygmies for tangible proof of the animal's presence yielded no result.

Around Ouesso, the natives talk of a big animal which does have a horn on its nose- though I don't know whether it has one of several. They are just as afraid of it as the Kelle people.

Around Epena, Impfondo, and Dongou, the presence of a beast which sometimes disembowels elephants is also known, but it dose not seem to be as prevalent there now as in the preceding districts. A specimen was supposed to have been killed twenty years ago at Dongou, but on the left bank of the Ubangi and in the Belgian Congo.

This report is particularly interesting, as the man in question recognised the print as being that of a rhinoceros - one of the few animals capable of killing an adult hippo. (The hippopotamus is one of the most dangerous animals in Africa. Despite the cuddly Disney image, this animal has it is in reality totally unpredictable and highly territorial. It also possesses a huge mouth armed with immense, curving tusks, that can bite a man in two, or rend a boat asunder.) In the Congo this horned animal is called *Emela-ntouka.* This translates as 'killer of elephants'. Places where both hippos and elephants are scarce or absent, are reputed haunts of this aggressive creature, who gores the former animals to death with its horn.

Iise von Nolde spent ten years in eastern Angola, and in 1930 reported events much like the ones related previously. Natives told her of a monster called "*Coje ya menia*" or 'water lion'. The name seemed to relate to the roaring sound the animal produced rather than to any resemblance to a lion. She heard its rumbling cry for herself on several occasions. It was said to inhabit the water but was also seen on the bank. In the rainy season when the Cuanza river was in flood it moved to smaller rivers and swamps.

One day, she met a native in hippopotamus-skin sandals. She asked him if he had killed the hippo himself, and he replied that he had found the animal dead - killed by a *Coje ya meina*. On another occasion, a Portuguese lorry driver told her of how he had heard of one of these creatures killing a hippo on the previous night. He intrepidly set off to investigate with several native hunters and found the beast's tracks. The hippo's tracks ran for several miles and seemed intermingled with the tracks of its pursuer - but none of them could identify them. Finally, they came upon an area where the grass and bushes had been smashed and crushed. The mangled cadaver of the hippo lay in the centre of the devastation. It looked as if it had been hacked and ripped by a huge bush knife. None of the carcass had been eaten. It would seem that the only thing capable of inflicting such wounds would have been a massive horn.

For me, the clinch in this animal's identity is a photograph taken in 1966 in the Congo by French photographer and naturalist Atelier Yvan Ridel. The photo shows a large three-toed footprint - one of a set that led out of a mass of reeds, up a steep bank, across a small beach and into the river.

The tracks are instantaneously recognisable to any zoologist worth his salt - they are the foot prints of a rhinoceros. The nearest rhino populations to the Congo are 1000 miles away in the Cameroons and the Central African Republic. These are black rhino (*Dicerocs bicornis*) - the smaller of the two African species and much smaller than the reports of the *Emela-ntouka*. The toes seem a little more elongate than those of other rhinos, and this may be an adaptation to a marshy environment. The rhino's close relatives in the order perissodactyla (odd toed ungulates) - the tapirs - display slightly elongated toes and are invariably found in swampy biotopes.

The *Emela-ntouka/Chipekwe* is most likely to be not a ceratopsian dinosaur, but a giant semi-aquatic rhinoceros. The idea of a water dwelling rhino may seem strange, but the great Indian rhino (*Rhinoceros unicornis*) spends almost as much time in water as a hippopotamus. It feeds mainly on lush water plants such as reeds and water lilies. The Indian rhino also bears only one horn - much like the *Emela-ntouka* - and unlike the two savannah dwelling African species who both have two horns.

This unknown species must be a veritable giant. Natives say that it rivals the elephant in size. The largest known rhino is the African white rhino (*Ceratotherium simum*), that can reach five tons in weight, and is second only to the elephants as the largest land-mammal. A white rhino would have no trouble despatching a hippo, but if the *Emela-ntouka* does *indeed* kill elephants, it would need to be even more massive. One prehistoric rhino - *Indricatherium* - was the largest land mammal of all time reaching twenty tonnes in weight - bigger than the largest mammoth. One group of rhinos - the *Amynodontids* - specialised in an aquatic lifestyle. These flourished in the Oligocene Epoch - 38 to 25 million years ago - finally dying out about 10 million years ago. Could one species have survived into the present? This is by no means impossible, but it is perhaps more likely that our unknown giant is a modern species that has avoided detection, rather than a prehistoric survivor.

But what of the ivory horn? Rhino horn is made from keratin - a fibrous material that also forms human fingernails - and very different to ivory. This is the only sticking-point with the rhino theory. Could the natives be mistaken on this point? I think the answer has to be 'yes'. However much we want this creature to be a dinosaur, the bulk of the evidence points towards a giant aquatic rhino.

So it seems that our *first* horned 'dinosaur' is no such thing. But what of the *second* possible dinosaur that lurks in the African rain forest. This is a very different beast.

Lewanika was a king who ruled over the remnants of the Bartose Empire on the middle of the Zambezi river. Prior to the 1920s, Barotseland lay in the north-western district of what is now Zambia. King Lawanika was fascinated by the animals of his kingdom and studied them in detail. His subjects repeatedly told him of a vast, aquatic reptile - larger than an elephant. The King gave orders to be notified immediately the next time such a creature appeared. The following year three men came to his court, and told him they had just seen a monster on the edge of the marshes. They described it as taller than a man, with a snake-like head on a long neck. On seeing the men, it slid on its belly into the deep-water. The King rode at once to the spot, and saw the depression made by the creature, and the channel where it had slid into the swamp. He told the British Resident - Colonel Hardinge - that the channel was *"as large as a full sized wagon from which the wheels had been removed"*.

The wagons used by the Boers at the time, were 1.40 metres wide, so whatever made the track was a substantial animal. Hardinge found out that the natives called the creature *Isiququmadevu.*

The description given by the King's three subjects, is one we see time and time again across sub-Saharan Africa. An elephant-sized beast, with an elongate-neck, terminating in a small head, a barrel-shaped body with four sturdy legs, and a long whip like tail. The description is reminiscent of a group of saurischian (lizard-hipped), herbivorous dinosaurs called sauropods. These included such well-known dinosaurs as *Diplodocus, Apatasaurus,* and *Brachiosaurus.* One species - *Amphicoelias* - may have been the largest animal that ever lived. At possibly 200 foot plus in length, and 200 tons or more in weight, it would have dwarfed even the blue whale. Many kinds of sauropods were found in the African continent such as *Vulcanodon* and *Aegyptosaurus.* The jungles of central Africa have remained largely unchanged since the Cretaceous Period, and many believe that they still harbour dinosaurs.

The first western involvement with these creatures came in 1913 when the Likuala-Kongo German expedition penetrated the northern Congo. It was led by Freiherr von Stien zu Lausnitz - a colonial officer. The endeavour was due to last two years, but was cut short by the outbreak of the First World War. Lausnitz's report was never published, but parts of the manuscript were obtained by pioneering cryptozoologist Willy Ley. Ley discovered that during their travels, the Germans collected reports of a giant aquatic water-animal much feared by the natives. It haunted the lower Ubangi, Sanga and Ikelemba rivers and was known as *Mokele-mbembe.* Lausnitz said that the characteristics of the animal had been repeated to him by several experienced native guides who had no knowledge of each other.

The creature is reported not to live in the smaller rivers like the two Likulalas, and in the rivers mentioned only a few individuals are said to exist. At the time of our expedition a specimen was reported from the none navigable part of the Sanga River, somewhere between the two rivers Mbaio and Pikunda; unfortunately in a part of the river that could not be explored due to the brusque end of our expedition. We also heard about the alleged animal at the Ssombo river. The narratives of the natives result in a general description that runs as follows:

The animal is said to be of a brownish-grey colour with a smooth skin; its size approximating to that of an elephant; at least that of a hippopotamus. It is said to have a long and very flexible neck and only one tooth but a very long one; some say it is a horn. A few spoke about a muscular tail like that of an alligator. Canoes coming near it are said to be doomed; the animal is said to attack the vessels at once and to kill the crews but without eating the bodies. The creature is said to live in caves that have been washed out by the river in the clay of its shores at sharp bends. It is said to climb ashore even at daytime in search of food; its diet is said to be entirely vegetable. This feature disagrees with a possible explanation as a myth. The preferred plant was shown to me; it is a kind of liana with large white blossoms, with a milky sap and apple like fruits.

A sauropod with a horn? One sauropod - *Amargasaurus* - sported a crest of spines on its upper neck. These were believed to have been used for defence against contemporary predators, and to have been rattled - like porcupine spines - for communication and warning. These seem very different to the single horn spoken of here. The great Belgian cryptozoologist Bernard Heuvelmans has suggested that some confusion exists between the *Mokele-mbembe* and the *Emela-ntouka*. Both are large aquatic animals, both are rarely seen, and now probably exist only in the most remote reaches of the central African rainforest. It seems that some of their characteristics have been transposed upon each other. The horn of the *Emela-ntouka* is erroneously placed on the *Mokele-mbembe*, whilst the long tail of the latter is sometimes attached to the former - a feature never found in rhinos. It should be noted that these confusions only occur in a small minority of reports.

Having said this, there is a possibility that the *Mokele-mbembe* does sport a horn, albeit one much smaller than that of the *Emela-ntouka*. Air security-officer, A. S. Arrey, told cryptozoologist Philip Averbuck of a sighting of two Long Necked monsters he had as a child. Arrey was living at Kumba in Cameroon during 1948-49. He was swimming with friends in Lake Barombi Mbo. Also present were some British soldiers. Something began to make the waters at the centre of the lake boil, and everyone swam to shore. Looking back, they saw a long-neck - some twelve to fifteen feet high - break the surface. A few minutes later, a second, slightly smaller neck, rose around 200 yards from the first. Both were covered by smooth scales. The larger of the two - which Arrey assumed to be the male - bore an eight inch horn on its two-foot long head. The smaller creature was hornless. The monsters remained at the surface for an hour before the 'female' submerged, followed soon after by the 'male'.

Lucien Blancou - whom we met earlier - was also aware of this second kind of water monster. In the 1930 the *Linda Banda* people of French Equatorial Africa, described to him an animal they called "*Ngakoula-ngou*". It was a gigantic snake-like animal that killed hippos without leaving any sign of a wound, and browsed on trees without leaving the water. 'Snake-like' seems to refer to the creature's necks as no true snakes eat vegetation.

Blancou was told by Yetomane - a chief and hunter of great renown - that in 1928, one of the monsters had crushed a field of manioc belonging to the chief, and left tracks 1.90 metres wide. This probably meant the track left by the animal's body rather than individual footprints. The size is quite comparable to that left in the marshes of Barotseland. The same animal was said to have killed a hippo (what is it with African water monsters and hippos?) in the River Brouchouchou. The corpses was eaten by the villagers.

The Baya people told Blancou of an identical creature they knew as Badigui. a man called Moussa related how he had seen the beast in his youth:

When he was about 14 years old and the whites had not yet come (probably around 1880), Moussa was out laying fish-traps with his father in the Kibi stream, which runs into a tributary of the Ouaka called the Gounda in what is now the Bakala district. It was one o'clock in the afternoon in the middle of the rainy season. Suddenly Moussa saw the badigui eating the large leaves of the roro, a tree which grows in forest galleries. Its head was flat and a bit larger than a python's (Moussa spread his hands and put them together to show me the size). Its neck was as thick as a man's thigh and about 4.50 metres long, much longer than a giraffe's; it had no hair but was as smooth as a snake, with similar markings. The underneath of its neck was lighter - also like a snake's. Moussa did not see its body.

His father told him to follow him and run away. The animal gave no cry, but Moussa had heard its cry at other times when he had not seen the beast himself. He did not imitate it for me.

According to him, the old men believed the badigui does not frequent places where you find hippopotami, for it kills them.

Along the Cavally river in Liberia - close to the border with The Ivory Coast - there are similar stories. This river rises in the Niam Mountains - in a still-unexplored area. At a place known as Juju Rock, a grey dinosaur-shaped animal is said to live. Natives say it is larger than a crocodile and carnivorous. The diet here seems to be at odds with reports from other areas of Africa, but as we shall see later there may be an explanation for this. To my knowledge, this creature has never been investigated by western science, and due to Liberia's current unstable climate it will probably remain so.

Jorgen Birket-Smith of the Institute of Comparative Anatomy at the University of Copenhagen, was resident in the French Cameroons during the winter of 1949-1950. He was based at Case du Nyong along the River Nyong. He was told by two old hunters, of a large animal that inhabited the River Sanaga. He was told that it was larger than a crocodile or hippo, and that it had a long neck like a giraffe. Smith, who had heard rumours of African dinosaurs, drew a picture of an *Apatasaurus*. The natives instantly identified it as the creature:

...the guard remembered, that when he was a boy – that must have been sometime in the twenties – they caught one in the village. Its size was between a hippo and an elephant. The whole village had eaten from it for a week....

...it ate from the trees, by which they meant the trees in the gallery forest leaning over the water or turned over into the water. It hardly ever came onto dry land. It is supposed to browse mainly at night, and it stays submerged during daytime.

James Powell, member of the crocodile specialist group of the International Union for Conservation of Nature and Natural Resources, was studying crocodiles in Gabon, along the Ogowe and N'Gounie rivers, when he heard stories of a dinosaur-like animal. The Fang people - former cannibals who had been gradually migrating towards Africa's west coast from inland for some two-hundred years - told of a monster they named *N'yamala*.

Powell befriended a Swiss dentist from the Albert Schweitzer hospital who had married a Fang girl. He accompanied the dentist up the Ogowe to his wife's village. There he became aquatinted with the village witch-doctor, Michel Obiang, and found the septuagenarian to be highly intelligent. Powell showed the old man pictures of Gabonese animals such as leopards, gorillas, crocodiles and hippos. The witch doctor identified them all. Powell then showed him a picture of a bear, an animal not native to sub-Saharan Africa. This was unknown to him. Then he was presented with a picture of *Diplodocus*, a sauropod dinosaur. He answered, matter of factly; "*N'yamala*". He added that this animal fed on jungle chocolate; a plant with nut-like fruits that grows near river banks and lakes. This recalls Lausnit's description of the *Mokele-mbembe*'s food source half a century earlier.

The witch-doctor was insistent that the *N'yamala* had no horn, and rejected pictures of other dinosaurs as unknown to him. A *Pterodactyl* was not unreasonably identified as a bat.

The following day Powell travelled 80 miles downstream to study the narrow snouted crocodile (*Crocodylus cataphractus*). He repeated his experiment with the population of a small village. The results were the same - *Diplodocus* was instantly identified as *N'yamala*. The villagers told him that it lived in remote lakes in the jungle. None of them had seen it personally. The area was sparsely populated, and according to the American Embassy in the country, Gabon is *still* 80 percent unexplored.

Powell made a return to the witch-doctor's village at a later date, and talked to him again. This time Obiang told him of his own encounter with the *N'yamala*. In 1946 he had been half way up the River N'Gounie, where the Ikoy tributary branches off. He had camped for several days by a small cove off the main river, where the waters were deeper. He observed the monster leaving the water at around 5.00 a.m. and feeding on jungle chocolate. It was around ten metres (thirty-three feet) long, and as heavy as an elephant. Obiang said it was as strong as one of the caterpillar tractors used at the construction of the hospital. It had thread-like filaments running down its neck, and two 'pouches' in the vicinity of the front-legs. These - Obiang stated - were used for storing food, much like a hamster's cheek pouches. This may seem odd, but sauropod dinosaurs possessed a crop much the same as that which birds have. Because they only had small peg-like teeth for nipping off vegetation and totally inadequate for mastication, they processed their food with the crop. This was a highly muscular section of the throat where fibrous plant matter was crushed into a digestible pulp. Sauropods swallowed stones known as gastroliths for this purpose, and stored them in the crop for grinding food (the dinosaur equivalent of dentures!) These stones can still be found today, recognisable due to their highly polished nature.

Powell asked Obiang to take him to the spot where his sighting occurred. The witch-doctor obliged, and Powell discovered a remote lake in the dense jungle, swarming with ants and flies. The lake was some thirty metres (100 feet) across, by 5.5 metres (eighteen feet) deep. Obiang was very scared that the *N'yamala* might still be in the area, though nothing was seen. When asked if any hunting trophy such as a skull, bones, or skin were ever preserved Obiang replied "*Oh no, no the N'yamala is king of the waters. It never dies. No one ever kills a N'yamala.*"

Obiang suggested that to see a specimen, Powell should travel down The Ogowe towards the coast. On an island in the middle of a wide part of the river, a *N'yamala* had killed a hippo but lack of time prevented Powell from doing this.

Once home, Powell contacted Paul W. Richards - an authority on the African rainforest.

Richards identified the "jungle chocolate" as a species of Landolphia - a large group belonging to the dogbane family - or Apocyanaceae that includes vines and lianas.

In January 1980, Powell together with Dr. Roy P. Mackal - a biochemist from the University of Chicago and vice president of the International Society for Cryptozoology - mounted an expedition to look for surviving dinosaurs in the Congo. Early on in their trip they met an eye witness at a Mission. Firman Mosomele claimed to have seen the *Mokele-mbembe* some 45 years before, at a bend in the Likouala-aux-Herbes river just below the town of Epena. He saw a snake-like head supported on a three metre (ten foot) neck break the water. Terrified, he paddled his canoe away, as the beast's two metre (seven foot) back surfaced. The animal was a reddish-brown in colour. Mosomele said that in the Epena district natives were afraid to go to the river-bank in late afternoon, as this was when the creature came ashore to feed.

The dread which this animal installs in natives was illustrated by the beliefs attached to the *Mokele-mbembe* by locals. Some of these were related to Mackal and Powell by Marien Ikole - a pygmy from the village of Minganga:

- To tell any one of a sighting or even *talk* of the beast you will die, this obviously hampers investigation, and implies that the vast majority of sightings go unreported.

- When the monster appears, it causes a miniature tidal-wave that will wash onto the bank, and then suck you back into the water to be drowned.

- The *Mokele-mbembe* is so huge that it can bridge the river.

- Once, in a time of war, a tribe escaped from their foes by running across the creature's neck, back, and tail, as it positioned itself across the river.

These beliefs have analogues in many ancient dragon legends around the world, and argue for the existence of actual creatures rather than mere myths.

Pascal Moteka - another pygmy who lived near Lake Tele (infamous for sightings) - recounted to the expedition of a killing of a *Mokele-mbembe* shortly before his birth, (around 1950). The fishermen were too afraid of going out onto Lake Tele - due to the monsters who entered it via waterways or *molibos*. The tribesmen cut down some trees of about fifteen centimetres (six inches) in diameter, and trimmed off the branches. Then they sharpened one end of each, and rammed the blunt ends into the mud at the bottom of one of the waterways to form a barrier against the monster. One of the creatures tried to smash its way through, and whilst entangled on the spikes the pygmies managed to spear it to death.

There was a great celebration, and the animal's carcass was butchered and eaten. However, all who ate the flesh of the *Mokele-mbembe* were poisoned, and died soon afterwards. This recalls the almost universal belief in the toxicity of dragon blood. In many British dragon legends, so much as a drop may be lethal, and many victorious heroes met their end by spilling the blood of their terrible foes. This tale was latter confirmed by other fishermen in the area.

Pascal had seen the animals himself, mainly in mid-morning. He related seeing their long necks rise two metres (seven feet) from the water, and on occasion a rounded back surfacing like a buoy. His intense fear of the creatures prevented him from approaching them, and consequently he only observed them from a distance.

Other witnesses saw the animal at much closer range. Nicolas Mondogo said that his father had seen a massive animal with a long neck come out of the river and onto a sandbank. It left dinner-plate sized tracks and a great furrow where its tail had dragged in the wet sand. This occurred between the villages of Mokengi and Bandeko, on the upper Likouala-aux-Herbes river. Close to this spot, Nicolas had his own sighting when aged seventeen. It had been 7 a.m, and he was on his way to a Catholic Mission at Bandeko. He had paused to hunt some monkeys, when a huge animal rose from the river. The water in the area was only a metre (3.5 feet) deep, so he could observe the underbelly and legs of the animal. The beast stayed in view for three minutes. It had a long neck (as thick as a man's thigh) a head that bore a comb like a rooster, and was reddish brown in colour. It was a mere twelve metres (forty feet) away, and was some ten metres (thirty feet) long. It stood two metres (seven feet) high, and possessed a neck of a similar length, giving a height of approximately four metres (fourteen feet), quite comparable to that of a giraffe. The tail seemed longer than the neck.

David Mambamlo, a school teacher, saw it even closer. Only three years before, he had been canoeing just upstream from Epena at about 3 p.m. when a two metre (seven foot) head and neck broke the surface only ten metres (thirty feet) from his vessel. He was mesmerised with horror, as it rose further out of the river, exposing its upper breast. The monster was grey in colour with no visible scales. David picked out a picture of an *Apatasaurus* from a book and said that the animal most resembled that. He subsequently showed the expedition the location of his sighting - a cave in the river bank, a kilometre (half a mile) from the village. The water-level had dropped revealing the cave but no occupant was spied.

Daniel Omoa, Ministry of Agriculture worker, said that in July of 1979 a *Mokele-mbembe* had taken up residence in a pool close to the river. This was just north of Dzeke - eighty kilometres (fifty miles) downstream from Epena. The people saw it leave the jungle, and enter the river by a sand-bar that had become a small island during the dry season. Elephant-sized tracks were found on the island, and a pathway of crushed-grass two metres (seven feet) wide, was found at the river bank.

Mackal and Powell had to return to the States soon after. Though they had not seen the *Mokele-mbembe,* both were now convinced of its existence as a rare but real biological entity, as opposed to just a native myth.

In October 1981, Mackal returned to The Congo, this time accompanied by Richard Greenwell from the University of Arizona. Greenwell was also the secretary of the International Society of Cryptozoology. This time they came closer than ever to seeing the *Mokele-mbembe*.

Whilst travelling upstream from the village of Itanga, they came to an area where the trees briefly thinned out along the river bank, and were replaced by elephant-grass. As they rounded a sharp bend, something dived off the 1.5 metre (five foot) bank, and into the water with a great splash. Whatever it was, it was large, as it caused a wash to flow over the expeditions dug-outs. Due to the shaded nature of the area none of them got a good look at the creature. The pygmies were in no doubt of the creatures identity and screamed out *"Mokele-mbembe"* in terror. The group searched the area for half an hour, but the monster (if that was what it was), did not reappear. The water into which it dived was found to be seven metres (twenty-three feet) deep.

They travelled to Dzeke, but found that the animal dwelling in the nearby pool had departed some sixteen months previously, in the June of 1980. A villager called Appolonair, related his sighting of the animal. Whilst hunting monkeys, he saw its long head and neck rear up into view and feed on *malombo* (another name for jungle chocolate).

They were also told that the creatures were once common - before the coming of the white man. When motorboats began to come up the river, they retreated to more remote areas.

At the village of Bozenzo, they were told of a *Mokele-mbembe* that reached with its neck from the river and seized goats. The creature then devoured them. This seems at odds with the insistence elsewhere, that the animal is a herbivore. Village men plucked up the courage to tackle the brute after several livestock losses. They attached ropes to their spear-shafts and harpooned the monster. It was cut up and eaten. After this the village became cursed. Houses burnt down for no apparent reason, illnesses broke out, and there were strange deaths. As a result, the *Mokele-mbembe* became a venerated animal. This occurred around 1908.

Perhaps this animal has some sort of toxin in its flesh. This is far from impossible. Poisonous birds have recently been discovered in New Guinea, and South America's poison-dart frogs are some of the most toxic animals known to man. Alternatively, food poisoning could arise if the meat of this unknown animal was not properly cooked. Either way an outbreak of illness and death would be attributed to a magick curse from the creature.

At Dzeke they found a track smashed through the jungle at a height of two metres (seven feet), and a trail of twenty-five centimetre (twelve inch) prints. The village folk still feared the pool where the monster had laired, and would not approach it. Had they investigated the pool upon the first expedition they may well have found their quarry.

Since then there have been many attempts to find the *Mokele-mbembe*. Herman Regusters, an engineer from California, led an expedition into The Congo with his wife in September 1981. Originally Regusters had planned to co-run Mackal's second venture but then changed his mind without adequately explaining why. He claimed he saw - and photographed - a *Mokele-mbebme* but his shots were hopelessly under exposed and of no value. This sort of bad-luck seems to habitually dog cryptozoologists. Much to the delight of sceptics (who are generally armchair zoologists), cameras seem to be absent, or to fail, whenever an unknown animal appears. The next expedition suffered a similar fate.

A search for the monster by Congolese scientists took place in the spring of 1983. Lake Tele was visited by a group from The Ministry of Water and Forests. It was led by Dr Marcellin Agnagna - a zoologist from The Parc de Zoologie. On 1st May - whilst filming monkeys in the forest - Agnagna was approached by an excited local who bade him to come quickly to the lake. Wading into the water, he saw the back and neck of a large animal some 700 feet away. The strange animal turned its head as if it had heard Agnagna approach. As he raised his camera and began filming he realised he could not see anything through the viewfinder. He had foolishly kept the camera on the 'macro' setting. In the time that it took him to realise this and switch the setting, his film had run out! Despite this mother of all frustrations, he watched the animal through the telephoto lens obtaining a detailed sighting. The head was held around a metre out of the water, and turned from side to side as if listening. It was reddish-brown, with a long, slender muzzle, and crocodile-like oval eyes. Just behind the neck was a black hump. Agnagna was sure the beast was a reptile - but *not* a crocodile, turtle, or python.

He and two - particularly brave - villagers waded further into the lake. The animal submerged, but then surfaced again, staying in view for 20 minutes. Agnagna took some shots with a small 35 millimetre camera, but the pictures were too indistinct for identification.

British explorer Bill Gibbons led two expeditions. Operation Congo took place in 1986 and was an Anglo-Congolese effort. Despite being hampered by bureaucratic problems from the Congolese side, they rediscovered Mackal's *Mokele-mbembe* tracks from his second trip thus independently verifying them. They were also told that Lake Tele itself is not the home of the monsters, but that they live in three sacred lakes in the surrounding jungle. These lakes are holy to the Boha people who claim ownership of Lake Tele. Two expedition members were allowed to spend a day at one of these lakes, never before seen by white-men. They were informed that the *Mokele-mbembes* use Lake Tele as a feeding ground - and for transit - but actually reside in the smaller bodies of water. However, no evidence for their presence in the sacred lakes was uncovered.

Gibbons met up with American journalist Rory Nugent at Epena. Nugent was conducting a solo expedition by boat, plane, and on foot. At Lake Tele he saw a black periscope-shaped object break the surface. It was some 1,000 metres away, and beyond the range of his camera. He tried to photograph the object, however, but once again the pictures were far too blurred.

The second Operation Congo expedition took place in late 1992. Though no further evidence was gathered, two unexplored lakes were visited - Lake Tibeke and Lake Fouloukou.

Most recently, English explorer Adam Davies attempted to solve the riddle. Impressively he self-financed his trip and travelled solo - no mean feat in such an unstable and dangerous country. He was told by *mokele-mbembe* witness Dr Marcellin Agnana, that Lake Makele - some 1.25 miles from Lake Tele - was the best place to look for the beast. The pygmies told him that they believed that only the male of the species bears a horn. The confusion with the horn seems to continue. Sadly, Adam did not catch site of the monster himself in the limited time he had in the area. Hopefully, one day an expedition will have the luck to prove conclusively just what this most enduring of 'neo-dinosaurs' actually is.

The *Mokele-mbembe* probably exists. The native accounts (save for the horn) are very consistent. But is it a dinosaur?

The answer is almost certainly no.

The two major factors against this idea are the same as those that applied to the *Emela-ntouka*. We have seen that there are no fossils that suggest any kind of non-avian dinosaur survived the extinctions at the end of the Cretaceous Period. Other 'prehistoric survivors' such as the okapi - a short necked giraffe from the Central Africa - and the coelacanth - a primitive fish of the 'extinct' order *Crossopterygii* - have fossil precedents for their survival.

Secondly, and perhaps more importantly, as mentioned briefly earlier in this chapter, sauropod dinosaurs, (or any dinosaurs for that matter) were not aquatic. The notion of aquatic dinosaurs had its sorry genesis with Victorian scientists who perceived these giant animals as being too heavy for their legs to support them for very long on dry land. They envisioned sauropods as spending ninety percent of their lives in water, buoyed up to relive them of their vast weight and feeding on soft water plants. Only when they needed to lay eggs would they leave this safe environment. (It was once believed equally as wrongly that carnivorous dinosaurs could not swim! In fact they were the best swimming of all dinosaurs).

This ridiculous theory has long been disproven. Sauropod bodies were adapted for life on land, with thick pillar-like legs to support them, and hollow vertebra to lighten their body-weight. Their lifestyle could be compared to that of modern elephants or giraffes - huge herd dwelling herbivores that browse vegetation. Fossil track-ways show sauropods to have been social-animals, and that the young travelled with the herd and were not abandoned in lakeside nests as once thought. Lastly, it was physically impossible for sauropods to have been aquatic on account of their long necks. Previously they were pictured as strolling along lake beds with only their heads above the water. Some species like *Brachiosaurus* had their nostrils on top of the head on an elevated crest. Again this was thought to be an adaptation to aquatic living, a type of 'snorkel'. However, the water-pressure on a sauropod's neck would have caused it to cave-in, and if it tried to take a breath its lungs would have collapsed. Obviously sauropods entered water from time to time - as do modern elephants, in order to bathe, cool off, and rid themselves of parasites - but they were not habitual water dwellers.

The *Mokele-mbembe* does seem to be genuinely aquatic and hence is unlikely to be a dinosaur.

If it is not a dinosaur, then what is the *Mokele-mbembe*? The creature that most fits the picture is a giant monitor-lizard. In the previous chapter we encountered Australia's *Megalania prisca*. If giant monitors can exist in the Antipodes then why not elsewhere? The African animal seems radically different to *Megalania*, but this may be due to its aquatic habitat.

Many monitors favour a semi aquatic existence. Most of these amphibious species - such as the water monitor (*Varanus salvator*) - have elongated necks. Monitors are primarily carnivores, but are very adaptable. It is not out of the question that an omnivorous variety could have evolved. One must remember the stories of the Mokele-mbembe eating goats; this lends weight to the omnivore hypothesis. Dr Ralph Molnar - an expert on Australian fossil monitors - believes that some of them were aquatic and bore crests on their heads. This instantly brings to mind the native descriptions of the *Mokele-mbembe*.

A ten metre (thirty foot) aquatic, omnivorous monitor seems much more likely than a sauropod species having survived for 65 million years.

But the mighty Congo has not yet given up all of its monsters. After giant crocodiles, unknown crocodiles, and giant monitors it still has another surprise. Whilst showing dinosaur pictures to natives on his first expedition Roy Mackal was astounded when one girl picked out a *Stegosaurus* as an animal known to her. These herbivorous Ornithischian (bird hipped) dinosaurs, were typified by a double row of diamond shaped plates that ran in alternating rows along the back of the animal. At first thought to be defensive spikes, we now know these highly-vasculated structures were thermoregulatory devices that helped the creature control its body temperature. When wanting to raise the temperature of its body, a *Stegosaurus* would present its flank to the sun. This would warm up the blood as it flowed through the wide plates. If alternatively it wished to cool down, it would turn away from the sun's rays. An elephant's ears serve a similar purpose today. Defence was in fact catered for by sharp-spines on the powerful tail. These differed in number from species to species.

They flourished during the mid to late Jurassic period, then fell into sharp decline when replaced by other families of herbivorous dinosaurs in the Cretaceous. They lingered on in the Indian sub-continent until the late Cretaceous.

The girl - Odette Gesognet - was in her early 20s and lived in the village of Bounila. She related that the animal was known to her ancestors and she had been warned to hide behind a tree if she ever saw one. The animal had 'planks' growing out of its back. These were festooned with algae, as it spent most of its time in the water. The animal was called *Mbielu-mbielu-mbielu*. Her story was backed up by Bruno Antoine - a 65 year old man who had worked for thirty-five years in the French Administration. Antoine had been awarded The Congolese Medal of Honour, by former president Marien Ngouabi. He told the expedition that one of these creatures had been seen at Ebolo some 200 metres upstream from Epena. It was mainly observed just before dusk at around 4.00 p.m to 6.00 p.m. It was coated with weeds and was fully observable when it left the water.

The reader will now be expecting me to stress how there were no aquatic stegosaurs and how no non-avian dinosaurs survived the end of the Cretaceous period! That said, we cannot glibly ignore these reports. The people were obviously likening a *Stegosaurus* to some animal they knew. My guess is that if this creature exists it is a giant freshwater-turtle with a spined-shell. In the Pleistocene epoch a giant spined tortoise called *Meiolania* existed in Australia. Today some chelonians - such as the Bornean hillstar tortoise - sport spines. A giant, spiny-terrapin lurking in The Congo must surely be possible – especially when compared to some of its more outlandish neighbours!

The African 'dinosaurs' seem to be a mixed bag of spectacular animals - none of which are in reality dinosaurs. A mixture of ignorance and wishful thinking has transposed the mantle of 'dinosaur' upon them - but does this hold for the rest of the world?

Let us now move away from the 'dark continent' and widen our search to other continents and other creatures. South America must surely show some promise, after all it was in Venezuela that Conan Doyle set his novel *The Lost World*. In the dim, primal, Amazon jungles there must be room for archaic saurians?

In fact the neotropics have produced far fewer 'neo-dinosaurs' than The Old World. What meagre tales there are, I will recount here.

The most dramatic of these adventures was alleged to have taken place in October of 1907. A German called Franz Herrmann Schmidt, and his companion Captain Rudolph Pfleng, had travelled up the Solimoes river in Colombia. By the twelfth day of the expedition, they had reached a remote valley with a plant-choked, shallow lake. Fed by hot springs, the vegetation was exceedingly luxuriant, though both men noticed a lack of fauna.,

Some massive tracks were spied leaving - then returning to the lake. There were three sets, one adult and two apparent youngsters. Nearby trees had been browsed to a height of around fourteen feet.

Next day - whilst canoeing down the lake - a splashing and crashing was heard from the vegetation on the bank. Monkeys in the trees went wild, and a huge shape loomed from the shadows. The Indian guides panicked and paddled further out into the lake, then:

The head appeared over bushes ten feet tall. It was about the size of a beer keg and was shaped like a tapir, as if the snout was used for pulling things or taking hold of them. The eyes were small and dull and set in like those of an alligator. Despite the half dried mud we could see that the neck, which was very snake like, only thicker in proportion, was rough knotted like an alligator's side rather than his back.

Evidently the animal saw nothing odd in us, if he noticed us, and advanced until he was not more than one hundred and fifty feet away. We could see part of the body, which I should judge to have been eight or nine feet thick at the shoulders, if that word can be used, since there were no forelegs, only some great heavy clawed flipper. The surface was like that of the neck. For a wonder the Indians did not bolt, but they seemed fascinated.

As far as I was concerned, I would have waited a little longer, but Pfleng threw up his rifle and let drive at the head. I am sure that he struck between the eyes and that the bullet must have struck something bony, horny, or very tough, for it cut twigs from a tree higher up and further on after it glanced. I shot as Pfleng shot again, and aimed for the base of the neck.

The animal had remained perfectly still till now. It dropped its nose to the spot at which I had aimed and seemed to bite at it, but there was not blood or any sign of real hurt. As quickly as we could fire, we pumped seven shots into it, and I believe all struck. They seemed to annoy the creature but not to work any injury. Suddenly it plunged forward in a silly clumsy faction. The Indians nearly upset the dugout getting away, and both Pfleng and I missed the sight as it entered the water. I was anxious to see its hind legs, if it had any. I looked again only in time to see the last of it leave the land- a heavy blunt tail with rough horny lumps. The head was still visible though the body was hidden by the splash. From the instant's opportunity I should say that the creature was thirty-five feet long, with at least twelve of this devoted to head and neck.

The monster dived under the dugout, and resurfaced about an eighth of a mile away. The creature began swimming towards them, and on seeing the impotency of their bullets, the men paddled frantically away, finally losing their

110

giant pursuer behind an island.

This story appeared in the *New York Herald* on Sunday 11th of January 1911. Pflend is said to have died of fever in March 1908, so the tale was never backed up by a second testimony. The monster itself is a hopeless hybrid of dinosaur, turtle, and tapir. It sounds like a complete construct. It is interesting to note - however - that at one time sauropod dinosaurs were believed to have trunks much like tapirs. The nasal openings in sauropod skulls are placed high up between the creature's eyes (or on top of the head in some species). This is much like the placement of the nasal openings on elephant skulls. This led some to conclude that sauropods had small trunks like the beast previously described. However, sauropod nasal openings lack the tiny diagnostic-scars left by muscle-attachments as seen in elephants. This theory has, therefore, largely been abandoned.

It also goes without saying, that an animal with the flipper-like limbs reported by Schmidt and Co. could not have left the elephant-like tracks they also reported.

In 1931, Harald Westin - a Swedish explorer - was travelling down the Marmore river in the Mato Grosso region of Brazil when he happened across an odd animal sauntering along the bank. The twenty foot beast had an alligator-like head and possessed a body resembling a boa constrictor, but with four lizard-like legs. Westin kept up the tradition and took a pot-shot at the animal. It made clucking noise but seemed unharmed.

The description of this creature ill-fits any dinosaur. Apart from the elongate body this thing (if it existed at all), sounds more like a crocodilian than anything else.

Sebastian Bastos was an elderly jungle guide who had been educated in Switzerland. In 1975 he met a businessman from Geneva with whom he became friends. Bastos confided many things with his friend, including an alleged encounter with a supposed dinosaur. In the early 1970s he had been canoeing in the rainforest, whilst the water-levels were unusually low. He was proceeding on foot - pulling his vessel behind him - towards a native friend, whom he had arranged to meet at this particular point. Disturbed by a noise behind him, Bastos looked back and was appalled to see an immense monster rear up from the river, and smash his craft like matchwood. He and the Indian ran away in terror, pausing only to see if the horror still pursued them. To their intense relief, the brute had dived beneath the surface again. The Indian explained that the natives went in great fear of these animals. They laired in deep holes in the river in the jungle interior. At night they would sometimes come ashore. Their heads necks and backs measured eighteen feet (suggesting an overall length of nine metres or thirty feet).

This whole story is as suspect as a puppy next to a pile of poo! The exact area of the Amazon that this adventure is supposed to have occurred in is not identified, the businessman has never given his name, and once again our 'dinosaur' is aquatic.

Colonel Percy Fawcett, whom we met along with his suspiciously slender giant anaconda in the last chapter, had this to say about dinosaurs in the Amazon:

... some mysterious and enormous beast has frequently disturbed the swamps-possibly a primeval monster like those reported in other parts of the continent. Certainly, tracks have been found belonging to no known animal-huge tracks, far greater than could have been made by any species we know.

I've already made clear my opinions on Percy Fawcett's stories, and I have the same feelings on South American 'dinosaur' reports.

One can, at a push, conceive of dinosaurs in South America, but in North America, in the icy wastes of the Yukon? Just such an outlandish tale surfaced in Paris in 1905. It related the story of Georges Dupy - a French-Canadian missionary and banker from San Francisco. He - with two companions - was gold-prospecting at Armstrong Creek near the McQuestern River. The men were hunting moose for food, when one of the animals that they were stalking let out a bellow of alarm, and took flight with its fellows. Upon investigation of the area the men discovered the imprint of a huge animal in the snow. The body seemed to be thirty feet long by twelve feet wide, and impressed itself two feet deep. There were also four footprints measuring five feet by two and a half feet. These seemed to bear twelve-inch claws. The animal's tail had also left a furrow some ten feet long and eighteen inches wide.

The group tracked the uncommon spoor for six miles, until it ended at the foot of a ravine. They had the impression that the brute had leapt up the side of the cliff. Sometime later a concerted search for the monster was made with the Canadian Mounted Police. One evening, after a fruitless day of trekking across the tundra, they set up camp on the summit of a rock gulch and lit a fire. Dupy took up the story:

We lay by the fire, relaxed our aching limbs, and let our eyes roam over the marsh, glittering with icicles and hoarfrost crystals, that we had just crossed. The tea was steaming ready in the pail when, on a sudden, we were startled by the sound of falling stone tumbling down into the bottom of the ravine, followed by larger boulders. Then came a harsh appalling roar. We sprang to our feet and I don't mind saying that my teeth chattered and it was not cold, either! Right across the ravine, on the side opposite to that were we were camped, the boulders were rolling heavily into the bottom, as a gigantic black and hairy animal slowly and heavily ascended the grade. From the corner of its mouth a blood-stained frothy slime dripped. Its horrid jaws were munching, munching, munching. The priest, the sourdough, and Buttler unconsciously clasped each other by the arms and tried to shout, but could not utter a sound. And well for us that we were stricken dumb! Our Indians crouched on the ground, their faces ashy and their bodies trembling like aspen leaves. They pressed their faces to the ground and shut out the sight. Buttler suddenly got up and tore down the hill.

"Luckily, the monster had not sighted us! He stopped barley 100 paces from us. Then popping his huge belly on a big flat rock, he stood motionless gazing into the glaring eye of the red and setting sun! It was a sight that may not have been unfamiliar to our giant forefathers in a remote age. The monster stood still for 10 minutes, as did we. He actually swivelled round his huge neck, and still did not see us. I calculated he was about 50 feet long. He had a sort of rhinoceros horn on top of his jaws and his carcass was covered with black stiff bristles like those of a wild boar. The hair was plastered with mud and frozen muck. I'd put his weight at 50 tons.

"As we watched, a sound like the crunching of bones came from his dripping jaws. Then he reared up on his hind legs , emitted a horribly hollow roar, gave a terrific leap, and vanished up the ravine. We made no attempt to follow him.

Dupy and Co. went to Dawson City and requested a party of fifty armed men and mules from the Governor. The Governor did not buy the story, nor oblige Dupy in his request. The Dawson City *Daily Nugget* had a field-day mocking the whole affair. However the creature was apparently seen again some five years later. The priest from their original encounter, Pere Lavagneux, wrote to Dupy after his return to France:

Ten of my Indians and myself have seen again that horrible beast of Partridge Creek. It was on Christmas Eve, and the monster was passing like a whirlwind over the frozen surface of the river, breaking off with his hind feet enormous blocks of ice from the frozen surface. His fur was covered with hoarfrost and his little eyes- that was why he probably did not see us when we met him, some five years back, when you were here my son- glittered like fire in the dusk. He had in his jaws something that looked to me like a caribou. He moved at a rate of more than 30 miles an hour. The temperature stood at 45 degrees below zero. At the corner of the cut off, the monster vanished.

It is evidently the same monster we saw before. Together with the chief Stinehane and his two sons I followed up the trail of the horrid beast. They were exactly like the track you and I and the rest saw when you were here. Then they were embedded in the muck of the moose lick. Eight times on the snow we measured the prints. They were the same and so was the enormous body. Not a 20th of an inch difference! We trailed them to Stewart, fully three miles, when the snow fell and obliterated the tracks.

It is hard to know just where to begin in picking fault with this.

- Firstly, the description of the monster sounds a little like *Ceratasaurs* save for the size, twice as large as that dinosaur.

- Secondly, no known dinosaur bore fur (though some had feathers).

- Thirdly, Dupy's statement inferring 'giant' human ancestors living alongside dinosaurs shows his gross ignorance.

- Fourthly, the fact that the animal had not grown a fraction in five years.

- Fifthly, the extremely low temperatures sited that are not conducive to giant reptiles.

The hairy Yukon dinosaur, I think, can safely be thrown into the cryptozoological out tray.

Canada is not exactly a tropical zone, but there have been other 'dinosaur' reports from here as well.

In 1970, herpetologist Ken Strong was working in the Provincial Museum cataloguing specimens. During this time he was contacted by a Mrs Henderson who was inquiring about bipedal lizards about a foot in height. She wished to know if there were any records of such creatures on Vancouver Island. She explained that her father had told her that he had destroyed a nest of such creatures whilst blasting to install a line for the Esquimalt & Nanaimo Railway. She thought little of this until the 1960s, when a man told her of finding a desiccated lizard carcass in a graveyard in Cumberland. The description fitted her father's. Sadly when they returned to the cemetery, the corpse had vanished.

Strong filed the report away, but later that year the creatures apparently re-appeared. He received a telephone message from a man in a state of hysteria. The museum secretary who took the message, managed to work out that he was a logging contractor on Texada Island. His loggers had walked off-site on account of twelve to eighteen inch tall bipedal dinosaurs that were running around the area.

Strong tried to contact the man several times, ringing the number the terrified fellow had left, but never got an answer. He passed the story on to Mrs Henderson whose natural history society examined the area but found nothing.

The affair is strikingly similar to events that supposedly took place in Colorado. In a letter published in the August 22nd 1982 issue of *Empire* Magazine, a Myrtle Snow of Pagosa Springs, claimed to have seen dinosaurs several times! In May 1935, when she was three, she saw five 'baby dinosaurs' close to her home. Shortly after, a farmer shot one after it had killed some sheep. Her father took her to see the body.

"It was about seven feet tall," she recalled, "was grey, had a head like a snake, short front legs with claws that resembled chicken's feet, large stout back legs and a long tail."

She saw another in a cave in 1937, but this one had dark-green skin. Her third sighting was on October 23 1978, as she was returning from Chama, New Mexico. At around 7.30 p.m she watched one walking through a field in driving rain heading to the location of the previous sighting.

All this is very interesting but who can remember accurately things from when they were only three years old? I myself have a couple of "false memories" from my childhood, where fact and dream have become muddled due to the passage of time and my then very young age. We must also inquire why we have no other reports, and wonder at the whereabouts of the shot specimen.

Herpetologist Nick Sucik has collected reports of these creatures. He refers to them as 'river dinosaurs.' In one sighting, a woman and her daughter saw one of the creatures rush out in front of their car as they were driving in the Yellow Jacket area. At first they thought it was a young deer on account of its size. They described it as having a long neck and skinny legs like a bird's. The creature was featherless, however. The arms seemed to sprout from its upright neck rather than its body, and all in all it resembled a cross between a dinosaur and a bird. They estimated the thing to be five feet long.

Moving further afield, let us examine the world's greatest continent, Asia. There are many reports of dragon-like creatures here in their legendary home, but few that resemble dinosaurs.

Lake Tian Chi or 'Heavenly Lake' lies in the crater of Baitoushan volcano, in Jilin province, China. In 1980, a group of meteorologists were visiting the area, when they encountered a 'water dragon'. The creature was described as being larger than a cow, with a metre long (three foot) neck, and a flattened duck-like beak. One of the scientists took a shot at the creature, (dragons are apparently no longer sacred in China.) It seemed unharmed, and dived back beneath the surface. More sightings were reported in 1994, and film crews from China, Japan, and a team of North Korean scientists visited the remote lake. A photograph was taken, but in true monster snap-shot tradition, it was too blurry to be of any use

The North Korean group would have done just as well to stay at home, as a near identical monster has been re-ported in their own country. Chang Bai Tien or Long White Heaven Lake has a duck-billed denizen. Like its Chi-nese counterpart it is remote and rarely visited.

It has been suggested that these animals are surviving hadrosaurs or "duckbilled" dinosaurs. These were herbivo-rous dinosaurs with flattened jaws superficially resembling a duck's beak, and includes such species as *Anatosau-rus, Parasauorlophus,* and *Corythosaurus* Unlike ducks, their bills were packed with teeth - up to 2,000 - more than any other dinosaur. These tiny file-like teeth were used to shred tough, fibrous food such as pine-needles, twigs, and seeds. They were once believed to be aquatic on account of their bills, and a singular specimen with fossilised skin still attached. (This is ultra rare as soft tissue usually decays soon after death). The digits of this in-dividual appeared to be webbed - re-enforcing the idea of amphibious hadrosaurs. It was soon found out however, that in life the skin of the dinosaur's foot bore pads like those of a camel. The skin had shrivelled after death to give the appearance of webbing. This, together with the dentition adapted for dealing with land plants, pointed to a defi-nite terrestrial lifestyle. Clearly the duckbilled oddities in these lakes *cannot* be hadrosaurs.

Heading south to the Malayan peninsula we come to Lake Tasek Bera and its odd inhabitants. The local Semelai people speak of long-necked, aquatic animals that dwell here. The animals are harmless to humans, and feed only on water-plants. The small head at the end of the neck is furnished with two small, soft horns.

In the late 1950s, an officer with the Malayan Police Force went swimming in the lake. After mooring his boat be-side Tanjong Keruing - a small headland - he dived into the water. Looking back over his shoulder he saw a huge neck rearing up over a clump of rassau weed some thirty-six metres (120 feet) away. Two silvery-grey curves showed behind the neck. Panicking, the man swam back to the boat, and paddled away as fast as he could. Looking back one last time, he saw the monster watching his retreat.

The man's commander passed on his account to Stewart Wavell, a producer for Malayan radio, commenting on the man's fine record and reliability. So impressed was Wavell, that he travelled to the lake in 1957 in the hope of re-cording the animal's call which was said to resemble an elephant's trumpeting.

Wavell made camp with his two guides on Tanjong Keruing. Whilst preparing his wire recorder and camera, the monster's cry boomed out across the lake:

A single staccato cry from the middle of the lake…It was a kind of snorting bellow, shrill, strident like a ship's horn, an elephant trumpet, and a sea-lion's bark all in one.

He switched the recorder on, but the call did not come again. In 1962 an R.A.F expedition visited the lake but found no monsters.

The aquatic nature of these animals once more rules out dinosaurs. The small soft horns sound remarkably like those of a giraffe. These curious appendages are called ossicones and are possessed only by the giraffe and its smaller relative, the okapi. So, an aquatic giraffe? Maybe not, but the beasts of lake Tasek Bera do not seem to be any kind of known dinosaur.

Oddly - these beasts are referred to as nagas, even though they are not snakes. They seem to have thick, substantial bodies. In Malaysia the term 'naga' seems to be used for any kind of water-dwelling monster, and not exclusively for giant snakes. But it seems that both the thick bodied animals, and the more traditional naga serpents, may have inhabited Tasek Bera side by side.

About a year after the police officer's sighting, another officer of the armed forces threw a grenade into the lake and reported seeing a huge snake rear up. A sixteenth century Portuguese traveller reported seeing – in the same lake - a snake so vast that it took forty men to carry its dead body.

In 1967 when a drought affected the area, and water levels were low, many sightings were reported.

Recently Dr Karl Shuker has received word that Tasek Bera is now hopelessly polluted by run-off from surrounding banana plantations. The area has become a foul quagmire and its inhabitants must sadly have died out or moved on.

Another naga-haunted body of water is Lake Chini south east of Pahang in Malaysia. British engineer Arthur Potter, his clerk - Inch Baharuddin bin Lajan - and two labourers named Lajan and Malik, *all* saw the creature in May 1959. Mr Potter claimed that he was in his house-boat on the lake at about 10.30 pm when it appeared to rain. The rain ceased - then started again. He continued:

Then we saw the attap roof of the boat being raised and I shouted to Baharuddin to flash his torch on it. The roof was about 8 ft from the floor of the boat. When the torch was flashed wee saw a gaping hole in the roof nearly 3 ft across. And we saw, too, a red eye peering down at us. It was the size of a tennis ball.

We couldn't see much more as the torch was not very powerful and the attap blocked the view. Whatever the thing was, it looked exactly the colour of attap. It then disappeared from view. We all thought it was a huge snake and did not think any more about it until the next morning, when we found the tracks the monster had made where it left the water.

Starting from the water edge we found tracks 18 feet wide. It looked as if something slimy had gone over the ground. The tracks continued for only 4 ft and then stopped. But we picked them up again more than 100 yards away. They were of the same width but stretched nearly 200 ft.

The sighting earned Mr Potter the nickname 'Dragonwick'.

In the early 1960s, a team of Royal Air Force frogmen dived in the lake but found nothing.

Explorer, Stewart Wavell, visited Lake Chini in the 1960s, and was told of the ancient practice of human sacrifice to the naga around a great pillar of rock that rose up out of the waters. These were believed to pacify the naga. One of his guides, Che Yang, told him of a great flood that had come to the town of Pekan a couple of years previously. Many people had wondered if the naga was demanding sacrifice, even though the practice had been stopped generations ago. One day a girl out washing her clothes, fell from her raft and was drowned. It was noticed that the waters immediately receded. The townsfolk believed the naga was now satisfied - having taken its victim.

Australia, that lost-continent of primitive mammals and giant reptiles, *also* has its stories of living dinosaurs - and furthermore ones more savage than anywhere else in the world.

In the remote area of north-west Australia called Arnhem-Land, The Aborigines tell of a giant, bipedal, flesh-eating monster a full nine metres (thirty feet) tall, that they call "*Burrunjor*". The descriptions fit *Tyrannosaurus rex*, as no other carnivorous dinosaur grew this large. Even so, *T. rex* is known only from North American strata - its fossils never having been found in Australia. Such 'trivia' is of no interest to those who have claimed an encounter with it. One such fellow was a policeman who was trailing explorer and bushman Bryan Clark. In the mid 1970s - whilst mustering cattle in the Urapunji area - he lost his way in the bush. It took him fully three days to find his way out of the wilderness, and back to his homestead. Unknown to him a mounted policeman and two aboriginal guides had picked up his trail and were following *him*.

On the first night of the search they camped out on the edge of the *Burrunjor*'s territory - despite the frightened protests of the guides. In the middle of the night, the policeman awoke to find his companions screaming in a state of panic, and madly attempting to pack their saddle-bags. The ground was shaking as if monstrous foot-falls approached, and the snorting of a huge animal was heard. The policeman made like his somewhat more alert colleagues, and beat a hasty retreat. He later warned Bryan never to return to the area, because if he became lost again, he would be on his own - the policeman refused to go near the place, period.

Others claim much closer encounters than this. Between Queensland and Northern Territory in the coastal borderlands is another of the *Burrunjor*. Here in the 1950s, cattle-men lost stock to something that left half-eaten bulls in its wake like so many breadcrumbs. It also left what were - apparently – bipedal, reptilian tracks. Gathering a posse, they followed the trail with cattle-dogs into swampy scrubland. Suddenly, the dogs turned back, and in the distance some of the men were said to have spied a thirty foot tall reptile standing erect amongst the trees. The posse then rapidly lost its enthusiasm.

Another man who claims to have seen one of these brutes, is Johnny Mathews - a part-aboriginal tracker. He saw a twenty-five foot tall reptile in 1961, stalking through scrub near Lagoon Creek on the Gulf Coast. "Hardly anybody outside my own people believes my story, but I know what I saw," he said to researchers.

Other down under 'dinos' are less aggressive. The Central Australian Aborigines have a creature in their folklore called "*Kulta*". According to their traditions, *Kulta* lived in swamps and ate only plants. The people feared it because it shook the earth when it walked. It was a quadruped, with a long tail, and a long neck ending in a small head. It was believed to be so large that if it entered a forest its head would protrude from one side and its tail from the other. When deserts overtook the central plains and the swamps dried up, *Kulta* died out.

"*Ipilya*" was a similar creature from the legends of the tribes around The Gulf of Carpentaria. It was said to be 100 yards long, and lived in swamps. The tribespeople associated it with thunderstorms on account of its booming voice. (Dragon/Rain association again!)

"*Wanambi*" is another dinosaur-like creature from aboriginal folklore. It was identical to the creatures above, except for a colourful crest that ran down its neck and back. Some sauropod dinosaurs did indeed have crests. This was most evident in *Amargasaurus*, a small sauropod we met earlier, with a row of spines along the neck for defence and - via rattling them porcupine-style - communication. Folklore aside, some claim to have seen these latter-day Aussie long-necks.

In the Singleton district of New South Wales, stories of the 'Dinosaur Swamp Monster' have been circulating for generations. This little-known tract of remote swamp, stretches beneath the Blue Mountains. The modern sightings began in 1953, when some duck hunters - Ernie Millington and Horrie Chilvers - were out in the swamp. About thirty metres (100 feet) away, behind some tall reeds, the men noticed a strange animal. Ernie later said:

All we could see was this long necked beast with a snakelike head, whose neck was thicker than a man's leg, standing about six feet out of the water. We could see the ripples as the animal moved about, but we could not get a look at it's body which was obscured by the tall swamp grass. It moved away to disappear in the grass and swamp scrub. We did not see it again, nor did we want to, and we did not wait around.

Years later, the same creature (or at least an individual of the same species), was still haunting the swamps. Peter Garland believes that what he saw on a remote dirt track in 1981 was a dinosaur. He was attempting to locate a farm recently acquired by a friend, and took the wrong turn on a remote road - a turn that led him into Dinosaur Swamp:

Recent rains had eroded the track, and deciding it was too rough for my new car I stopped, got out, and began walking some distance ahead to see if driving conditions would improve. I wasn't even sure now that I was on the right track to my mate's place.

Anyway, about this time I had to answer a "call of nature". I walked off the road for a moment. I was about to leave when I looked to one side of me at the sound of rustling shrubbery and stood petrified. There, only yards ahead of me and looking straight at me, was a large, greyish, scaly, reptilian beast, something like a brontosaurus approaching me!

Coming to my senses, I turned and ran for the car- but not before I noticed it had a large serpent like head on the end of a long, thick neck. I couldn't see the end of it's tail in the foliage but it must have been long. I reckon the animal was up to 25 feet in length. It stood about 3 feet off the ground on four powerful looking legs.

The car was about 500 yards away. As I ran towards it, I could see the creature crashing it's way into the scrub in the opposite direction. I lost no time in leaving the place, which I found out later, was not the road to my friend's place at all.

We must remember that these accounts are coming from areas that also have reports of giant monitor lizards. Monitors *are* known to stand on their hind-legs. Monitors *can* have long necks. In the last chapter we met *Megalania prisca* - the giant monitor said to be still existing in the outback. Non-avian dinosaurs died out 65 million years ago, *Megalania* conversely was around until only ten-thousand years ago. Now in the 'existent today stakes' which pony would *you* back? The so-called dinosaurs of Australia, are probably giant monitor lizards.

Finally, for the most outlandish account of living dinosaurs we must move to New Guinea.

Explorer Charles Miller and his new bride were honeymooning among cannibals in New Guinea. (Top marks for originality there, I hope I can marry a girl who's up for this kind of honeymoon!) Miller claimed to have uncovered a lost tribe called the Kirrirri. One member of the tribe was using an odd tool to break open coconuts. The object appeared to be some kind of horn or tusk. When enquiring about its origin to The Village Elders, Miller uncovered a remarkable story. Wroo - an old man from the village - drew a long-tailed, hump-backed lizard in the sand. About its neck he drew a frill, and he adorned its back with triangular spines. The beast was said to be twelve metres (forty feet) long. The horn had come from just such a brute. The natives called it the *Row* after its cry - somewhere between a snake's hiss and a roar. Miller determined to see the animal for himself. The natives told him that the monster's lair lay two or three days to the north-west.

Taking guides, he travelled to a triangular marsh in the hill, where his native companions became nervous. Then - out of a stand of reeds - a gigantic animal emerged. Miller's new wife clutched at the grass, paralysed with fear. The following turgid narration is entirely Miller's, and I take no responsibility!

As if in obedience to my wishes, the colossal remnant of the age of dinosaurs stalked across the swamp. Once it's tail lashed out of the grass so far behind it's head I thought it must be another beast. For one brief second I saw the horny point. I heard it hiss- Roooow-Roooow- Roooow.

Miller started to film the monster but the thing seemed to become alerted to his cameras whirring.

Suddenly it stopped, reared up on it's hind legs, it's small forearms hanging limp, and shot it's snaky neck in our direction. It was a full quarter of a mile (400 metres) away, it couldn't possibly hear the camera, but I found myself cowering back as if that snapping turtle-shaped beak would lash out and nab me.. I gasped with relief when the creature settled back. Twice more the Row reared up, giving me a good view of the bony flange around it's head and the projecting plates on along it's back bone. Then with a click my camera ran out just as the Row slithered behind a growth of dwarf eucalyptus.

This film, if it exists, has never been shown to zoologists. Miller never produced so much as a still from it in his book *Cannibal Caravan*. In the copy of the book that I have read, the chapter including Miller's adventure has been excluded. Perhaps it was omitted from later editions. Moreover, as Bernard Heuvelmans - The Father of Cryptozoology - noted in 1955. the *Row* is a hopeless hybrid of several totally different dinosaur species. The beak and frill belong to a ceratopsian dinosaur such as *Triceratops*, the plated-back belongs to *Stegosaurus*, and the elongated neck and tail are those of a sauropod such as *Diplodocus*. I would add to this the bipedal-gait and car-nivorous-nature of *Tyrannosaurus rex* or *Allosaurus*.

The *Row* is a hopeless hybrid, akin to something dreamed up by Toho studios - of Godzilla fame - and must vie with the hairy Yukon dinosaur for the title of "least likely monster".

The outlook for the survival of non-avian dinosaurs is poor, worse it is non existent. There is not a shred of evi-dence that these magnificent animals persisted beyond the end of the Cretaceous Period, 65 million years ago. But what if they had other descendants than birds? Ones that due to their very nature could leave no fossil trace. Just such a theory was put forwards by Peter Dickinson, in a remarkable book published in 1979.

In *The Flight of Dragons*, Dickinson attempts something not done since Charles Gould's *Mythical Monsters* - to explain fire-breathing, winged dragons as *real* animals within the known zoological frame-work.

Impressed by the universality of dragon-legends, Dickinson believed that they had a basis in fact. The main stum-bling-block was the sheer size of dragons - animals that after all were supposed to have flown. Looking at mediae-val reconstructions of dragons, he reckoned their weight to be around 9,000 kilograms (20,000 pounds). In order to be able to fly by the muscular power of its wings, a dragon of this weight would need a wingspan of over 180 me-tres (600 feet) - far too massive to be real. And how could an animal possibly breath out fire? These problems seemed insurmountable, until a chance viewing of the crash of *The Hindenburg*.

...one day I happened to see on television an old newsreel film of the wreck of the airship Hindenburg, an almost in a flash all my ideas changed. As I watched the monstrous shape crumpling and tumbling in fiery fragments, with the smoke clouds swirling above, I said to myself, it flamed and it fell, and my mind made the leap to Jordanus. All the pieces I had been considering shook themselves into a different shape. I saw that the Hindenburg was not just a very big machine which flew-it was a machine which could fly only because it was very big. Other answers slotted into place.

Dragons could fly because most of their bodies were hollow, and filled with a lighter- than- air gas.

Dragons needed an enormous body to hold enough gas to provide lift for the total weight of the beast.

Dragons did not need enormous wings, because they used them only for propulsion and manoeuvring.

Dragons breathed fire because they had to. It was a necessary part of their specialised mode of flight.

Dickinson's theory held that dragons evolved from large fast moving carnivorous dinosaurs like *Tyrannosaurus rex*. They developed huge, chambered, stomachs that they filled with hydrogen gas, thus achieving flight. The hy-drogen was formed from a mixture of hydrochloric acid in the gut, and calcium from the bones of their victims, and controlled partial-digestion of their own bone structure. The calcium taken from their own bones was being con-stantly replaced with a regular intake of limestone. This may explain the dragons legendary love of lairing in caves.

The vast-body was filled with this gas, and the animal acted - in essence - as a living dirigible. As any chemist will know, hydrogen mixed with oxygen is highly flammable. This is where the dragon's most famous attribute - its fiery breath - came into play. Dragons needed to breathe fire in order to control their flight. To rise, they filled their gas-bag stomachs, and to descend they burned-off gas by breathing it out - possibly with a chemical catalyst, as fire.

The fiery-breath doubtless doubled up as a formidable weapon - a punishing jet of flame with which to destroy prey and as a display to other members of its species. A similar weapon is employed by the bombardier beetle (*Brachinus*) that spews a jet of boiling chemicals at its enemies. The two chemical components are produced from different glands, and do not reach such high temperatures until it is outside of the beetle's body.

The wings were formed from the extended ribcage - much like that of the modern lizard *Draco volans*, a small gliding species often called the 'flying dragon'. These were covered with a bat-like membrane and were used in navigating the animal in flight.

Dickinson also believes that he can explain some of the more esoteric aspects of dragon legends. The cult of dragon-worship would have sprung up from primitive people's fear of such a terrifying creature. The famous 'dragon hoards' would have been built from offerings made to appease the monsters. Dickinson says that dragons would have used gold as a nesting material as it is non-combustible and fairly soft. Their fondness of virgins may have its genesis in human worship and sacrifice of high-born victims, perhaps born and raised specifically as sacrifices to dragons.

The theory also provides a good reason why there are no known dragon fossils. In life, a thick mucous-lining in the stomach-walls kept the powerful hydrochloric acid needed to produce hydrogen in check. After death, the mucous-lining was no longer generated, and the acid destroyed the animal's body. The creature literally digested itself. Hence no dragon bones and no dragon fossils. It is for this very reason that Dickinson's theory is impossible to prove. In effect he his hoist by his own petard, and his wonderful theory must - for the time being - remain just a tantalising possibility.

So far, we have considered the possibility that dragons were some kind of physical creature. Perhaps we are barking up the wrong tree. Can such a magickal, powerful beast be confined to mere flesh and bone? Could the origins of dragons lie outside the boundaries of standard zoology or even Cryptozoology? In the next chapter we shall explore the possibility that the dragon is of a truly paranormal nature.

CHAPTER FIVE

The Esoteric Theories

"I know that a bird flies, a fish swims and a deer runs. For the deer a net can be made, for the fish a line, and for the bird a corded arrow. But the dragon's flight to heaven on the wind and clouds is something beyond my knowledge."

Confucius (551-479 BC)

 ne of the downright strangest stories in the annals of paranormal research, occurred in the late 19th century in Somerset county, Pennsylvania - at a country school-house. The location was the township of Jenner. The school-house had been built beside a crossroads to replace an older school that was far from the road. William Johnson - a 16 year old student - and his classmates would often attend night-time functions in the building. Often they found the door barred by an object - over which they had to step - before entering.

The obstacle was a huge snake coiled around the building. (This brings to mind the way lindorms in Scandinavia were supposed to coil around churches and crush them). Neither its head or tail were ever observed, and it was believed that the extremities were hidden beneath the school. Its coils were about twelve inches in diameter, and covered with sharp-scales. Whoever was foolish enough to step on the coils were thrown to the ground violently.

Oddly, the monster only appeared when there was no moon. Stranger still - not everyone could see it, but even those unaware of its presence would be thrown down by it. Many - often under the influence of drink - tried to attack it with stakes and other weapons, but could do it no harm. Johnson moved away from the area aged thirty, but the school serpent was still manifesting.

This just one of the legion of cryptozoological cases that cannot be seen within a purely zoological framework. Pure cryptozoology is the study of mystery animals, those erroneously believed to be extinct, and those unknown to modern science. But reports of unknown animals rub shoulders with cases and creatures that are so bizarre that they refuse to slotted into a "natural" order. These include monsters that appear and disappear in front of witnesses, creatures that seem immune to any weapons, beasts that rear their heads amidst other unexplained phenomena, and things the seem to generate fear at truly incredible levels.

This latter power is possessed by perhaps the most famous of living dragons, the Loch Ness Monster. In the penultimate chapter we will examine the monster and its kin throughout the world in detail, but for now we will confine ourselves to the stranger aspects of Scotland's most celebrated denizen.

One of the earliest and most famous of 20th century sightings, occurred on July 22nd 1933. Mr George Spicer - proprietor of a firm of London tailors - and his wife were enjoying a motoring holiday in The Highlands. There enjoyment was rudely interrupted at 4 o'clock in the afternoon as they drove from Dores to Foyers via the winding loch side road.

We were midway between Dores and Foyers on the south bank of the loch when my wife exclaimed "What on earth is that?". I was looking ahead as my wife spoke, I observed the most extraordinary form of an animal crossing the road. It was horrible – an abomination.

First we saw an undulating sort of neck, a little thicker than an elephant's trunk. It did not move in the usual reptilian fashion but, with three arches in its neck, it shot across the road until a ponderous body about four feet high came into view.

When we reached the part of the road it had crossed, we stopped, but there was no sign of it. It had been a loathsome sight. It seems futile to describe it because it was like nothing I have read about or seen. It was terrible. Its colour, so far as the body was concerned , could be called a dark elephant grey. It looked like a huge snail with a long neck. I reported the affair to various scientific bodies all of who seemed incredulous. I am willing to take an oath, and so is my wife, that we saw this Loch Ness beast.

Spicer estimated the monster to have been 7.5 to 9 metres (twenty-five to thirty feet) long. From his description it is obvious that the creature badly frightened him. He later called for the Loch to be dynamited.

This recoiling of the mind has been shared by many other witnesses. Mr Richard Jenkyns and his wife saw the horror from their lochside house on the 30th September 1974. The couple watched the monster through binoculars for half an hour. It seemed to be around eighteen metres (sixty feet) in length. The monster had a lasting effect on them. Later Richard commented:

I felt the beast was obscene. This feeling of obscenity still persists and the whole thing put me in mind of a gigantic stomach with a long writhing gut attached.

Mrs Greta Finlay - an Inverness house-wife - had similar feelings toward the thing she encountered at close range on August 20th 1952. She had gone fishing with her young son, and was on the north-east shore of the loch near Aldourie pier, off Tor Point.

I was sitting outside the caravan when I heard a continual splashing in the water. After several moments passed and realizing this was not the usual wash from a boat I walked round. To my surprise I saw what I believe to be the Loch Ness Monster. My son and I stood looking at this creature in amazement. Although I was terrified, we stood and watched it until it submerged, which it did very quickly causing waves to break on the shore. We had an excellent view as it was so close to the shore. Its skin was dark in colour and looked very tough. The neck was long and held erect. The head was about the same width as the neck. There were two projections from it, each with a blob at the end. This was not a pleasant experience. I certainly never want to see the monster again.

Mrs Finlay was interviewed by the late Tim Dinsdale - perhaps the greatest 'Nessie'-hunter of them all. She confessed to him that she had been paralysed with fear, and that her son had been so utterly horrified, that he had given up fishing all together. This "terror effect" is not confined to the Loch Ness Monster. The most extreme case involved a relatively diminutive lake in Ireland.

In 1954 Miss Georgina Carberry - a librarian from Clifden - and three friends were on a trout fishing trip to Lough Fadda. This small Connermara lough, lies in Derrygimlagh - a bog of some thirty-five square miles, dotted with small lakes connected via streams. The friends enjoyed a good day's fishing, but in the late afternoon an event occurred that changed their lives forever. She was later interviewed by veteran monster hunter F.W. Holiday.

Holiday: *Could you tell us what you saw on Lough Fadda when you had the sighting of this object?*

Carberry: *Well, it was a very long object. We sighted it rising...coming out from an island. At first one of our company thought it was a man swimming in the lake...then she said: "Oh, now look at it!" And she was quite right only it wasn't a man swimming, but a very big object which we watched...oh, for a long time...coming leisurely towards us...swimming along slowly. So we kept watching it and eventually, through time, it got very near to us. Anyway, next thing, we began to get a bit worried. I was sitting nearest to it and it came in I suppose, oh, to within twenty yards of us. I was the first to move and jumped back and the other three who were sitting behind me did likewise.*

122

And as soon as we moved it just came right around...swung right round a rock which was near the shore and dived and we could see these awful big rings in the water as it was sinking. Before two minutes it had gone practically up to the island again when it surfaced. We could distinctly see two big humps showing behind its head out of the water. And the tail we noticed, when it swung around the rock, 't'was kind of a fork - a V-shaped tail. And the mouth which was open when it came in quite close to us at the shore and the eyes and that I can't really remember. But I distinctly remember that the whole body had movement in it.

Holiday: *What do you mean by "movement"?*

Carberry: *It seemed like...wormy. You know - creepy. The body seemed to have movement all over it all the time.*

Holiday: *What did the head look like? Was it like any thing you've seen before?*

Carberry: *No, it wasn't. The only thing the mouth resembled, open, was like shark-shaped.*

Holiday: *Did you see teeth? What did the mouth look like?*

Carberry: *Just...oh, a huge great mouth. I can remember white inside but as regards teeth and eyes, I can't remember what sort of eyes it had because we were so frightened to see such an unusual object.*

Holiday: *How high was it standing out of the water...the head and humps you mentioned?*

Carberry: *Oh, they came right up. As it swam towards us we could see the two humps behind the head very clearly.*

Holliday: *And how high out of the water did the head stand?*

Carberry: *Well...higher than the humps. It was a fair distance out of the water.*

Holiday: *Was there a neck to speak of?*

Carberry: *There was, yes. It seemed to come up just in one long...(curve?)*

Holiday: *And you jumped back?*

Carberry: *We certainly did! I was the first to move being the nearest to it.*

Holiday: *Could you see how wide it was or whether it was a narrow object of...?*

Carberry: *Well, now, it was fairly wide in the girth – a good span.*

Holiday: *And the head was up – clearly visible?*

Carberry: *Oh very clear... and the mouth.*

Holiday: *Was it that dark that it was silhouettish?*

Carberry: *Oh, no, it was a bright evening...a beautiful evening. I can always remember it was so fine – one of the fine summers we had some time ago.*

Holiday: *Were you effected by this at all?*

Carberry: *I certainly was! I don't think I went back to that lake for six or seven years after. And when we went back we would never go alone. Never alone.*

Holiday: *Thank you very much.*

To scare someone away from a place for seven years takes a lot, but the fear exerted by this being didn't end at that. Whilst driving home, Carberry found herself watching for the monster, in fear that it had slithered out of the bog and was pursuing them. She suffered from nightmares about the thing for weeks afterwards. One of the other witnesses had a mental breakdown, and was hospitalised.

One man - Captain Lionel Leslie, who had been investigating Irish lake monsters for some time - did what George Spicer had suggested years before – he dynamited Lough Fadda. On October 16th 1965 he set a 5lb charge against the rock where Miss Carberry had seen her dragon and at 16.30 hours detonated it. Ten seconds after the blast something surfaced thirty-five metres (150 feet) from the shore, and thrashed violently on the surface for a while. But if this was the dragon of Fadda it was unhurt, as no body was found.

The Captain later told *The Irish Independent* that he was "satisfied beyond any doubt that there is a monster in Lough Fadda."

Early in 2001 Chris Moiser, a personal friend and one-time lecturer in biology at Plymouth College of Further Education, took a party of students on a field trip to The Gambia in west Africa. He enquired about a creature which had been reported in the 1930s - known as *Ninki Nanka*. To his amazement he found that far from being a forgotten relic of a bygone era, *Ninki Nanka* was a living tradition - and one that engendered extreme terror.

Many people refused to speak of *Ninki Nanka* point blank, being too afraid to even discuss the monster. These included well-educated people like school-teachers. Others spoke of people that had seen the creature, and were so terrified that they we still having psychological problems years later.

It is described as having a horse-like head, a long neck with a crest or mane of spines, and a bulky crocodile-like body. Locals believe the monsters swim in from the ocean and come up river. They make their lairs in deep holes in the mangrove swamps. Chris was shown a former *Ninki Nanka* hole. It had been filled in and a tree planted to stop the beast returning.

A few years ago, one of the dragons was supposed to have risen out of the river, and smashed a bridge to matchwood. Several people were tossed into the water and drowned. Chris asked a local jeweller to make him a model of the dragon in silver. The man obliged but said it would upset his local customers. The results resembled nothing so much as a Welsh dragon.

Funds permitting, I intend to take an expedition from the Centre for Fortean Zoology down the Gambia River to search for *Ninki Nanka* in the ill-explored mangroves, and the swamps in the country's interior.

This intense fear seems peculiar to creatures that seem supernatural in origin. Other 'impossible' entities have had this effect. Tony Healy - one of Australia's foremost cryptozoologists - cites many cases where intense fear is a factor. Most involve Yowies - huge, bipedal, ape like creatures. Australia - as every zoologist knows - is a land almost devoid of placental mammals; in short there have never been any primates living wild in Australia except man. Nevertheless, both Aborigines and white settlers, have reported encountering these brutes from the earliest colonial times to the present day. He cites two examples of the fear they can engender.

The first concerns two men who saw an ape-like creature peering at them trough their car window one night. One man was paralysed with fear whilst his companion fainted. The latter man moved away from the area and refused to visit the place ever again.

Another case involved two 18 year old youths in a campsite just outside of Canberra. The lads were confronted by a tall, hairy creature that seemed to move with impossible speed – cutting off each escape-route they tried. One of the besieged pair phoned his mother from the campsite's pay phone. Upon her arrival the yowie had departed, but she found the two young men crying like babies. Like Georgina Carberry the lads kept a fearful watch out of the car during the journey home, dreading that the monster was following them.

The author has a personal friend who has encountered a creature of seemingly un-natural origins. The fear it created in him caused vivid nightmares for years afterwards, and still festers within him to this day. He is now a well-respected scientist and understandably insists on anonymity. For the purpose of recounting his story he calls himself 'Gavin'. Gavin encountered one of England's strangest phantoms one summers evening in 1988. Whilst walking with his girlfriend 'Sally' (also a pseudonym), through the coastal woods near Mawnan Old Church in Cornwall. Their touch-beams fell upon a creature perched in a tree some fifteen feet above the ground. The monster resembled a huge brown and grey owl with glowing yellow eyes. Where a beak should have been, was a wide, black, crescent-shaped mouth, and horn-like structures rose from its head. The thing had a three metre (ten foot) wingspan, and its wings bore claws like some archaic, prehistoric bird. In lieu of talons on the feet, the creature had black pincers like giant crab claws.

The monster leapt backwards out of the light, whilst Gavin and Sally ran for their lives. What they had seen was the Cornish Owlman - although he says it resembled a giant nightjar as much as an owl - an infamous entity that has been seen in and around the woods beside Mawnan Old Church since the mid 1970s. Now is not the time or place to discuss Owlman, but what is interesting is the lasting effects it had on Gavin. Ones much like those the dragon had on Miss Carberry. Gavin says:

What is Owlman? I think its like a ghost and no way is it a real animal. More to do with the human mind than the world of zoology. Several years ago I began having nasty dreams featuring similar creatures. The were always malevolent, but not generally harmful. There's dreams for you. I particularly remember one were I had to hunt and kill a man with a bow and arrow, and I was being watched by a black and white Owlman standing at the base of a birch tree.

Gavin has confided in the author that after his sighting he felt that the Owlman had somehow followed him home (sound familiar?) to the south-east of England. He felt he could see it in a copse of trees close to his bedroom window, and that it was watching him. Despite being in his mid twenties at the time of writing, Gavin still becomes afraid when speaking of his experience. I have seen this first-hand several times, and was flabbergasted at the change that comes over him. Gavin changes from a confident scientist to a frightened schoolboy. I doubt if any "real" animal could have quite the same effect.

But enough of the Owlman we must away, back to the inky waters of Loch Ness.

In 1899 a flamboyant character arrived in Inverness. He purchased the brooding Boleskine House on the shores of Loch Ness for twice the amount the building was worth, becoming the self-styled 'Laird of Boleskine'. The man was Aleister Crowley, and he had good reasons for paying over the odds for the remote foreboding house.

Crowley was born in Lemington, Warwickshire, in 1875. Rebelling against his ultra-strict Christian upbringing, he became the most flamboyant and colourful character in British occultism. His magickal and sexual experimentation shocked the prudish Victorian society. Crowley revelled in this and wove an intricate web of myths about himself.

He chose Boleskine on account of its occult architecture. Previously he had scoured Britain for an abode to suit his needs and found none. Once in Boleskine he intended to carry out the ritual of Abra-Melin - an ancient rite that took eighteen months to perform.

The ritual harkened back to the 1400s. The ritual was translated by a Jewish scholar called Abriham the Jew, from a north African manuscript. Abriham was wandering The Middle-East looking for true magicians from whom to learn. He finally came upon a wizened mage called Abra-Melin who passed the rite onto him. It dealt with the summoning of demonic forces. The ritual demanded idiosyncratic architecture, and Crowley had previously tried to replicate this in his London flat. Though not having the desired effect strange things happened there. In 'The Great Beast's' own words:

During this time magical phenomena were of constant occurrence. I had two temples in my flat; one white, the walls being lined with six huge mirrors, each six feet by eight; the other black a mere cupboard in which stood an altar supported by the figure of a Negro standing on his hands. The presiding genius of this place was a human skeleton, which I fed from time to time with blood, small birds and the like. The idea was to give it life, but I never got further than causing the bones to become covered in a viscous slime.

Exactly whose skeleton it was, and how Crowley came by it is unclear, but it featured in one of his most notorious and amusing spells. Althoea Gyles - a local artist and lover of one of Crowley's poet rivals W. B. Yeats - was sent to visit Crowley. Yeats had her scratch his foe's hand with a brooch and carried a drop of 'The Beast's' blood back to her spouse. Yeats allegedly used this as a spell component to invade Crowley's dreams. But more of the precious fluid was needed and Gyles was sent back. This time, 'The Beast' was ready and had already sprinkled Gyles apartment with a "magick potion". Upon arriving at Crowley's flat, she became overcome with lust for the skeleton and made love to the blood and slime festooned cadaver. After this "boneing" she was promptly rejected by Yeats.

Yet more happened at Crowley's flat, apparently on account of the occult décor:

The demons connected with Abra-Melin do not wait to be evoked; they come unsought. One night Jones and I were out to dinner. I noticed while leaving the white temple that the latch of the Yale lock had not caught. Accordingly, I pulled the door to and tested it. As we went out, we noticed semi-solid shadows on the stairs; the whole atmosphere was vibrating with the forces we had been using. (We were trying to condense them into sensible images.) When we came back nothing had been disturbed in the flat; but the temple door was wide open, the furniture disarranged and some of the symbols flung about the room. We restored order and then observed that the semi-materialized beings were marching around the room in almost unending procession.

When I finally left the flat for Scotland, it was found that there was no way to take the mirrors out except by way of the black temple. This had, of course been completely dismantled before the workmen arrived. But the atmosphere remained and two of them were put out of action for several hours. It was almost a weekly experience, by the way, to hear of the casual callers fainting or being sized with dizziness, cramp of apoplexy on the staircase. It was a long time before those rooms were re-let. People fled instinctively at the presence of something uncanny. Similarly, later on, when I gave up my rooms on Victoria Street, a pushing charlatan thought to better himself by taking them. With this object he went to see them. A few seconds later he was leaping headlong down the five flights of stairs, screaming in terror. He had sufficient genuine sensitiveness to feel the forces, without possessing the knowledge, courage and will required to turn them to account, or even endure their impact.

Crowley's attempts to perform the ritual at Boleskine failed. No-one knows quite why, but the rite was never completed. The semi-formed shadows that he evoked in London seemed to have been called again, however. John Symonds - his biographer - recounts that the house's lodge and terrace became peopled by shadowy shapes. The place seemed to have a strange and violent effect on people. A workman employed to renovate the villa went berserk and attacked Crowley, who had to knock the man out and lock him in a coal-shed. His lodge-keeper - who had been a teetotaller - went on a three-day drinking-binge and tried to murder his own wife and children. Crowley finally left in 1918 but some believe he left *something* behind.

Subsequent owners of Boleskine have also reported disturbances. Musician and former member of the supergroup Led Zeppelin, Jimmy Page brought the house in the 1970s. His friend and custodian of Boleskine, Malcolm Dent, has experienced the house's dark side on several occasions:

Most of the oddities occurred during upheavals in the house. I am not talking about wallpapering, but structural alterations. Any time there was any thing major, it was almost as though the house didn't like it. If we didn't get on with the job and get it finished, something would let us know about it. We would be wakened up during the night with heavy doors banging all over the place and carpets and rugs being rolled up. It was though it was a reminder to get on quickly and get the job over.

Another time, Malcom and some friends, saw a statue of The Devil rise up from a mantelpiece, float to the ceiling then smash to the floor. The most horrifying event happened early one morning when the disturbances reached a crescendo:

I was awakened in the wee small hours and just knew something was wrong. I was petrified. Something outside the bedroom door was snorting, snuffling and banging. It sounded like a huge beast. I had this clear picture in my mind of what it looked like, but there was no way I was going to open the door. I had a knife on my bedside table and I opened the blade and just sat there. The blade was so small it wouldn't have done any good, but I was so frightened that I just had to have something to hang on to. The noise went on for some time but even when it stopped, I still could not move. I sat in bed for hours and even when daylight came, it took a lot of courage to open that door. Whatever was there, I have no doubt it was pure evil.

Could it be that the daemon-summoning ritual had worked in a way that Crowley had not foreseen?

Modern day wizard 'Doc' Shiels thinks this may well be the case. Whilst engaged in the magickal "Monstermind" experiment described later in this chapter, Doc made the acquaintance of a man named Patrick Kelly. Kelly claimed to have photographed a lake monster in Lough Leane, in 1981. This however was not the most fantastic of his claims.

He said that he was a direct descendent of Edward Kelly, the notorious scryer of Dr John Dee. Dee was the court magician to Queen Elizabeth 1st, and claimed to 'speak with the dead' via a young medium whom he had trained.

The modern day Kelly also claimed his father, Laurence, had met Aleister Crowley in Paris in 1933 shortly after he had left the Abbey of Thelema. Crowley told Laurence that he was very interested in the Loch Ness Monster - whose first major flap of the 20th century was occurring.

Finally, Patrick Kelly and his father *both* claim to have seen the Loch Ness Monster on May 1st 1969 close to Boleskine. Fantastic assertions indeed - but at least for this last one there may be some evidence. In June of the same year, three American students were exploring the 17th century cemetery below Boleskine House. They came upon a curious object. It was an old tapestry wrapped around a conch-shell. The tapestry was decorated with serpent-like symbols embroidered in gold thread. It measured four feet by five feet, and seemed to be old and threadbare. There were reddish-stains at each corner, as if objects had been placed there.

All in all it looked like an altar-cloth. The shell was about five inches long, white and inscribed with two parallel grooves and a lotus blossom. When blew it produced a harsh braying sound. The objects were taken to the Victoria and Albert Museum to be studied by experts. The tapestry was latter identified as being Turkish in origin. The snake-like symbols were Turkish script for serpent. We should also note that today, Lake Van in the east of Turkey, is said to be inhabited by a dragon whom we shall examine in the penultimate chapter.

Lotus flowers - like the one on the conch-shell - along with roast swallows, were said to be the favourite food of dragons in China. They were often used as offerings to dragons in oriental lakes, to appease them and ensure rainfall. Could Patrick Kelly and his father have been performing some kind of ritual at Loch Ness? Perhaps they were disturbed and had to leave behind their artefacts as they hurriedly retreated. If this were the case then it seems that the Kellys were successful in their endeavour.

Infamous wizard, surrealist, and performer Anthony 'Doc' Shiels instigated the largest monster raising experiment ever in 1977. 'Doc' had been in contact with seven professional psychics from around the world for some time. The group called themselves Psychic Seven International or P-S-I. The seven decided to try and contact or called up aquatic dragons by using their powers. 'Doc' took part in a number of spectacular rituals involving sky-clad [naked] witches, beside various bodies of water in Ireland and Scotland. His colleagues concentrated on other lakes around the globe. The experiment commenced on the last day of January or more importantly the Pagan feast of Imbolc.

'Doc' saw the results for himself on the 21st of May. He had travelled to Scotland with his wife Chris. And on the 20th he had preformed a ritual invocation involving the *Niddnidiogram*. This is 'Doc's' sigil used in monster raising rituals. It resembles an eye with a trident resting atop it.

The following day, he was in the car-park of the Inchnacardoc Lodge with four friends, when they all saw three humps gliding through the water about 900 feet away in the direction of Fort Augustus. The humps slipped with hardly a ripple beneath the surface. None of the group had a camera on them at the time. 'Doc', though elated at the beast's presence, was understandably frustrated. Little did he know that he would later that day take what are widely regarded to be the finest pictures of the Loch Ness Monster ever obtained.

'Doc' and Chris had hitch-hiked to Drumnadrochit, and from there walked to Urquhart Castle, overlooking the Loch. At four p.m, he was ensconced in a ruined tower, looking over the water from a window, this time with his camera.

Quite suddenly, a small dark head on the end of a long sinuous neck broke the surface of the water, about a hundred yards away. It was, undoubtedly, the Loch Ness Monster, proudly erectile, ready to be snapped. I instantly raised my camera and shot two pictures during the few seconds the creature was visible. Its neck was four or five feet long, greenish brown, with a yellowish underside. Its open mouthed head was tiny in relation to the muscular neck. The animal turned away from me, straightening its neck before sinking vertically.

I stood there mesmerized by the brief dreamlike vision. My heart beating rapidly, hands shaking as I lowered the camera, whispering expletives, ecstatic.

Doc's friend David Clarke arranged for the high speed Ektachrome film to be developed by Newquay Colour Services, who handled most of the colour transparency work for *Cornish Life* magazine. The two snaps were startling in their clarity, showing the muscles in the beast's neck and its open mouth. The gleam of an eye even seems to be visible.

Martin Gilfeather of the Glasgow based paper *Daily Record* (that, ironically, was the paper that printed the first photo of Nessie back in 1933), asked Doc to send him both slides. Prudently Doc decided to send just one. The next day Gilfeather asked to see the other snaps on the roll of film. These were the before and after shots, mainly innocuous holiday snaps, but the journalist wanted to see if edge numbers of the photos all matched up. The roll was dispatched and after the snaps were examined to Gilfeather's satisfaction, the pictures were published in the *Record's* national sister newspaper the *Daily Mirror.*

It was then the backlash started. Many investigators have noticed it. It plagues them with ill-luck that can range from camera-failure to serious illness. Some call it the 'Loch Ness Hoodoo', Doc calls it 'psychic-backlash'. The *Daily Record* had promised to return Doc's pictures promptly. He got his slide back after an agonizing two-week wait. His roll of film, the precious negatives, were never returned. The paper said they had been mislaid. Doc has not seen them since.

David Benchley, a Falmouth based photo-journalist, made a glass copy negative of the second monster shot. Doc sent this to fellow Monstermind participant - American psychic Max Maven. It was sent in a sealed package to Boston, Massachusetts. The package arrived but the picture had disappeared. To top this off, another journalist, Frank Durham, had made copy slides of the first Nessie photo. The day these arrived, the glass negative of monster shot two was dropped and smashed.

Doc wrote an affidavit declaring the photos to be genuine. Veteran monster hunter Tim Dinsdale sent this, together with the slide of the first shot, to Dr Vernon Harrison. Dr Harrison was a photographic scientist and former president of the Royal Photographic Society. Dr Harrison wrote back with the following analysis:

Dear Mr Dinsdale

I have examined the photographic transparency stated to have been taken by Mr A. N. Shiels on Saturday 21st May 1977 from the shore of Loch Ness in the vicinity of Castle Urquhart. This examination has been made through a binocular microscope at all magnifications up to x100. I find the transparency to be quite normal and there is no evidence of double exposure, superimposition of images or handiwork with bleach or dye.

The object depicted is certainly not a branch of a tree, a trick of the light or an effect of uneven processing. Under magnification a small reptilian head is seen looking towards a point on the right of the photographer. The lighting comes from behind, and somewhat to the right of the photographer; and the foreshortening of the water shows that the object was photographed from a considerable distance trough a long focus lens. The creature has a wide mouth, partly open, and light is reflected strongly from the lower lip, which is presumably wet. There is an indication of two eyes and a stubby nose. The head is attached to a long neck whose girth increases as it approaches the water. The neck is smooth and reflects the light strongly, and it appears to be paler in colour on its lower side. The course of the neck can be traced some inches below the surface of the water until it is lost to view because of the turbidity of the water. The image of the submerged part is distorted by the surface wavelets of the water, and I find these distortions to be entirely naturalistic. There is even a wavelet that has been reflected back from the left side of the neck and caught the light of the sun.

It is not possible to say from a single still transparency what the photograph represents. The obvious explanation is that the photograph depicts a living creature strongly resembling a Plesiosaurus. However it could be a hoax. For example, a diver might have a model of the head and neck and be holding it above the water while he himself was submerged. A third possibility is that the photograph is not of an outdoor scene at all, but is a reduction of an imaginative painting by a competent artist. To produce a sufficiently deceptive painting would require a detailed knowledge of the effects of light reflected from, and transmitted through rippled water; and it is just these effects I find so impressive in the photograph.

While I feel the alternative explanations I have suggested are not very plausible, they can only be excluded by a study of any independent evidence that may be available.

Yours sincerely,
V. G. Harrison.

The results worldwide were spectacular - 1977 was a year filled with monsters. A gigantic aquatic dragon was sighted off San Francisco Bay. Champ, the monster of Lake Champlain appeared. A twelve metre (forty foot) monster was seen in Lake Kol-Kol in Kazakhstan (in what was then Soviet Central Asia). Miss M Lindsay took two pictures of Morag, the monster of Loch Morar on 31st of January. On the same day a monster was spotted in Loch Sheil by John Smith. The Loch Ness Monster was seen on at least three occasions. Mr and Mrs Alex McLeod, Pat Scott-Innes, and a Mr Flemming and his daughter Helen. Three colour photographs of Morgawr - the Cornish sea dragon were taken by Gerald Bennet from Parson's Beach - and the monster was spotted again by Ray Hopley off Trefusis Point.

A spectacular set of sightings, but they came at a cost - if one gives credit to Doc's psychic backlash theory. Dr David Hoy - one of the American participants in Monstermind - suffered a heart-attack. Another member - Major Leslie May M.B.E, of Edinburgh - also fell ill, and many other members of the team from the former USSR, Mexico, and India have seemingly vanished. Doc has heard nothing of them since 1977. Doc himself was attacked by a mob in Plymouth, accidentally set his beard on fire, had a son involved in a motorbike crash, had his daughter thrown by a usually docile horse, had another daughter stricken by abdominal pains, and lost two cats to some unidentifiable malady. Ted Holliday - another long-term monster hunter reported a similar "curse" that seemed to banjax him some years before.

The idea that the Loch Ness Monster was a malevolent supernatural entity reached its peak some years before Monstermind in the early 1970s. In 1973 one man believed things had gone on too long, and decided to exorcise Loch Ness. He was the Reverend Dr Donald Ormand. Dr Ormand was perhaps the 20th century's most renowned exorcist. During his long career he'd dealt not just with ghosts and demonic possession, but with latter-day vampires, phantom black dogs, and areas of the sea where people were drawn by a strange siren-like urge to drown themselves. These cases, fantastic as they are, pale into children's games, when compared to the Doctor's strangest case.

Dr Ormand's first encounter with a lake monster happened in 1967 whilst on a caravanning holiday on the shores of Long Loch in Ross-shire. One morning, he set out to walk to the village of Ardelve. His route took him past Loch Duich. As he looked out over the loch, the calm water suddenly became violently disturbed, foaming and heaving. For one absurd moment the Reverend thought a submarine was breaching in the loch. But the object revealed itself to be some immense, aquatic-animal, with two huge humps, that reared out of the water. Then - just as swiftly as it had surfaced - the beast sank, leaving only concentric ripples as a clue to its manifestation.

It was not until the following year that Dr Ormand began to suspect that these monsters were not conventional flesh and blood creatures. In June 1968 he had a far more alarming encounter with a sea-serpent. The Reverend was holidaying with his friend Captain Jan Andersen in Norway. Andersen had offered to show Dr Ormand the "eeriest waterway in Norway" - the 'Fjord of Trolls' (note the link with hairy giants). The entrance to the fjord is hidden, and was used by British craft during The Second World War. The men travelled along the long, narrow, waterway screened on either side by gargantuan cliffs. But it was only on their return journey, that the exorcist began to feel something was badly wrong. A feeling of growing menace began to creep over the area. As they approached the entrance to the fjord the water began to seethe.

"What on Earth is it?" asked the Reverend.

"It can be only one thing", replied the Captain. "It would be useless to try and avoid it."

Two massive humps appeared, much like the ones the Doctor had seen in Scotland but much closer. The massive animal bore down on their boat with terrifying speed. And the frightened cleric braced himself for an impact that would turn the vessel to matchwood.

"It will not hurt us, they never do", shouted The Captain. Sure enough the monster veered to the starboard at the last moment and submerged.

"Shall we follow it?" inquired the Reverend, eager to see more of the fantastic animal.

The Captain's reply was cryptic:

Sufficient unto the day is the evil thereof. The further we kept away from that thing the better. When I said evil its what I really meant. This is the third time I have seen it. On the other occasions it was further north, closer to the North Cape. They are what our ancestors called the Sea Serpents. Today people regard them as existing only in legend. But when you have seen them you believe in them.

Dr Ormand questioned his reasoning. "But why are they evil? That one might have easily capsized our boat, but it did us no harm."

The Captain's answer was even stranger than before:

They don't do physical harm. They want to convince any who see them that they are harmless. The evil they do is to men's characters. The serpent in the Garden of Eden was no ordinary snake, and what you have just witnessed is no ordinary creature.

Dr Ormand enquired as to their true nature.

I don't know for certain, but I think their character was described in the first book of Genesis.. I am not sure even that it exists physically or not- there are things which do not exist and yet may be visible to man.

The more Dr Ormand thought on Andersen's words the more convinced he became that the monsters were paranormal in nature.

The explanation for these extraordinary appearances, in my submission, lies not in the field of science, but in the realm of the supernatural. What has been seen, and is still visible to some on occasion, is not a concrete present-day monster, but a projection into our day and age of something which had its habitat in Loch Ness and its surroundings, millions of years ago.

Commenting on modern witnesses he says:

What they saw was not something that was taking place at that precise moment. The gigantic creature they were so privileged to see was no longer in the land of the living. It was something seen out of time. The so- termed Loch Ness Monster is not physical but psychical, a spectre of something which existed in the waters and on the shores of the vast lake in the dim recesses of the past.

He had his ideas backed up in 1972 whilst attending a meeting of the Organisation of Enquiry into Psychical Disorder in Sweden. An eminent Scandinavian neurologist delivered a report concerning the monster of Lake Storjsson. The report was about the malevolent effect that the monster seemed to have on those who hunted for it, or who had seen it regularly. It resulted in shocking moral degeneration. Similar patterns were found, or so the neurologist claimed, in Irish and Scottish cases.

At almost the same time, Dr Ormand received a letter from F. W. Holliday - the renowned monster hunter who had recently come to similar conclusions to the Doctor. The letter congratulated him on his insight.

With these encouragements, the Doctor made up his mind to exorcise Loch Ness. The Reverend believed that the monster's manifestations were not in themselves evil, but rather that evil had attached itself to the phenomenon and to the area. He believed that he could purge this evil, and leave the monsters intact. This theory was not shared by F. W. Holliday who believed the creatures themselves to be overwhelmingly evil.

The Doctor decided to seek the advice of a fellow exorcist, Reverend Dom Robert Petipierre, a monk of the Anglican Order of St Benedict. Dom Robert took a large map of The Loch, and drew a cross upon it. The top of the crucifix was at the Inverness end of the loch, and the base near Fort Augustus. The intersection terminated on the left at Drumnadrochit and on the right at a point between Inverfahigaig and Dores. The men planned preliminary exorcisms at each of these points. The final rite was to be carried out in the centre of the cross - in the middle of the loch, in a boat. All the points of entry and exit along waterways, were 'bound against evil' to stop the contamination spreading during the ritual.

Between them, the exorcists drew up a rite from German, Spanish, Roman, Greek, and English sources. On June 2nd 1973 the ritual took place. Accompanied by Holliday, Dr Ormand exorcised all of the points, and eventually on a small boat he rowed to the centre of the dark peaty loch. There, floating on 800 feet of cold, black, water, he gave the final exorcism:

"I adjure thee, thou ancient serpent, by the judge of the quick and the dead, by Him who made thee and the world, that thou cloak thyself no more in manifestation of prehistoric demons, which henceforth shall bring no sorrow to the children of men."

After the ceremony, Dr Ormand felt drained and fell into a deep sleep. He believed his exorcism to have been a success and subsequently went on to exorcise Lake Storjsson in Sweden.

Quite a story, all in all. What are we to make of it? Are these the ramblings of a fundamentalist Christian madman with his worldview set in The Dark Ages, or was the Doctor *really* grappling with some supernatural force in the form of a monster? Exorcism is not confined to Christianity - many other faiths have practicing exorcists. Muslim priests cast out "djinn", pagan wizards and witches drive out malignant spirits with spells. But if these creatures *are* of paranormal origin just what are they?

131

There are two schools of thought on this, each with some merit.

- The first is that they are somehow created by ourselves, unwittingly, through the power of our minds.

- The second is that they exist independently of us, either unseen on this world, or in some other dimension or reality from whence they occasionally stray.

Let us examine the former theory first.

The Buddhist monks of Tibet, Nepal, and other parts of the Orient have long claimed to be able to create tangible objects with the power of their minds alone. Through deep concentration, and extreme mental discipline, it is said they can create a kind of spirit being - an artificial ghost if you will - that is so convincing that it is often mistaken for a real person or animal. These mind beings are called "tulpas". Westerners have experimented with them to varying degrees of success.

Perhaps the most renowned of these was a remarkable Frenchwoman called Dame Alexandra David-Neel. Born in 1868, she lived during a period where women were considered very much as second class citizens and were expected to live their lives as dutiful obedient wives. This makes her 100 year life as an explorer and mystic even more incredible. She travelled extensively in the Himalayas and eventually became a Lama, (the highest ranking Tibetan Buddhist – or Lamaist - priest) in Tibet.

She created a thoughtform or tulpa herself, with remarkable consequences. She relates the happenings in her book *Magic and Mystery in Tibet.*

I could hardly deny the possibility of visualising and animating a tulpa. Besides having had a few opportunities of seeing thoughtforms, my habitual incredulity led me to make experiments for myself, and my efforts were attended by some success. In order to avoid being influenced by the forms of the lamaist deities, which I saw daily around me in paintings and images, I chose for my experiment a most insignificant character: a monk, short and fat, of an innocent and jolly type.

I shut myself in doors and proceeded to perform the prescribed concentration of thought and other rites. After a few months the phantom monk was formed. His form grew gradually fixed and lifelike looking.. He became a kind of guest, living in my apartment. I then broke my seclusion and started for a tour, with servants and tents.

The monk included himself in the party. Though I lived in the open, riding on horseback for miles each day, the illusion persisted. I saw the far tulpa, now and then. It was not necessary for me to think of him to make him appear. The phantom preformed various actions of the kind that are natural to travellers and that I had not commanded. For instance, he walked, stopped, looked round him. The illusion was mostly visual, but sometimes I felt as if a robe was lightly rubbing against me, and once a hand seed to touch my shoulder

The features which I had imagined, when building my phantom, gradually underwent a change. The fat, chubby-cheeked fellow grew leaner, his face assumed a vaguely mocking, sly, malignant look. He became more troublesome and bold. In brief, he escaped my control.

Once, a herdsman who brought me a present of butter saw the tulpa in my tent and took it for a live lama.

I ought to have let the phenomenon follow its course, but the presence of that unwanted companion began to prove trying on my nerves; it turned into a "daymare". Moreover I was beginning to plan my journey to Lhasa, and needed a quiet brain devoid of any other preoccupations, so I decided to dissolve the phantom. I succeeded, but only after six months of hard struggle. My mind creature was tenacious of life.

Another remarkable woman who had experience with tulpas was Violet Mary Firth - better known by her pen name of Dion Fortune. In perhaps her best-known work, *Psychic Self - Defence*, she describes how such creatures can be created inadvertently. After being severely wronged, she lay brooding on her bed one night. In a state between sleep and wakefulness, she began to think of Fenris - the demonic wolf who devours Odin in Ragnarok, the death of the gods in Norse myth. After a strange drawing-out feeling from her solar-plexus, she was horrified to see a huge, snarling, wolf materialize on the bed next to her.

I knew nothing about the art of making elementals at that time, but had accidentally stumbled upon the right method - the brooding highly charged with emotion, the invocation of the appropriate natural force, the condition between sleeping and waking in which the etheric double readily extrudes.

I was horrified at what I had done, and knew I was in a tight corner and that everything depended on me keeping my head. I had enough experience of practical occultism to know the thing I had called into visible manifestation could be controlled by my will provided I did not panic; but if I lost my nerve and it got the upper hand, I had a Frankenstein monster to cope with.

She got an idea of the phantom's power the next day, when several of her housemates complained of nightmares about wolves. She came to the conclusion that the wolf was really part of herself, extruded and after revenge. She made the decision to forgo her revenge, and attempt to reabsorb the beast. She called it forth into her room once more.

I obtained an excellent materialization in the half-light, and could have sworn a big Alsatian was standing there looking at me. It was tangible, even to the dog like odour.

From it to me stretched a shadowy line of ectoplasm, one end was attached to my solar plexus, and the other disap-peared in the shaggy fur of its belly, but I could not see the actual point of attachment. I began by an effort of the will and imagination to draw the life out of it along this silver cord, as if sucking lemonade up a straw. The wolf form began to fade, the cord thickened and grew more substantial. A violent emotional upheaval started in myself; I felt the most furious impulses to go berserk and rend and tear anything and anybody that came to hand, like the Malay running amok. I conquered this impulse with an effort, and the upheaval subsided. The wolf form had now faded into a shapeless grey mist. This too was absorbed along the silver cord. The tension relaxed and I found my-self bathed in perspiration. That, as far as I know, was the end of the incident.

Fate magazine ran a story in 1960, written by Nicholas Mamontoff the son of one of a group of Russian occultists who studied under a Tibetan guru. The mystic had told the 'Brotherhood of the Rising Sun', that western scientists had never known how powerful the human mind, is or what miracles it could work. In 1912 he led the group in an experiment to create an *egrigor* - another term for a tulpa. One of The Brotherhood had suggested they create a dragon, but the guru suggested that they create something harmless. They decided on a 'Puss in Boots' character, and concentrated on the image for about half an hour. Gradually, a cloud began to form, that condensed into a red-haired cat. Its clothes, however, were ill-formed. The guru suggested that they gave it only boots, eschewing the hat, coat and other items. This improved the creature's clarity:

Within a few moments the features of the cat stabilized and on its hind feet were a pair of Russian boots. The egrigor was motionless and looked like a poorly developed photograph.

The author himself has experimented with tulpa creation. The story of 'The Great Leeds Spider Plague' is blackly comical, and may seem in parts like an irrelevance, or a grand prank in appalling-taste. However, it illustrates how relatively easy it is to create such a being, and how its continued persistence can be ensured.

The story begins in February 1996 whilst I was at University in Leeds. My student-digs were in a three-story house built in suburbia at the beginning of the 20th Century. It had a large and rambling cellar that was unused due to its dank and musty nature. I was twenty-six at the time, and was throwing a party to celebrate ten years of being a "Goth". To those humble souls not in the know, Goth is a youth sub-culture. The illegitimate offspring of punk and new-romantic. Its adherents dress like members of the Munsters or the Adams Family, and revel in the dulcet tones of such bands as *Bauhaus*, *Joy Division*, *Fad Gadget*, and *The March Violets*. An attraction to all things dark, strange, and unwholesome is also a bonus. The whole movement began in Leeds in the late 1970s and had its hey-day in the early 1980s. I felt that ten years of dressing like an undertaker, and listening to *Siouxsie and the Ban-shees* needed something special to mark it.

Naturally I wanted to hold this party in the cellar. I decorated the rooms appropriately, and as a centre-piece erected an altar to *Atlach-Nacha* - a fictional spider-god created by the peerless horror writer Clark Ashton-Smith in his deeply strange and disturbing 1934 story *The Seven Geases. Atlach-Nacha* was an appalling, subterranean-deity said to dwell beneath the fabled land of Hyperborea. He was constantly spinning a gargantuan web, and it was said that if this mammoth-task was ever finished, the world would come to an end. Ashton-Smith describes him thus:

A darksome form, big as a crouching man, but with long spider-like members… He saw there was a kind of face on the squat ebon body, low down amidst the several jointed legs. The face peered out with a weird expression of doubt and enquiry and terror crawled through the veins of the bold huntsman as he met small crafty eyes that were circled about with hair.

The altar consisted of an antique set of drawers, upon which sat a chalice of black ichor (in fact nothing more eso-teric than black food-colouring), sat in the centre of a red pentagram. At each point of this five pointed star was a black candle. Below it was attached a script written in Arabic - the translation of which runs:

That is not dead which may eternal lie
Yet in strange eons even death may die.

This was written by Ashton-Smith's friend and contemporary author Howard Phillips Lovecraft, and refers to the eternal "Great Old Ones" - a group of appalling alien gods he and others created in their bizarre writings in the early part of the 20th century.

Below the altar stood a porcelain nun with an inverted crucifix, and above it hung a large web made of muslin. The god himself was represented by nothing more exotic than a large toy spider - an battery-powered device activated by sound. In response to a sharp or loud sound it would scurry down a wire with its eight-inch legs flailing in a predatory dance.

The party was a roaring success. We had a fire-eater from Manchester who managed to burn through our washing line, and set our rubbish bags alight (causing much curtain-twitching from the neighbours). I masqueraded - like Erik in *The Phantom of the Opera* - as Edgar Allen Poe's 'Red Death'. We had black punch that I dubbed "Giant Squid Ink", and, being students, all got very drunk.

The bad thing about parties is the realisation, with cold sobriety, that one must clean up. The next morning - after fifteen bin-liners full of assorted rubbish had been collected - I came upon the altar-room. I just didn't have the heart to take down my lovely (well in my gothic eyes), creation. Then the idea struck me to leave the altar *in situ*, and use it as a focus for a series of thought-form experiments.

Each evening, I would descend to the cellar, with a ritual-sword and dressed in black robes. These accoutrements were not necessary, but helped to focus the mind, like an actor's dress rehearsal. I would open a circle - a practice common in magick, whereby a "magickal space" is opened for the user to work in. Then I would concentrate on visualising the spider. I would empty my mind of everything but my objective (an act that is far more difficult than you would think). I visualized a massive, slate-grey crab-spider with legs three-feet across. It had a bulbous body the size of a human-head and marked with a pattern resembling a grinning skull. Its own head was as large as an orange, and furnished with six green, bioluminescent eyes. Its one inch fangs were constantly dripping green venom. I imagined it squatted on the altar, its head jerking from side to side as if constantly listening. Sometimes I visualized it scurrying about the room in my peripheral vision, in the odd shadows cast by the candles, accompa-nied by a sound akin to the rustling of dead leaves.

I poured mental-energy into the thing. I also experimented with other forms of energy raising. I chanted the creatures name over and over until the words ran into one an other, and became a mantra, *"Atlach-Nacha, Atlach-Nacha, AtlachNachaAtlachNacha"*. I tried Dervish-whirling, and staring into dancing flames. My fire-eating friend had left behind a strobe-light at the party. I found this most efficacious in the aid of entering altered mental states. After experimenting with the strobe's settings, I found one that was particularly hypnotic.

After a few weeks, a distinct change came over the cellar. It was noticeably colder. When one was in the altar room, a feeling of being watched prevailed, and I would often find the hairs on my neck standing on end upon entering. When the lights were turned off the feeling of not being alone was palpable. To get a second opinion I called an a friend of mine; Steve Jones. Steve is a practicing witch and psychic, and one of his talents is the apparent power to detect spirits in any given place. He has used this in the investigation of several haunted buildings. On entering the altar-room, Steve declared that he could definitely sense *something*, but that it seemed unfocused. I tried switching off the lights, and this had a dramatic effect. Steve instantly got the unpleasant feeling that his bare fore-arms were being wrapped in cobwebs. Steve, who is an arachnophobe found this most distressing.

A couple of weeks later, there was an interesting development. I entered the room as normal only to be greeted by an image of a gigantic white spider upon the far wall. The image seemed two-dimensional, flat like a photograph. It was about four feet across, and did not much resemble the spider I had been visualising. I had imagined a crab-spider with angular, spindly-legs, this thing more closely resembled a tarantula with thick legs. As I looked to one side, the vision followed my moving eyes. and appeared on the right-hand wall. As I looked to the ceiling, it followed and appeared there. It was as if the spider was attached to my retina. The effect was akin to the one you get by staring for a long time at a white image on a black background – then, if you turn away, the image is retained for a few seconds. Whether it had any objective-reality is debatable, but it meant one thing to me, I was succeeding!

A few days later I saw it again! This time it was outside the altar-room, at the bottom of the stairs leading down into the cellar. This meant the tulpa was growing stronger and more independent. However, the summer-holidays loomed, and I had to return to the Midlands. Without me on hand to feed it, I thought that the tulpa would become weakened. I was very wrong.

Upon my return I went immediately to the cellar to find that the creepy atmosphere remained unchanged. I also found out that my "offspring" had been busy in my absence. Over the summer of 1996, Leeds, Wakefield, and the surrounding areas had suffered a plague of giant spiders. Panicked locals called the police and took captured specimens to wildlife experts believing them to be dangerous exotics. In fact they turned out to be *Teginaria domestica* - the common house spider, but these specimens had grown to *twice* their natural size. If this were not enough, a worker at a Morrison's warehouse in Wakefield was in for a nasty jack-in-the-box style surprise

Michael Haigh was unpacking a consignment of bananas from Brazil, when in his own words:

All of a sudden I realized that a giant spider was attacking my face. It was so huge it blocked my vision totally making everything dark. The spider bit me on the left cheek. It was terrifying!

A Brazilian huntsman spider (*Hetropoda spp.*), with a nine inch leg span, had leapt out of the bananas and buried its fangs in Mr Haigh's cheek. He was taken to the Tropical Medicine Department of Saint James' Hospital in Leeds, were he was kept waiting for eight hours! The doctor's brilliant diagnosis was that if he was still alive the spider could not have been a very poisonous one!

Mr Haigh decided to sue the banana company for damages, and mental stress. His solicitor said:

Frankly, if the day has come that a man cannot go to his place of work without being attacked by giant spiders, then frankly something is drastically wrong.

That must have been one of the strangest lines in legal history, but it didn't impress the banana company, who insisted it was Mr Haigh's fault for doing such a dangerous job as unpacking bananas in the first place! In a statement that reminds one of the *Monty Python* sketch 'How to defend yourself against assailants armed with pieces of fruit', they issued this statement:

He exposed himself to sustaining an accident such as he alludes befell him.

It seems to be pushing coincidence too far to think that all of these odd, spider-related stories, occurred at the same time that I was involved in spider thought-form experiments. It was as if the experiments had swollen beyond the bounds of the cellar and were effecting the mindset of the whole population, as well as having physical effects on the area. The best, however, was still to come.

It soon rolled round to the next year and I threw another party. This time I had the express intent of getting the whole crowd of my guests involved in a mass visualization of the creature.

I soon had thirty people sitting around the altar. These included several girls who had been passing by the house. One of the other guests had asked them if they wanted to come and join the party. I'm sure these poor unwitting girls still tell stories about what happened next. The whole scene was reminiscent of the classic *Dr Who* story *Planet of the Spiders*, in which Buddhist monks summon giant, psychic, transdimentional spiders into an English country house, via arcane rituals. I began by describing Atlach-Nacha in detail, and telling the crowd to visualize it on the altar. Then, they began to chant the spider's mantra over and over. Such a multiple raising of energy would empower a tulpa greatly.

I realized, that this being my last year at university, I would soon have to move out, and would no longer be able to continue feeding the tulpa. I needed to find a secondary, way of keeping belief and energy flowing into my creation. I came up with some novel "triggers" to keep my child in the pink.

In my bedroom there was a tiny door in one of the walls. When unscrewed, this led to a crawl space some six feet long by two feet wide by three feet tall. I knew that it would be human nature for any inquisitive mind to do what I had done, and look behind the door. I procured a rusty old biscuit-tin into which I placed a number of pseudo-occult items. These included pieces of jewellery inscribed in Sanskrit and Arabic, a huge dead spider that I covered in black wax, spells written on parchment that had been dyed and singed to give the illusion of age, and an occult diary. The diary was by far the most important of these.

The diary - in a way - was a fictionalised account of my experiments. It followed a young student who moved into the house and began a series of rituals. He finds a tome in an antiquarian bookshop in Hebden Bridge and uses it to contact a spider-demon. Starting in an understated manner, with only the suggestion of something un-natural afoot, it builds slowly up into an ever-mounting crescendo of horror. The diary charts the student's descent into the black pit of madness. He glimpses vistas of hell described in stomach-churning detail, page after page, and finally kills himself on the remotest wind-blasted Yorkshire moors. But not before the spider god has clawed its way into our world.

I left this 'box of delights' in the crawl-space, and screwed the tiny door back into place. It was my ardent hope that someone of a nervous-disposition would find them. At the same time I was preparing another trigger in the cellar.

I decided to leave the altar-room intact - for my successors - in all its mind-blasting glory. I added to the already unwholesome décor with giant red pentagrams on the walls. I decided that an ungodly stench was needed to add to the "evil" atmosphere. I concocted a foul brew of rotting fish, eggs, and meat, that I poured into the wall-cavities. I rigged the light-bulb in the room to explode upon being switched on. I also left a convenient torch beside the door. I intended the next tenants to open the door, and be greeted by a foul-stench, fumble for the light switch and in the brief illumination of the explosion to see the Spider-God's altar. Then upon finding the torch they would play the wan, shaky beam over my play-pen of evil.

It worked better than I could have ever hoped for. I revisited Leeds several months after my course was over. A friend of one of my old housemates whom had stayed on in Leeds, related some interesting information.. Apparently the student that had been given my room that term was a born-again Christian. He had indeed opened the little doorway to the alcove. He had indeed found the box of esoteric items. And he had indeed read the madman's diary.

This gullible fellow had descended to the cellar and in the exact sequence of events I had planned for, he found the alter of *Atlach-Nacha*. He had two priests in to exorcise the house and the altar was burnt in the back-yard!

This may all sound like a student prank in poor-taste, but it was done for a reason. The belief that this farcical affair would have generated in the minds of the residents would be huge, and tulpas *thrive* on belief. You are feeding the spider-god *now* by reading these words. It doesn't matter if you don't believe in it as long as you *think* about it. As for the exorcism, in many cases this makes matters worse. If the exorcist is not properly trained, and does not possess sufficient-skill, it can stir up a whole psychic hornet's-nest. A poor exorcist will also confirm a person's belief that something uncanny is afoot, thus feeding the tulpa.

All of this begs some questions.

- Firstly if an untrained and cluttered mind can achieve such results, what could a clear, well-trained, concentrated mind achieve?

- Secondly, could minds work in a gestalt, together as one, perhaps unknowingly to create tulpas on a huge scale?

We already have the case of the "Puss in Boots" created by the Brotherhood of the Rising Sun and there is evidence that points to the unknowing creation of tulpas as well.

Robin Furman is one of Britain's best known parapsychologists. He runs 'Ghostbusters U.K' - a company that investigates paranormal occurrences such as hauntings, poltergeist outbreaks, possessions, and other manifestations. The author has met Robin on several occasions and has always found him to be honest, likable, wise, and deeply-fascinating. Well respected in his field, Robin has witnessed many strange beings for himself. He suffered an unpleasant childhood at the hands of his violent father. Once - after being sent to bed with a thrashing - he had a very strange visitor.

I looked up to see an enormous dragon walking straight through my bedroom wall. It was green with huge wings. The thing I remember most about it was its tail that it held up in the air in long coils. I wasn't afraid of it. It just walked through my room and out down the corridor. I ran down stairs shouting for my parents to come and look at the dragon but they could not see it.

Perhaps Robin's dragon was an 'unconscious tulpa'. Maybe his subconscious had created a 'guardian' for him in the shape of the biggest, fiercest, creature it knew - a dragon.

Another example of involuntary thought-form creation, is mentioned in W. Y. Evens-Wentz in the book *The Tibetan Book of the Great Liberation.*

Mediums in the Occident can, while entranced, automatically and unconsciously create materialisations which are much less palpable than the consciously produced tulpas by exuding "ectoplasm" from their own bodies. Similarly, as is suggested by instances of phantasms of the living reported by psychic research, a thoughtform may be made to emanate from one human mind and by hallucinatory perceived by another, although possessed of little or no palpableness.

Further clues to the 'gestalt' thought-form can be gleaned from the case of one Franek Kluski. His real name was Teofil Modrzejewski, and from an early age he knew that he was "different". As a boy, he claimed to be able to see dead relatives and animals. He also had out-of-body experiences. Importantly, other children with him at the time, claimed to also be able to see 'the dead', as if he were passing on his power to those around him.

When Kluski grew up, he worked partly as an engineer, and partly as a professional medium. His speciality was the 'materialization' of spirit-animals, and he seemed to have a whole phantom menagerie at his beck and call. Sitters at his séances saw a big cat like a lioness that would stalk around them, lashing its tail, and leaving behind a strong, acrid smell that lingered for some time. Another beast was christened *Pithecanthropus* by witnesses after the now defunct name for the primitive human *Homo erectus*. The creature seemed part-ape part-man. The brute seemed benevolent in nature but possessed vast strength. One witness, Colonel Norbert Ocholowicz noted:

It could easily move a heavy bookcase filled with books through the room, carry a sofa over the heads of the sitters, or lift the heaviest persons, in their chairs, to the height of a tall person.

Other sitters felt the 'ape-man' rub its furry hide against their cheeks, and lick their hands, revealing that the creature could be felt as well as seen. It too left behind a foul odour.

Another member of Kluski's 'Zoo' was an owl-like bird that would apparently materialize in mid air and fly noisily around the room. On August 30th 1919, at a séance in Warsaw, the bird was photographed perching on Kluski's head. The shot revealed the bird to be remarkably similar to *Caprimulgus europaeus*, the European nightjar.

Observant readers will have noticed something. Kluski appeared to have been manifesting three of the great monster archetypes of the 20th century.

- Firstly, the phantom nightjar.

We have already noted that the Cornish Owlman resembles a giant nightjar. Both owls and nightjars are almost universally thought of as birds of ill omen due to their nocturnal habits and eerie eyes. A monster nearly identical to the Owlman is said to haunt the jungles of Senegal in West Africa. The natives know it as *Kikyaon* and describe it as being half-owl half-man. They believe that it exists both physically and psychically. Witch-doctors use the beast to destroy their enemies. On the physical plane *Kikyaon* destroys men's bodies with its beak and talons, and on the spiritual plane it eats their souls. Its name means "soul cannibal".

Another Owlman known as "Chick Cherney" is reputed to live in the pine forests of the Bahamas. In Japan the Tengu were a whole race of malevolent bird men. But perhaps the most infamous of owlman's relatives is a creature the media dubbed "Mothman". This was a man like figure with dark wings, no discernable head, and huge glowing eyes. The monster haunted an old WW2 munitions dump near Point Pleasant in West Virginia. Mothman was seen by over 100 people during the mid 1960s and was said to emit a high pitched squeaking sound, had strange hypnotic powers, exerted extreme fear, and pursued cars at speeds of 100 miles per hour. The creature appeared alongside other anomalous phenomena such as UFO sightings, and cattle mutilations.

Some months prior to its appearance in The States, an identical creature was seen by two young couples in Hythe, Kent. John Flaxton, Mervyn Huchinson and their girlfriends had been walking along a country road when Flaxton pointed out what looked like a bright star descending behind a group of trees. The object reappeared alongside them some 75 metres (250 feet) away, and revealed itself to be a golden, glowing oval six metres (20 feet) across. The object again hid itself amidst trees, but soon a figure came lumbering out of the shadows towards the teenagers. It was described as dark, headless, tall and possessing bat-like wings. The lovers were overtaken by blind panic and fled..

- The big cat - one of our most persistent archetypes.

There are reports of out-of-place exotic cats in many parts of Europe, Australia, New-Zealand, the USA and even Russia. It is in Britain however that the creatures are most celebrated. Although records of such beasts go back centuries, it was not until the 1960s that they grabbed the public's imagination with the case of the 'Surrey Puma'. These animals are given dramatic names like the "Beast of Bodmin", the "Peak Panther", and the "Beast of Exmoor". They are usually described as being pumas *(Felis concolor)* or melanistic (black) leopards *(Panthera par-*

dus).

There can be little doubt that there really are populations of these animals living and breeding in Britain. Up until The Dangerous Wild Animals act of 1976, one could quite legally keep such cats as pets and many did. The Act required stringent safety regulations, and – usually - a hefty licence fee. Met with such a law, lots of private keepers turned their cats loose in the countryside. Even *more* amazingly, up until 1981, absolutely anyone could open a zoo! As a former zookeeper, I saw enough incompetence in supposedly professional zoos, never mind those cobbled together by unqualified amateurs. Escapes must have been commonplace, and most were probably not reported.

With no competition, (wolves, bears, and the like, being long-extinct in Britain), and a healthy supply of prey species, from rabbits to deer, these animals have profited, and the ones seen now are probably at least third-generation descendents from the original escapees. In 1980 a female puma was even captured alive by the late Ted Noble on his farm at Cannich, Scotland. Many believe that these cats are now fully naturalised, and have become part of our fauna. But some reports - both here and abroad - seem to be of something other than flesh and blood animals.

One such odd case occurred at 8.30 pm on April 10th 1970 near Olive Branch, Illinois. Mike Busby was driving along the little used road alongside the Shawnee National Forest, when his car engine faltered and stopped. As Busby got out to check beneath the bonnet he notice a pair of green cat like eyes glowing in the shadows. A black, panther-like creature emerged from the darkness *walking on its hind legs*! The animal attacked Busby, dragging him to the ground and slashing his arm, abdomen, and chest with its claws. Luckily, a passing lorry frightened the creature off and the victim escaped in his car - that strangely worked once more. Once he reached Olive Branch, he was able to find the lorry driver who confirmed his story.

Cats *may* rear up on their hind legs to scratch at enemies, but they do not - and indeed are incapable of-walking on their hind legs. This case is far from unique. Herman Belyea was attacked by an identical beast nineteen years earlier in Queen's County, New Brunswick. On November 22nd 1949, a black cat-like creature, six-feet tall, and walking erect like a man, forced him to run for his life. The monster dodged his axe-blows and chased him until he came near to town.

At other times creatures seem to be bulletproof - like the "panther" shot at by police near Atlanta, Georgia in April 1958. The patrolmen were searching some woods after a report of the animal. Their torch-beams illuminated glowing, yellow eyes, and the creature charged. The men opened fire, and the beast sped past them totally unaffected. Officer J. F. Porter recalled:

Both of us were firing at point blank range. I don't see how we could have missed it.

- Giant apes or ape-men have been reported from every continent-including Antarctica!

In Asia they are called *yeti, dremo,* and *almas.* In Africa the *agogwe, tokoloshe, chemosit* or Nandi bear. In South America, *mono grande* and *ucumar.* In North America *sasquatch* or *bigfoot*, in Europe *troll* or *woodwose*, and in Australia *yowie* or *yahoo.* As with the big-cats, it is almost certain that some of these monsters are *real* animals – in this case unknown species of great-ape. In Asia, fossil remains of a giant - probably bipedal - ape have been uncovered in China and India. Known as *Gigantopithecus blackii,* this creature flourished in the Pleistocene epoch - a period of Earth's history that ended only 10,000 years ago. Like some other creatures mentioned in this book, *Gigantopithecus* may well have survived to the present day. Biological samples from the yeti have fallen into the hands of western scientists who have examined them with surprising results.

Bones from a yeti hand preserved in the Pangboche monastery in Nepal, were stolen by cryptozoologist Peter Byrne, and subsequently smuggled out of the country by the actor Jimmy Stewart. The bones were examined by several primatologists - including Dr. W. C. Osman Hill, of the Zoological Society of London - who believed them to be from a very primitive human, perhaps even a Neanderthal. He and his team from the University of California - later revised this view, and stated that the bones belonged to an unknown primate. Fred Ulmer – the Curator of Mammals at the Zoological Society of Philadelphia - stated that the metacarpals were massive even for a mountain gorilla (*Gorilla gorilla berengi)* - the largest living primate.

Skin samples were also taken and analysed, and found not to be from a human or any known species of ape. Sadly these specimens have again, since been lost. However, Byrne also brought back alleged yeti-droppings that were analysed by Dr A. Fain of the Tropical Medicine Institute of Anvers. He discovered the egg of an unknown parasitic-worm. As individual species tend to have their own parasites, the stool was believed to have come from an unknown animal.

Hair samples from a yeti that had supposedly brushed against a tree in central China, have recently been examined by laboratories in China, the UK, and the USA. By using proto-induced X-ray emission, the relative concentration of elements in them has been revealed. This is different for every species - allowing a database to be made. All three labs came to the same conclusion; an unknown species of primate.

The case for the yeti as a real animal is a good one, but when reports emerge from areas where there have never been any apes - even fossil ones - the nature of their reality comes into question. North America is a fine example. Of all the mystery apes, the Sasquatch is the most reported. But other than man, no species of primate has ever been known to naturally occur in this area. It is also from North America that we find some of the strangest reports on record. The by now familiar pattern of bulletproof creatures appearing alongside UFOs, cattle mutilations, poltergeist outbreaks, and other phenomena is common.

Let us examine a couple.

In August 1972 Randy and Lou Rodgers moved into a farmhouse in Rochdale, Indiana. Shortly after, 'something' began to rip apart their chickens. The attacker did not eat the birds, but needlessly tore them to shreds. The culprit was spotted on a number of occasions and resembled a large gorilla. The Rodgers shot at the monster from point blank range but the bullets seemed to past straight through it. Mrs Rodgers said:

We would never find tracks, even when it ran over mud. It would run and jump but it was like it wasn't touching anything. And sometimes when you looked at it looked like you could see through it.

Policeman and wildlife officer William Woodall also saw the brute but could never find any physical evidence.

One night in 1964, Lew Lister - and the 18 year old girl who would later be his wife - were sitting in a parked car at around 11 p.m, about a mile from the family farm in Point Isabel Ohio. Lew turned on the car's headlights, and illuminated a horrific figure bounding towards them across a nearby field. The obviously inhuman thing walked clean through a three-strand barb wire fence like a ghost, and grabbed at Lew as he frantically wound up his window. The future Mrs Lister described the creature as being six feet tall, and covered with "yellow fuzz". It had a head pointed at the top, and with a narrow chin, and wrinkled brow. The ears and nose were pig-like, and the mouth bore fangs. The eyes glowed orange, and had a hypnotic effect on the Listers. Mrs Lister described it as like a "time lapse" or "living in another time". (This distortion of time is reported in many fortean phenomena and we will return to it later.) As they watched, its hands became paw-like, and it fell down on all-fours - changing its form into a quadruped. This happened in what looked like slow-motion. Then, the monster simply vanished into thin-air. There are several other reports where bigfoot apparently 'dematerialises' in front of alarmed witnesses. The creature in this story sounds almost like yet another monster archetype - the werewolf.

Ohio seems to be a hot bed for these "weird" bigfoot reports. In 1981, a witness - referred to as "Ben", a Vietnam veteran - observed a banana-shaped object hovering above his farm in broad daylight. Soon afterwards, his farm-animals began to be attacked by a nocturnal predator, who bit off their heads. Armed with a gun, Ben stayed up one night to confront the attacker. Rather than the fox or racoon that he was expecting, he was confronted with a nine foot tall, ape-like creature with glowing, red eyes (red eyes again!) He fired at the beast, and it lumbered away. Next night it was back. Ben's wolfhound - a formidable dog - was beside itself with terror at the apparition. As the nights went on, Ben and his family realized that a number of creatures were visiting the farm. Their red eyes were seen glowing in the shadows. They were accompanied by strange, dancing-lights that shot beams down into the bushes. Sometimes these lights seemed to swell and transform into the apes.

The catalyst seemed to be Ben's teenaged son Andy. Andy would lapse into a trance when the lights appeared, and could not be woken. After the events he would have no memory of either the trance, or of the events that transpired.

Ben attempted to photograph one of the apes. Bizarrely, when the photograph was developed all that was visible was a reddish orange globe the size of a tennis-ball. The family split up under the pressure of these strange visitations.

W. C. Priestley was driving his car through the Monogahela National Forest, West Virginia, in October 1960. Priestley was following a bus containing his friends. Suddenly the car spluttered and stopped. Looking to the side of the road he saw:

...a monster with long hair pointing straight up towards the sky standing beside the road. I don't know how long I sat there, until the boys missed me and backed the bus up to where I was. It seemed this monster was very much afraid of the bus and dropped his hair (which had been standing on end) ,and to my surprise as soon as he did this, my car started to run again. The thing took off when the bus stopped.

A little while on, the car began to splutter again and ground to a halt.

I could see sparks flying from under the hood of my car, as if had a very bad short. And sure enough, there beside the road stood the monster again. The points were completely burned out on my car.

When the bus returned, the bigfoot left again, this time permanently. This adverse effect on electrical equipment is commonplace in paranormal occurrences from ghosts to UFOs. "Ordinary" flesh and blood creatures seldom have such an influence.

One could conceive of giant-apes in the wilds of Asia, or at a push the Pacific North-West of America but surely not in Britain? Surprisingly, bigfoot type creatures are reported from time to time in the British Isles. But from November 2002 onwards a massive 'flap' of these beasts was reported from all over the country.

One witness that I interviewed, was the owner of an articulated-lorry. He worked for The Forestry Commission, transporting logs. He was sleeping in the cabin of his lorry one night in November. The location was Fixton Woods in Sussex. At around 2.30 am, he went outside to relieve himself. Close to his vehicle was a large piece of equipment used for loading logs onto lorries. The machine had a large red light, so the drivers could avoid backing into it at night.

The witness noticed a huge figure standing next to the machine - apparently fascinated by the light (attraction to electrical equipment again). The man - a former solider - was trained to estimate size accurately. He reckoned that the creature was eight-feet tall. He returned to his cabin to get a torch. When he shone the beam on the thing, it turned and ran into the forest. He described it as black and ape-like.

Other reports came in from Sherwood Forest in Nottinghamshire, Cannock-Chase in the West-Midlands, Lancashire, and Scotland. But the biggest cluster of reports came from the woods around Bolam Lake in Northumberland.

As part of a team from the Centre for Fortean Zoology, I travelled to the area in January 2003. The witnesses we interviewed all seemed to be describing the same entity. Naomi - a 40 year old woman - and her 14 year old son, had just pulled into one of the car parks around the lake, when they heard a noise that the boy describes as sounding like 'Chewbacca' from the Star-Wars films. As they got out of their car they both saw a hulking, black shape watching them from the woods surrounding the lake. It was well over seven feet tall. Though standing stock-still, the thing seemed to emanate a feeling of rushing towards the witnesses. A feeling of wild panic seized Naomi and her son, and they both rushed back to the car, and drove quickly away. They did not look back, for fear that the thing was pursuing them. The feeling of rushing-terror and hostility followed them out of the park area, and onto the road.

Neil - another witness - was one of three night fishermen who saw what was to become known as the "Bolam Bigfoot" or the "Northumberland Yeti". The trio had been fishing, and were leaving the park at around 2.30 a.m. They were walking along a raised wooden-path above a marshy area of the woodland. One of their number stopped to tie a shoelace. The others looked back, and were horrified to see a massive, black, ape-like monster standing a scant six feet behind him. Even though it stood in the marsh rather than on the ramp, it still loomed tall - over seven feet. Neil cannot recall any facial features, apart from greenish eyes that glimmered in the moonlight. Needless to say, all three men ran pell-mell from the lake in terror.

On the second evening of our investigation, my friend and colleague Jonathan Downes – The Director of the Centre for Fortean Zoology - saw the phenomenon for himself, along with four other alarmed witnesses. The CFZ were being assisted by our old friend Mike Hallowell and about twenty from the *Twilight Worlds* paranormal investigation society in South Shields, Tyneside. At around 4.30 pm (whilst in the same car-park that Naomi and her son had their encounter in), one of the girls from the *Twilight Worlds* group said she could hear something large crashing through the undergrowth. Jonathan called for all the team's car headlights to be trained on the forest. In the illumination of six sets of car headlights something incredible was revealed.

Five people - including Jon - saw a powerful, black figure rushing through the trees. The thing was seen running left to right then right to left. It was matt black, fast, and strong-looking. Re-creating the sighting in daylight on the following day, it was established that the thing was 130 feet away from the witnesses. It was seven and a half feet tall and had moved through boggy, uneven ground with superhuman swiftness. Jon also got the feeling that the entity was two dimensional, flat. He describes it thus:

It was like a man-shaped moving hole cut into the backdrop of the trees. A man-shaped blob of nothingness.

Whatever the thing was, it seems to have little in common with the real flesh and blood mystery apes such as the yeti and orang pendek. Bizarrely we found out shortly after that a Buddhist monastery - Harnham Retreat Monastery - is located close to the lake. Is this merely a strange coincidence or is there a link? Some say that the monks have been observed performing rituals around the lake and woods at night. Could they be creating a tulpa, and if so to what ends?

It should be noted that the Buddhists at Harnham are Thai Buddhists, who have no tradition of tulpas. A Buddhist friend of mine - Bob Mann of Totnes, Devon - has pointed out that tulpa creation is not actually part of the Buddhist religion. The whole tulpa concept is from Tibetan and Nepalese folklore. This has been incorporated into the belief-systems and meditations of Buddhist monks in the area. So it seems that the Buddhist retreat at Harnham has little or no link with the man-beast of Bolam.

Phantom apes occur in many areas of Britain, particularly in the south west. Often times a legend will spring up around the phenomena in order to "explain" it as the ghost of some exotic pet owned by former-gentry in times gone by. Such is the case with Martyn's Ape at Athelhampton house in Dorset.

Some well-known reports have come out of Scotland. Ben McDhui in the Cairngorms is famous for its "Big Grey Men" - ape-like phantoms said to inhabit the cloud wreathed mountain peaks, and creating fear so intense than some mountaineers have literally ran off cliffs in their attempts to flee them. This recalls the fear felt by the witnesses at Bolam Lake. Much has been written about The Big Grey Men, but few know that they have a lowland cousin that haunts Dundonal Hill in Ayrshire.

Mark Fraser - a well-respected Scottish paranormal researcher - was told the following story by a man who wished to be known only as "Derek R". He was walking through some woods near his home at Torphins - around twenty miles from Aberdeen - with two friends. As they reached the edge of the woods, "Ben" - one of Derek's companions - saw what looked like the figure of a man, run from a stand of trees on the left to one on the right - about 200 yards away. He was suddenly overwhelmed with a sense of foreboding. The others dismissed this, until they too, saw a creature peering at them from the trees. Derek described the face as "human, but not human". It disappeared when a rock was hurled at it.

A couple of weeks later the trio saw it again, about two miles from their previous encounter. As they drove along the road to Torphins, a massive figure appeared from the side of the road. It was described as being hair-covered, muscular, and with red eyes. They accelerated, but the monster kept pace with them for about five minutes before stopping in the middle of the road.

It is interesting to note here that in Scottish folklore there is a creature called 'The Running Man', that was said to pursue horses, carriages - and later - cars at amazing speeds.

Derek also told Mark of a female friend of his who lived in a secluded cottage. She claimed twice to have seen a hairy-figure watching her cottage from the forest, before returning to the shadows.

It is obvious that a small temperate island like Britain could not support a population of unknown apes. This - together with the unnatural fear generated by them - must surely point to a supernatural origin. One only has to think of the legends of trolls, ogres, and giants so common in Britain to see that this is an ancient archetype.

Whatever Kluski was doing, it seemed that he was tapping into great monster-motifs. Some current, some ancient, and some yet to flourish. Dragons were noticeably absent, but Kluski's séances were held indoors, with hardly room enough for a dragon to manifest. One wonders what would have happened if he had tried an outdoor session - perhaps beside a lake? Whilst searching for the giant semi-aquatic snake - the naga - in Thailand, the author noticed some of the great archetypes once again. In Thai mythology there are three main monsters.

- The naga - a water dwelling serpent

- The garuda - a creature, half man, half bird, who is believed to bring the rains on his wings

- A giant golden lion.

These creatures are said to inhabit a mystic jungle. Perhaps the "mystic jungle" is the tangled reaches of our subconscious. Maybe Kluski was unconsciously manifesting the fears of the collective mind of the human race. This may sound absurd but there is evidence that such a thing actually exists.

British biologist Rupert Sheldrake infuriated adherents to academic dogma in 1981 when he published his revolutionary theories in a book entitled *A New Science of Life*. In this book Sheldrake raised the question of how - if every DNA molecule contained the coded information to make a specific creature - did the body know just what went where. For example, how did it know to grow skin-cells, and not - say - muscle-cells in the right areas. Also, many animals (like some lizards), can regrow lost-limbs, whilst others - such as echinoderms - can be totally destroyed, (for example by putting them in a liquidizer), but each piece will regrow into a fully-formed adult.

Sheldrake realised that - contained within the DNA - must be something akin to a 'blueprint' for each species - a life-shaping field *unique* to each life-form, that orders the DNA. He called his hypothetical 'blueprints' morphogenic-fields - or m-fields for short. The m-field theory might also explain how subjective information like emotions and memories are retained. The cells in our bodies are constantly dying and being replaced, and this includes brain-tissue. Yet we retain our memories and personalities – except under conditions of severe or maximum brain-damage, (even minimal to moderate brain-damage is self-repairable) - ergo *something* must be making the new atoms follow the exact patterns of their forbears.

This m-field template may be the key to understanding other biological mysteries such as migration. Darwin believed that this kind of information was passed on in the genetic-characteristics of the parents, but some startling experiments have challenged this view.

In the USA a series of experiments were carried out on rats. The rats had to learn how to escape from a pool of water without following the most logical course - as this had been rigged to give them an electric-shock. The first generation took a number of attempts to learn this. The young of these rats took less time to work out the problem. This seemed to be supporting the Darwinian idea, but identical experiments were being carried out in another country with rats that had no genetic relationship to the ones in America. These rats took even less time to solve the puzzle than the second generation of rats in the American labs.

Sheldrake believed that this was because of a *shared* m-field. He hypothesised the m-fields of all individuals of a species were linked to a huge gestalt m-field. He proposed that evolutionary changes, behavioural patterns, and information were shared at a subconscious level between the whole species. When individuals pick up advantageous new behavioural traits, it is incorporated into the gestalt. He believed this was passed on by resonance, rather like the way that the energy wave from a plucked string on an instrument can resonate onto another string on the same instrument that has not been plucked. This works because part of the unplucked string has the potential to resonate at frequencies in common with the vibrating string, and thus can resonate in harmony. In music this is called harmonic resonance. Sheldrake called his biological analogue, morphic resonance.

Of course the inverse of this also occurred, wherein the individual's behaviour is altered by the m-field of the species. Animals with fewer turnovers of generations - those with longer life spans - would have m-fields that work more slowly. But they work nonetheless. Some Einstein of the sheep-world worked out how to cross cattlegrids in Britain. The sheep curled up in a ball, and *rolled* across the grid! Initially only a few did this trick, but within weeks sheep all over the world were making P.O.W style escapes from farms.

This would seem to be the ideal was for gigantic "racial thought forms" to occur. Perhaps we should seek the origin of dragons and other monsters, in the jungles of our own minds, and in the fossil memories handed down to us in our genes from our remote ancestors.

Several million years ago, on the plains of East Africa, our remote ancestors were struggling to survive. *Australopithecus* had an existence fraught with peril. In moving down from the trees, and onto the grassland to exploit untapped food-sources, he faced new and deadly enemies. The crocodile was - and is - the biggest killer of mankind. The rock-python would also have found our ancestors easy prey. *Australopithecus* was small enough to have fallen victim to large raptors, and fossil evidence from South Africa supports this. Lions and leopards would have certainly preyed on our ancestors, and hunting-dogs may have also given them sleepless nights. *Australopithecus* and its descendents would have been in direct competition with other primate species. Some were smaller than itself - other, including the horrific giant baboon *Dinopithecus* - were larger.

Think about it. Here we have the genesis of mankind's monsters, the beginning of our species' bugbears. The dragon, the giant bird, the mystery big-cat, the phantom dog, the little people, and the hairy giant.

Sheldrake himself seems to support this notion.

In the early stages of a form's history, the morphogenetic field will be relatively ill-defined and significantly influenced by individual variants. But as time goes on, the cumulative influence of countless previous systems will confer an ever-increasing stability on the field; the more probable the average type becomes, the more likely that it will be repeated in the future.

Perhaps our fossil memories can be triggered by certain things in our surroundings. Maybe some kinds of electromagnetic-interference coupled with the right person, with the right brain chemistry, in the right place, at the right time, can create a monster. If the brain - an electro-chemical computer - is "shorted" it "re-boots" like an mechanical computer, and for a while switches to its most primitive "operating-system" In this condition, our m-field kicks

144

in, and together with our fossil-memories, creates a defence mechanism - the primal fear, 'flight or fight', taken to its extreme in the creation of something visible and (for a time at least), tangible.

But we have ignored some of the most important archetypes of the 20th century, ones that are pertinent to our search for the nature of dragons - the UFO and the "reptoid".

Strange lights have always been seen in our skies. They are recorded in ancient manuscripts from China and India, and are mentioned in The Bible. Their interpretation has differed through the ages. In the early part of the 20th century "waves" of sighting of what were then called "mystery airships" were reported from all over the world. In Britain some believed that they were the spearhead of an invasion fleet sent by Kaiser Wilhelm. In the Second World War, they were referred to as "foo-fighters". Both The Allies *and* The Axis Forces saw them, and each believed them to be new enemy technology. It was not until the post-war era that the idea that these phenomena may be alien spacecraft appeared. The phenomenon has "updated" itself, in keeping with the mindset of the era that it appears in. It is hence unsurprising that in an age dominated by technology, 'they' manifest as a technophoic nightmare.

In a more primitive age, one of mankind's greatest fears would have been of devouring predators. Maybe the UFO phenomenon - as viewed by our ancestors - were dragons. There are links between the two.

- Both dragons and UFOs seem to have an affinity with water, often appearing in or around lakes, seas and other bodies of water.

- Both seem far above the powers of mankind - the dragon, an unkillable monster of god-like power (in the early legends). The UFO a machine made by technology so advanced it seems god-like.

- Both appear suddenly, often causing panic, and then just as quickly disappear. Some myths state that as well as breathing fire dragons clutched fiery balls in their claws or pursued pearl like objects (pearls of wisdom in the orient).

Appearances by UFO "occupants" are another facet to this phenomenon. Early reports of "aliens" usually portrayed them as looking like very beautiful human-beings. They were usually tall, fair haired, and pale skinned. They first raised their heads in the post-war years and one has only to think of Hitler's putative super-race to explain their Aryan looks. "Contactees" such as George Adamski claimed to have met such beautiful space-people in the deserts of the American south-west. They span wild yarns of being taken to planets in our solar system - such as Venus - that were lush utopias. In such early cases, the "extraterrestrials" generally had some kind of warning for mankind to mend its ways, or suffer global catastrophe. The link to a post-war mind-set is obvious.

We now know that Venus is incapable of supporting life as we understand it, and that aliens are highly unlikely to resemble human-beings. This persistence of humanoid-aliens is one of my main reasons for rejecting the extraterrestrial hypothesis (ETH). It seems to be a kind of narcissus complex in the collective mind of mankind. Many of our past monsters have been humanoid too - trolls, elves, giants, angels, mermaids, vampires, werewolves, and satyrs to name but a few. I call this humanoid obsession 'The *Star Trek* effect'. One only has to watch a couple of episodes of this series to see the lack of imagination in the design of the alien races. Most of them look perfectly human, except for pointed ears or wrinkled foreheads. The chances of evolution on another biosphere being so like the chance-events on earth that spawned us, to result in a human-like lifeform are astronomical. To get a better idea of what something from another world might look, like I would suggest watching some classic *Doctor Who*. With far greater imagination, the costume-designers at the BBC produced some genuinely *alien* looking aliens.

As if growing directly with our knowledge, and perhaps liked directly to our minds, the UFO phenomenon has changed. Now the "aliens" look less human, and claim to come from other solar systems - such as Zeta Reticuli. The commonest alien type reported today is 'The Grey'. These are small in stature, with grey skin, lipless-mouths, flat noses and huge, dark eyes. In some ways they resemble the goblins of ancient legend. But the resemblance does not end there.

Beginning in the 1960s, a new facet to the UFO phenomenon emerged - the abduction. These scenarios involve the apparent kidnap of people, (sometimes several at once), by "aliens" who take them on board their vessel, and conduct medical-experiments on them - sometimes of a sexual nature. Often the abductee has no memory of the event, but finds they have "lost" several hours of time. The memories may come back during hypnotic-regression, or naturally bit-by-bit. They sometimes claim to have been "implanted" with small probe-like devices, although these have never been confirmed by scientists. Some female abductees claim that eggs have been taken from their wombs, or even that they have been implanted with human/alien hybrid-foetuses that are harvested later.

Students of folklore reading this, may find it all rather familiar - and with good reason. None of it is new. All the above have been claimed to be the work of fairies in times past. People abducted by 'The Fair Folk', were said to be spirited away to Faerieland. These victims often had little memory of their sojourn, but experienced lost-time. Time was said to be non-existent in Faerieland, so what seemed like a short stay there could account for days, weeks, or even years, in our world. The abductees were often returned with magickal silver-pins inserted into them - in some cases to render them mute. Most tellingly, fairies were supposed to be a waning race who wished to interbreed with humans to strengthen their racial stock. They would steal babies and leave sickly offspring of their own - known as changelings - in their place. There are many tales of fairies seducing mortal men and women, and mating with them to produce hybrid-children. The alien-abductee scenario is merely a high-tech update of this age-old story.

A fine example of this is recounted in historian Robert Hunt's book, *Popular Romances of the West of England*. The story concerns Ann Jeffries - a teenaged girl from Cornwall. One day in 1647 she was in her employer's garden, when she felt a whirling, floating sensation. She was approached by two small beings and then passed out. She came-to in Faerieland. Ann describes this place as colourful, flower-filled, and populated by strange creatures. The fairies seemed intensely interested in human sexual-reproduction. When returned, Ann heard a loud buzzing-noise and experienced the same floating sensation and blackout. After the encounter, she stopped eating certain types of food, and became a renowned psychic and healer. The relationship to modern abduction cases is startling.

Now the fairies are aliens, and the dragons may well be UFOs. But dragon-like creatures are still seen today - as the "Encounters with Modern Dragons" section of this book shows. The dragon-image refuses to be vanquished, and it may even have a new form from the ranks of the so called alien sightings.

I mentioned earlier, that aliens were becoming less humanoid (but still too man-like to be *true* aliens). One of their more recent forms, is known as 'The Reptoid'. This creature is a lizard-man resembling a human/reptile hybrid.

The following encounter was said to have happened to Ron and Paula Watson at Mount Vernon Missouri in July 1983.

During breakfast one day, the couple noticed flashes of light coming from a pasture across from their farmhouse. Looking at the field through binoculars, they were met with a strange sight. A black cow was lying motionless on the ground, whilst two silver-suited figures ran their hands over it. The animal seemed to levitate, and floated into a cone-shaped craft in a nearby clump of trees. The cone had a mirror-like surface that rendered it almost invisible.

Standing next to the strange craft were two lizard-men, that were described as having green skin, eyes with vertical slits, and webbed hands and feet. On the other side of the cone was a hairy bigfoot-type creature (quite a menagerie all in all!)

Ron wanted to have a closer look, but his wife would not let him go. They recounted what they saw to the owner of the pasture, when he mentioned that one of his cows was missing. The farmer would not listen to them, but his missing cow was never found. Later - under hypnosis - Paula claimed to have been abducted by the creatures.

Like most Western Dragons, the Reptoids seem malevolent. One of the most dramatic accounts of an encounter with one of these beings, happened to Charles Wetzel on the night of November the 8th 1958. Wetzel was driving his car near the Santa Ana River, in the town of Riverside, California, when a nightmarish-creature loomed out of the shadows and attacked his car.

Wetzel described his encounter:

It had a round scarecrowish head, like something out of Halloween. It wasn't human. It had longer arms than anything I'd ever seen. When it saw me it reached all the way back to the windshield and began clawing at me. It didn't have any ears. The face was all round. The eyes were shining like something fluorescent, and it had a protuberant mouth. It was scaly, like leaves.

In panic, Wetzel reached for his .22 pistol, and slammed his foot on the car's accelerator.

The thing fell back from the car and it gurgled. The noise it made didn't sound human. I think I hit it. I heard something hit the pan under the car.

Wetzel got away, but his attacker seemed unharmed - as it leapt out to petrify another motorist later that night.

An even closer encounter befell Mrs Darwin Johnson of Evansville, Indiana, who was swimming in the Ohio River on the 21st of August 1955. A large, clawed-hand seized her below the knee and yanked her under water. Each time she struggled to the surface, she was pulled under once again by her unseen attacker. Finally, she was able to make a lunge at an inner-tube that a friend was using as a swimming-aid. The thump of her body against the rubber apparently made the creature release her. The imprint of the creature's palm was visible on her leg as a green stain, and the scratches it left needed medical treatment.

The town of Loveland, on the Miami River, Ohio, has a tradition of such creatures dating back - once again - to 1955. In this year, a driver returning home from work at 3.30 in the morning spotted a trio of creatures some four feet tall, with leathery-skin, frog-like faces, and wrinkled heads. One of them held a device that emitted sparks. He parked his car, and watched them for three minutes before calling Police Chief John Fritz. Fritz investigated, but found nothing. Almost seventeen years later, two of his colleagues had a better look.

On March 3rd 1973, at one a.m, two Loveland police officers saw a creature - identical to the one described above - leap over a guard-rail, and scramble down into the river. Two weeks later one, of the officers saw the thing again. This time, it was lying in the middle of the road, and leapt up at his approach. Once again it scrambled over the rail, and into the river.

He took a shot at it but missed.

But the Loveland Frog saga may not be all it seems. Recently, one of the police officers involved was tracked-down and interviewed. He claims that the creature he saw was not bipedal and was merely a large lizard about a metre in length. He shot at the animal, and it scurried off the road. He says that the media hyped the story beyond belief, and that the infamous Loveland Frog was nothing more than an escaped exotic pet. But that does not explain the earlier sighting

A strange creature was seen in 1938 or 1939 by two Estonians, at Juminda on the Baltic coast. It had slit-like eyes and mouth, and browny-green skin. The thing was around three feet tall, with the general appearance of a frog. It seemed to have difficulty walking on land, but fled quickly when pursued.

Miniature versions of the frog-men were reported from a UFO encounter in Orland Park, Illinois, in 1951. Twenty-four year old steelworker, Harrison E. Bailey, was walking through some woods at eleven a.m, when he experienced a strange cramping and burning sensation on his neck. Looking behind him, he saw what he took to be a small, grey whirlwind. He then noticed a silvery-grey, oval-shaped object, at the edge of a meadow. As he drew closer, he saw it was a craft of some kind with windows. Peering from the windows were two "men" in what appeared to be green-tinted face shields. The men asked him where he was from, and where he was going. The pain seemed to wear-off, and he walked away - glancing briefly back at the craft.

The next thing Harrison remembered was awaking in the late afternoon. He was confused when a group of men asked him if he had come out of a flying-saucer on the previous day. In subsequent years, he began to suffer chronic health problems, and came to associate this with his encounter. In 1975 - under hypnosis - he recalled forgotten events that befell him that night.

He remembered being swarmed by a horde of bipedal frog-like creatures with large eyes, brown-striped skin, and three fingers. The creatures stood some 1.5 feet (eighteen inches), tall, and were accompanied by swarms of black beetles that scurried around erratically. The frog-creatures bit Harrison, and made him fall to sleep. He was taken on board the craft and given a telepathic message by the men in face-shields that they meant him no harm and wanted to communicate with mankind. They wanted Harrison as their spokesman.

Any Fortean investigator worth their salt will have seen several elements in this case that are repeated again and again.

- Firstly the powerful beings with messages for mankind. This phenomenon has always been around. In years gone by it was angels or even manifestations of the Blessed Virgin Mary who imparted these messages. They were often about mankind's poor moral-state. *Now* it is aliens with environmental messages, or warnings about atomic warfare.

- We can also note the witness's illness being associated with the encounter. Many people who experience UFOs and other Fortean phenomena claim to have either developed an illness or being cured of one. The author knows a man who after treatment for cancer found strange memories arising. During hypnotic-regression he recalled being abducted from a holiday caravan as a child, and examined by human-looking entities aboard a space-ship. They told him that they were his distant descendents who travelled back in time to do medical research upon him. The abduction was probably a false-memory brought on by the trauma of surgery and the nature of his illness.

In May 1976, Dominique [sic] Menuge was driving through north-eastern France, when he saw a bright light and observed about fifty tiny, green-coloured, "frog-men" scampering across the road in front of his car.

A factor that seems to link many of these reptoid sightings is water. The majority of them occur close to rivers, lakes, or swamps, and the following is no exception. On the 19th of August 1972, Robin Flewellyn and Gordon Pike said that they were chased off a beach on Thetis Lake, British Columbia, by a silver-scaled bipedal creature, that had risen from the water. The five foot tall creature bore six spines on its head, and had lacerated one of the witnesses with them.

Four days later, another two witnesses - Russell Van Nice and Michael Gold - watched the monster emerge from the lake, look around, and then return to the water. Their description tallied with that of the previous witnesses.

No less an authority than a State Conservation Naturalist, spoke out on the subject of lizard-men. Alfred Hulstruk claimed that a scale-covered man-beast regularly emerged from the red-algae choked waters of the Southern Tire in New York State.

At the time of going to press in the late spring of 2004, the most recent spate of reptoid sightings were those which came out of an area known as Scape Ore Swamp, Lee County, in South Carolina in 1988. The initial encounter went unnoticed by the press. Thirty-two year old George Hollomon was collecting water from an artesian well on Scape Ore bridge when a huge beast with big eyes leapt out at him from the woods. A week later, on June 30th the event that made the Scape Ore lizard-man a media star took place.

Seventeen year-old Chris Davis had just finished changing a flat tyre on his car. It was 2:00 am and he was parked on the Browntown road that runs through the swamp. Seeing something move out of the corner of his eye, he looked up to see a two metre (seven foot) tall creature running rapidly towards him from the bushes. Chris had just enough time to jump into his car and lock the door, before the monster was upon him. As he tried to drive away, he was horrified to see the creature keeping pace with his car at forty miles per hour. He saw that it was covered with green scales, had red glowing eyes, and had three fingers that bore long black nails. The lizard-man slashed at the car with its impressive claws and wrenched at the door handle. It then sprung onto the auto's roof before the frightened teenager finally lost his reptilian pursuer.

Initially Chris did not tell the police or the media, but the story was leaked and Liston Truesdale - the local sheriff - phoned Chris's father who confirmed the story. The monster instantly became a celebrity. Hundreds of people roamed the swamps looking (fruitlessly) for it. Stores sold lizard-man tee-shirts, caps, badges, and even lizard-man repellent spray!

On July 15th a man contacted the sheriff's office claiming to have struck a huge creature with an alligator-like face in his car. Police investigated but found nothing. By August the "lizard fever" died down, and the creature disappeared as quickly as it had arrived.

Although they have been reported only relatively recently, the reptoids seem to have a degree of antiquity. Human/reptile hybrids are recorded from many ancient cultures.

Sebek was the crocodile headed god of the Egyptian pantheon. He controlled the flow of the River Nile, and was associated with the fertility of the Nile Delta. When the river flooded in September, the delta would have been filled with crocodiles. He was also known as "the great devourer" - perhaps in reference to the crocodile's phenomenally powerful digestive system. This was seen as the natural circle - the life, death, and rebirth of all things. He is generally portrayed as a humanoid with a crocodile's head.

Despite his predatory nature, Sebek was a benevolent god. The son of Neith - the first Egyptian god - Sebek was said to be one of only two gods who would endure forever, as other god's powers would fluctuate. His cult flourished in the delta areas such as Fayoum, Thebes and Lake Moeris. In 1900, excavations at Tebtunis uncovered a temple dedicated to Sebek which was thirty metres (100 feet) long, and decorated with scenes of adoration, offerings, rituals, and great processions in his honour.

Another centre of his worship was Crocodilopolis (crocodile city). Here sacred crocodiles - believed to be avatars of Sebek - were kept in special, sacred pools. They were adorned with gold and hand fed milk and honey cakes by priests. The city was said to have been founded by King Menes, the first of the pharaohs. The legend tells of how he was set upon by wild dogs and fled into the waters of Lake Moeris. Here a crocodile offered to carry the king upon his back to the site that later became the city.

During the age of the New Kingdom (1400 BC) Sebek was seen as a manifestation of Ra the sun god, and Crocodilopolis became the pharaoh's favourite city.

Crocodiles - like all sacred Egyptian animals - were mummified. Specimens from thirty centimetre (one foot) hatchlings, to five metre (sixteen foot) adults have been found mummified. At Kom-Ombo small specimens were found stacked in their thousands and at the Maabdha Caves in central Egypt crocodile mummies were found stacked to a height of nine metres (thirty feet).

The reptoid rears its scaly head in Biblical scriptures too.

The human fear of snakes is apparent in the tale of the Garden of Eden, where Satan in the form of a snake tempts Adam and Eve to eat the forbidden fruit from the tree of knowledge.

In revenge a wrathful God damns the snake in Genesis 3:14-15 :

And the Lord God said unto the serpent,

Because thou hast done this, thou art cursed above all cattle, and above every beast of the field; upon thy belly shalt thou go, and dust shalt thou eat all the days of thy life.

This begs a question that has intrigued Biblical scholars for centuries.

If the limbless, crawling snake was due to a divine curse, what did it look like to begin with? In their book *Biblical Commentary on the Old Testament*, Carl. F. Keil and Franz Delitzsch commented:

If these words are not robbed of their entire meaning, they cannot be understood in any other way than denoting that the form and movement of the serpent were altered, and that the present repulsive shape is the effect of the curse pronounced upon it, though we cannot form any accurate idea of its original appearance.

Others had a very good idea of its appearance.

Egyptian carvings show the pre-cursed serpent as a human/reptile hybrid - a spindly creature with long arms and legs and a snake like head, tail and neck. In the Zohar or *Book of Splendour*, allegedly at least, a 13th Century Spanish commentary on the Pentateuch, (the first five books of the Old Testament), the original serpent was said to be a biped standing as tall as a camel. God smote off its limbs and split its tongue into a fork so its power of human speech was lost.

Artist have also portrayed Eden's villain as a reptoid. By the 12th century this was common. The creature often had a snake's body with the arms and face of a beautiful woman. Such creatures were given the name draconopides. Perhaps, due to it being the first name allocated to such creatures as a race, this is what we should really call the reptoids. Draconopides became associated with Lilith.

In Rabbinacal lore, Lilith was Adam's first wife, created before Eve, from the same dust as Adam. She refused to be subjugated by Adam (good for her!) and left him to become a daemon. Some texts say that she (and not Satan) was the serpent in Eden.

15th century painter Francois Forquet's work *Le Peche Originel* shows Lilith with a serpentine lower body coiled about the tree of knowledge, with the torso, arms and face of a woman and bat's wings. Another 15th century artist - Hugo van der Goes - creates an even stranger monster in his painting *The Temptation*. His serpent is an upright lizard with webbed feet and a woman's head sprouting horns

In reality, the snake's limblessness is a marvel of evolution, bestowing advantages rather than curses. The idea of a reptoid in the Garden of Eden is an intriguing one, and shows us just how far back this "new" archetype may actually go. There is one scientist, however, who has seriously considered the possibility of a race of humanoid reptiles!

Palaentologist Dr Dale Russell speculated that if non-avian dinosaurs had not become extinct at the end of the Cretaceous they would have evolved into a humanoid shape. Taking as his ancestral species *Stenonychus inequalis* - the most highly evolved known dinosaur which was a close relative of the more familiar *Velociraptor* - he postulated an upright, bipedal creature with binocular-eyes and a large cranium containing a large brain. The tailless beast was reconstructed with three long dexterous fingers, one of which was opposable. A reconstruction of the *dinosaurid* - as Russell christened his creation - is on show at the Canadian Museum of Nature in Ottawa, Canada. Russell believes that *had* such creatures evolved, their intelligence would have long since surpassed that of mankind.

Mammals as a whole would not have developed beyond small, shrew-like primitives if this scenario had come to pass.

It may be argued that Dr Russell was inspired in his theory by the BBC television programme *Dr Who*. The Doctor did battle with two races of super-intelligent dinosaur descendents - the Silurians and the Sea Devils. Both saw fruit well before Dr Russell's theories were published.

The reconstruction does bear a remarkable resemblance to reports of reptoids - in particular the Scape Ore swamp lizard-man. This has led some to conclude that reptoids come from a planet with a parallel development to Earth, but where dinosaurs continued their rule and developed into intelligent humanoids. The dinosaurid is totally hypothetical, and many say that it shows more about human narcissism than evolution. The tailless body, and human-like torso with the round face, all show a parallel evolution to humans. Would such a thing take place?

The idea of mankind as the pinnacle of evolution - the end to which all life developed - is a defunct, Victorian idea. High intelligence is not necessarily the end product of evolution. Life forms adapt to the environment, competition, and other pressures. If a large brain is not an advantage it will not develop or will even become scaled down.

An example of this is found in sauropod dinosaurs. As these creatures developed to browse higher vegetation and exploit treetops, their necks grew longer. Pumping blood up necks of twelve metres (forty feet) or more, became a problem even for their gigantic hearts. Sauropods countered this by developing smaller brains that required a smaller supply of blood when the neck was being held erect. It seems that our long obsession with human/reptile hybrids is where we should be looking to for the origin of lizard men and not to the stars.

There is, however, another possibility about the nature of dragons - a disquietening one. Namely that they are truly *real* creatures, not products of our minds but fully independent and living in another dimension.

The idea of other realities that co-exist with ours is not new. In the dark ages this place was called "fairyland". In the Victorian era it was known as the "astral plane". Modern writers have many names for it, John Keel calls it the "super-spectrum", Jerry Clark the "outer-edge" and F. W. Holliday the "goblin-universe". This *elsewhere* is the postulated domain of just about every monster, phantom, and weird-entity ever reported.

Perhaps this hypothetical dimension is separated from our own world by speed. We know that atoms oscillate at a certain frequency. Is it possible then, that other realities are composed of atoms that oscillate at different rates, either faster or slower than the norm? Such atoms could conceivably co-exist in the same space as the atoms in our dimension. Normally the objects made from these other atoms would be invisible to the naked eye. Perhaps these atoms can occasionally speed up/slow down for a time, and hence the things they compose become visible to us.

In Islamic lore there is a race of daemons known as djinn. This is where the western concept of the genie is derived from. Djinn were not one type of creature but came in as many kinds as there are animals in our dimension. The Koran devotes a whole chapter to them. They are said to inhabit our world, but are usually invisible to us and we to them. Sometimes the veil slips and the djinn are seen.

A Muslim friend of mine, Mohamed Bula, related several stories he had heard of djinn in India. One was seen sitting beneath a rose-bush. It grew from a tiny baby to an old man in seconds and then returned to its child form and repeated the process. Another witness reported that he had slipped through to the djinn's reality, and could see hundreds of robed figures apparently attending the funeral of one of their peers. Finally one man reported encountering a djinn on a remote beach. He saw a trail of footprints apparently stopping with no-one to make them. Looking back he saw a figure walking away in the distance and knew it was a djinn - for their feet are supposed to point backwards. This last point may seem odd but it re-occurs all over the world in many different supernatural creatures such as some of the British black dog sightings. These huge red-eyed daemon-hounds were often described as having their feet on backwards. The Brazilian *curupira* is a hairy forest spirit which is also said to possess these preposterous pads.

This slipping in and out of realities is also a common feature of Fortean events. The djinn stories are clearly indicative of this. Indian dragons are called Nagas and are seen as sprit creatures rather than flesh and blood.

Jerome Clark and D. Scott Rogo point out an interesting factor of monster sightings in their book *Earth's Secret*

Inhabitants. They note that most reported monsters resemble real animals either living or extinct.

Odd caricatures of the types of life-forms that populate the earth...these creatures represent the outcome of some evolutionary process paralleling life on this planet, but not exactly corresponding to it.

In other words, the monsters come not from some other sphere, but a parallel reality within our own.

On ancient maps, cartographers wrote "here be dragons" on areas that were still *terra incognita*. Dragons inhabited the depths of the sea and the heights of the sky. The dragon still manifests today, but perhaps its true domains are the depths of our minds, and the heights of the "super spectrum".

▲ The author with a ornamental carving of a naga, outside a temple in Thailand.

▲ Carving of the Lambton Worm at 'The Marsden Grotto', South Shields, Tyneside.

▲ Photograph taken of the 'Milford Monster' in March 2004, from 'The Shipwright Inn', Pembroke Docks, Pembrokeshire, West Wales.

Large Indopacific Crocodile - shot at the mouth of the
Howard River, Northern Territory, Australia, in 1945.

Picture courtesy of Flight Sergeant Selwyn Day

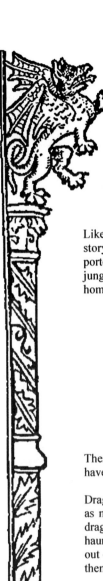

PART THREE

ENCOUNTERS WITH MODERN DRAGONS

Like nightmares come to life, dragons are not content with living only in story-books. Astounding as it may seem dragon-like creatures are still reported today from all over the globe. It is not only remote mountains and jungles that these reports come from; sometimes they are much closer to home.

- A flesh eating monster that devoured four teenaged scuba divers.

- The winged reptile that threw a US town into panic.

- An acid spitting giant worm lurking beneath the sands of the Gobi Desert.

- The dragon worship cult that practiced human sacrifice in the north-east of England well into the 20th century.

These sound like the scripts for horror films, but they were all alleged to have happened.

Dragons do not just belong in a world of castles and knights. They are just as much at home in a world of high-rises and computers. Like it or not dragons are part of the way the world is. They have always been here to haunt mankind, and they always will. When our distant descendents walk out onto new worlds I would not be surprised if they find dragons awaiting them.

CHAPTER SIX

Dragons of Land and Air

The sound of beating leather and the heat of melted stone
Rising through the sunlight is it circling our homes?

The Golden Apple *Dragon's Tale*
(from the album *Alive B-side*)

 n Sunday the 25th of June 1944, a whole townful of residents were engaged in a hunt for a giant reptile. They trampled through tangled, thorny briers, in an attempt to find the monster that had terrorised their neighbourhood for nearly three weeks. One would have been forgiven for thinking this was a group of peasants in medieval Europe, not sophisticated Americans in the middle of the 20th Century. But to them the monster - and the terror it generated - were as real as any of the dragon plagues that had terrorised their ancestors.

The story of what became known as the "peninsula python" began in a wooded valley near the Cuyahoga river, between Akron and Cleveland, Ohio. On June the 8th 1944, Farmer Clarence Mitchell saw what looked like a giant snake slithering through his cornfield. He estimated it to be some eighteen feet long, and said that it left a track as wide as automobile tyre. Similar tracks were reported two days later in fields belonging to Paul and John Salary.

A Mrs Roy Vaughn was the next to encounter the serpent. She saw the animal climb the fence to her chicken coop and consume a luckless fowl. In terror she phoned the fire department, (one wonders why not the police). By the time the bemused firefighters arrived, the monster had long departed.

At this point the media picked up the story. International news services ran stories on it that worried servicemen overseas who had relatives in the valley. Such was the excitement generated by 'The Peninsula Python', that the Columbus and Cleveland zoos both offered rewards for the snake captured alive.

Sirens were sounded on the 25th to report a sighting on Kelly Hill but the ensuing posse found nothing.

Two days later the snake reared its head again. It leapt down from the boughs of a dead willow tree in front of a Mrs Pauline Hopko. It so terrified her two milking-cows that they broke their halters in panic and fled. This puts one in mind of the stories of wyrms and dragons sucking milk from cows. Mrs Hopko's dogs cowered in terror behind her. This extreme fear is often reported in animals encountering "paranormal" entities.

The beast was also seen by Bobbie Pollard and some other local boys. Once again the Mayor's mob arrived too late and the python had departed.

The python had an uncanny ability to avoid those looking for it, perhaps something akin to the "hex" that seems to dog people trying to photograph lake monsters. The posse missed the monster again when it turned up in the back yard of Mrs Ralph Griffin. The frightened woman said it had reared up as high as a man.

The snake seemed to have a love of trees because the arboreal oddity appeared in the butternut tree of Mrs Katherine Boroutick. As she was throwing out some rubbish the giant snake came crashing down towards her. The posse later found broken branches but no snake.

Sighting continued throughout the summer and into the autumn. Residents assumed 'The Peninsula Python' would perish in winter, but no carcass was ever found - just a lasting legend of one of the strangest chapters in Ohio's history.

So was 'The Peninsula Python' merely someone's escaped pet? Today newspapers are full of humorous (and sometimes alarming) stories of exotic snakes turning up in unexpected places, from toilet bowls to car engines. However the exotic pet trade was virtually non-existent in small-town Ohio during the Second World War. Secondly, the snake was of a very large size. As far as I know the largest captive snake in Britain in recent years was a seven metre (twenty-three foot) Burmese python in the collection of Richard Blackmoore, a herpetologist from Exeter. A twenty-eight foot reticulated python called "Cassius" once resided in the now defunct Knearesborough zoo in Yorkshire. The zoo's owner, the late Adrian Nyoka provided animals for films and television shows - including Simba the world's largest lion. The current world record - recognised by the publishers of the Guinness Book of Records - is held by a Burmese python in the United States. 'Baby' is a 26.5 foot snake who weighs 403 pounds. After a meal this weight can increase to 450 pounds! Baby is on view at 'Serpent Safari - a reptile zoo situated at Gurnee Mills Mall, Gurnee, Illinois.

Massive snakes have been held in collections from time to time and are real crowd pullers. John Hagenbeck - the famous animal dealer - had a 8.5 metre (28 foot) reticulated python weighing 113.4 kg (250 lb) in his possession in 1905. A smaller but heavier snake of the same species was displayed at the Washington National Zoo. It was 7.5 metres (25 feet) long, and tipped the scales at 138.3kg (305lb). It's remains are now housed in the United States National Museum.

An eighteen foot specimen would be a prize exhibit (as shown by the local zoo's attempts to procure it). Zoo specimens this large are a rarity so the idea of 'The Peninsula Python' being an absconded pet is unlikely.

The U.S has a tradition of giant snakes. In a country where no such massive ophidians live, (the largest U.S Snake being the indigo snake, *Drymarchon corais,* that may exceptionally reach 10 feet) sightings of outsized snakes are common.

- As far back as 1833, giant snakes were reported in the US. In April of that year six people reported seeing a giant snake at Big Round Top, south of Gettysburg, Pennsylvania.

- A snake 25-35 feet long turned up in Allentown, Pennsylvania in 1870 and 1871, where it was reported to have eaten chickens and cats.

- Also in 1871, a snake measuring 39 feet 9 inches in length and 43 inches in circumference was supposedly killed near Fredonia, Kansas

- In 1875 the action shifted to Maryland, where a 15 foot snake dubbed an "anaconda" by locals was spotted. It left 15 inch wide tracks and ate pigs, a turkey, and a chicken set in a trap laid for it. The snake however escaped.

- In 1939 CCC workers in Bridgewater Massachusetts, were completing a project on King Phillip's Street at the edge of Hockomock swamp. They reported encountering a black snake as far around as a stovepipe. The creature lay coiled, then reared its spade-sized head, before disappearing into the swamp. Local legend said that the snake appeared every seven years.

Giant snakes are still reported in the area. Veteran fortean investigator John Keel was approached by a man from

Massachusetts after giving a lecture. The man recounted how he and a friend had been out hunting the previous year. They were travelling in a along a rugged dirt track surrounded by thick forest. A fox darted out in front of them swiftly followed by a huge brown and green snake as thick around as a truck tyre. Despite its fast pace the snake took several seconds to pass. The men estimated it that must have been at least 6 metres (20 feet) long. Neither felt inclined to get a closer look.

- A snake 13 feet 6 inches long was found dead behind the house of Clyde Myers near Doylestown, Ohio on May 1st 1944. It was 6 inches wide and had flattened the grass for 30 feet about it with it's thrashings. The body was put on display at a service station in Barberton before health officials buried it.

- D. A. Crane and his family were driving next to Spy Run Creek, in Fort Wayne, Indiana on June 13th when a blue-grey snake 18 feet long with a head as big as that of a bulldog slithered across the road. A local paper *The Fort Wayne Journal-Gazette* named the snake 'Pete the Python'. A hunt was organized by Sheriff Haarold Zeis but nothing turned up.

In January 1975 hikers in the northern Appalachian mountains reported seeing a twelve metre (40 foot) snake. Needless to say, the climate in the Appalachians during January is not conducive to reptiles. It may be that this creature was a member of that esoteric group of critters that inhabit what Ted Holliday called the "phantom menagerie". More than a dozen hiking parties have reported it since 1919. It is said to have its lair in old abandoned coal mines beneath Broad Top Mountain. Some researches claim to have come across the monster's trail, a trough in the earth six inches deep.

One of the most hair-raising encounters happened to Eileen Blackburn and her daughter in October 1978 near Cascade, Montana. Whilst driving in her car Eileen was reportedly attacked by what resembled a giant cobra. The nine metre (30 foot) creature had coils three feet in width. The creature apparently reared up and struck at the car. Cascade police chief Earl Damon had several other giant snake reports on file, all from the same area, but found nothing on investigation. Mrs Blackburn said:

It was between 20 and 30 feet long and its coils were at least three feet across. It covered my side of the freeway. It was standing with its head up, and it was taller than the hood of my car.

I tried to slow down and I'm sure I hit it or it struck at the car because it hit high on the left hand side of my car. It appeared to be a grey-white colour with a tan strip.

It had a flat head that came down to a point and the head was wider than the body. The body was about 6 inches in diameter at the widest point, and from the way it stood, and the shape of the head, it looked like a cobra. I've seen rattlesnakes, bull snakes and cobras and this looked like a cobra.

It is interesting to note that the world's largest cobra, the king cobra (*Ophiophagus hannah*) of south east Asia has a record length of only eighteen feet.

Willard Tollinger and his family came across a giant snake in 1946. The six metre (twenty foot) reptile lay coiled in shallow water near Flat Rock, Indiana. Pigs and other animals had been disappearing in the area all summer.

Back in June 1962, the citizens of Hazel, Kentucky were hunting a twenty-eight foot, stovepipe-thick snake that had been haunting the area. The *Madison Courier* of June 21st told how the townsfolk had enlisted the aid of a carnival snake-handler - Ernie Collins - and Murry State biologist Dr Hunter Hancock. They discovered trails indicating an ophidian of over six metres (twenty feet) in length. Squirrel nests twenty feet up trees, had also been raided. Mr Collins mused that it might be an Indian python from the description of its markings by witness Hildred Paschall. Needless to say no such animal was reported as missing.

Clifton Louviere shot a twenty-five foot snake on his pig farm near Ames, Texas on April 10th 1982. The carcass vanished overnight and Louviere realised, to his horror, that the beast had only been stunned.

In the spring of 1991 a man driving along Crenshaw Lane, off Route 25, towards Gallatin in Tennessee, saw what at first looked like a cedar-log beside the road. The log however was animate, and was curving back into the bushes. He estimated it to be six metres (twenty feet) long and eighteen to twenty inches around. It sported brown and black markings bordering on a reddish tone.

The Associated Press reported on July 21st 2000 that a monster snake was at large in Little River County, Arkansas. The creature, reported to be nine metres (thirty feet) long, was said to have eaten domestic cats and dogs. The Arkansas Wildlife Rescue and Rehabilitation Association were called in from Pulaski county to deal with the monster. Carol and Darryl Smith, who run the association planed to locate the snake's den, dig it out, and capture it alive. Carol told reporters:

It should be interesting, it could be a python, it could be a boa constrictor, it could be an anaconda. They thought it had been eating cats and small dogs. It's usually going to eat what is natural for it, rats, mice and other small animals.

I wish the Smiths luck, but as no-one has ever yet captured one of these giant snakes, I would not put money on their success.

As the creatures mentioned above could not survive the winters in the areas they inhabit, and have an uncanny knack of escaping capture a paranormal explanation would seem the most appropriate for them.

On the other side of the Atlantic, giant snakes have also put in an appearance from time to time. In the 1840s German settlers and native Russians lived close to the reed beds around the Dniester river in what is now southern Ukraine and the Crimea. They knew stories of a relatively recent date, that told of Cossacks encountering giant serpents, and of men and oxen being devoured by said beasts.

Men out in the corn fields discovered trackways made by some huge slithering animal, as wide as a corn sack. Some shepherds came upon one of these massive reptiles, and fled in terror, but not before the animal had killed one of their horses. A group of a hundred men sallied forth to hunt the beast. It was shot several times, but escaped into the trackless reed beds. It was estimated to be nine metres (thirty feet) long.

In the wilds of eastern Siberia, one of the least explored places on earth, giant snakes have raised their heads. In 1991 the Russian explorer and writer Alexander Remple interviewed a 71 year old man, Vladimir Semyonovich Kuzetsov. Kuzetsov was a seasoned hunter on the Russian taiga. Some years before the Second World War stumbled upon what seemed to be some pagan ritual being carried out by taiga nomads. He had spotted a bonfire and heard singing. He quietly approached the clearing and observed a semicircle of people around the fire, chanting songs in a language he did not understand. By the setting-sun he saw them performing incomprehensible gestures with their hands. They began to bow down. From the direction of the sunset, he perceived something huge crawling out of the forest. The shape resolved itself into a giant black snake around ten metres (thirty-three feet) long. Kuzetsov believes that he saw what looked like small front legs on the creature but cannot be sure. The people raised their voices in a guttural chant and Kuzetsov became afraid. Turning he fled madly through the trees not seeing the trail. He forgot how long he ran but his hands and face were covered with cuts when he finally stopped.

The Russian newspaper in Primorije published an account of another hunter in the late 1940s. The man went hunting in the vicinity of Khuntamy Lake. In the oakwoods of a nearby pass, he saw a ten metre (thirty-three foot) black snake lying among the branches. He shot at the monster with his rifle. It writhed about, smashing the branches with its immense strength. Scared at such a display of power, the man ran back to a nearby settlement. He returned with his sons - all armed with heavy duty rifles. The monster was gone, but it left an area of crushed foliage and smashed branches.

Whilst exploring a remote area of east Siberia, Alexander Remple, was told by natives of the Primorije region of giant snakes around the Angu River. G. E. Ribalko – a local man interviewed by Remple - saw a five metre (seventeen foot) specimen. In 1983 Alexander Vodyanin and his co-workers (also witnesses interviewed by Remple), were hay mowing when they saw a ten metre (thirty-three foot) snake. The following year a bus full of coal-miners on their way to work saw a gigantic black snake crawling across the road. At first they mistook it for a fallen log.

Swedish scientist Gunnar Olof Hylten-Cavallius published a book on giant snakes in his country in 1885. In *On the Dragon, Also Called the Lindorm* he published forty-eight verbatim accounts, half involving multiple witnesses. He writes:

In Varend (in southern Sweden) - and probably in other parts of Sweden - a species of giant snakes, called dragons or lindorms, continues to exist. Usually the Lindorm is about 10 feet long but specimens of 18 or 20 feet been observed. His body is as thick as a man's thigh; his colour is black with a yellow - flamed belly. Old specimens wear on their necks an integument of long hair or scales, frequently likened to a horse's mane. He has a flat, round or squared head, a divided tongue, and a mouth full of white, shining teeth. His eyes are large and saucer - shaped with a frightfully wild and sparkling stare. His tail is short and stubby, and the general shape of the creature is heavy and unwieldy.

He writes on the creature's hypnotic powers, its method of attacking prey, its terrifying effect on human witnesses, its hardness to kill and the foul stench of dead lindorms.

Kent cryptozoological researcher Neil Arnold, was told of a giant snake that supposedly haunted a remote quarry. A warden spoke of a massive python that resides in disused gas pipes in the pit. The monster is said to feed on the abundant rabbit population.

Ireland is famous for its lack of snakes but the monsters at large there in 1888 seemed not to have been aware of this. Pigs, sheep, and poultry were disappearing from an area of about twelve miles in diameter between Amraugh and Castleraine in County Sligo. Locals believed that the devil was taking them. Two detectives from Dublin were called in and saw livestock being taken by four and a half metre (15 foot) long dark skinned snakes. The *Dublin Freeman's Journal* ran a story that said the snakes had been turned loose by a drunken American showman in Amraugh in 1885. The animals had multiplied, and were turning up in the vicinity ever since.

Any one familiar with strange animal stories will recognise the "escaped/let loose from the travelling circus" story. This old chestnut is used all over the world as an explanation for odd animals. None of these careless establishments are ever identified and to use the "chicken and egg" analogy. It seems the animals appear first and the outlandish stories of mad show-owners spring up as a lame explanation later.

Back across the pond, dragons of a more traditional kind have also being reported from the United States. Inhabitants of the back woods in rural Arkansas, have a tradition of a six metre (twenty foot) lizard called a *gowrow*. The monster sports huge tusks and lurk in caves and under rock ledges. In 1897 William Miller, a travelling salesman claimed to have killed a specimen near the town of Marshall. He said that he had sent the body to the Smithsonian Institution. Unsurprisingly, however, there is no record of its arrival.

In the 1930s a gowrow was said to be lairing in Devil's Hole - a deep, wide mouthed cave on the estate of one J.E. Rhodes. After hearing a loud hissing coming from the cave, Rhodes bravely investigated. He was lowered via a rope for 200 feet below the cave opening, until the narrowing passage prevented further descent. The experiment was repeated using a large stone instead of Rhodes. It was lowered to the same depth as before, and a violent hissing was heard. When the rope was pulled up again, the stone was missing, and the rope had been bitten clean through.

As far as I know this creature has never been investigated by modern cryptozoologists. However, what may have been young specimens of this - or a related species - were seen in a remote valley in British Columbia. The *Vancouver Province* printed a story on May 12th 1978, about an encounter with horned lizards near Pitt Lake. Warren Scott, a woodsman, claimed that he and his wife had seen a number of five foot long lizards equipped with sharp teeth and horns. He managed to capture a small individual and preserved it in alcohol. Scott claimed to have sent the specimen to the biology department of the Simon Fraser University, Burnaby, British Columbia. Yet again, there is no record at the University of such a creature being received. With so many specimens going astray *en route* to academic establishments ,the more paranoid might believe that a cabal of disgruntled zoologists are amassing them in a warehouse somewhere, to keep the scientific *status-quo*.

Italy seems to be a Mecca for odd reptiles as well. In December 1933, a snake like animal attacked some farmers in Siracuse, Sicily. It was later hunted down and killed by peasants. The creature was eleven feet long, but its exact nature will never be known as the frightened farmers burnt the corpse.

Far stranger creatures have been reported from Italy. From the 1930s to the 1980s, creatures that seem to have absconded from medieval bestiaries have been seen roaming the country. In 1935, an eight-foot "dragon" was seen prowling the woods in Monterose north of Rome. The old man who reported it, claimed that he had seen the thing every ten to fifteen years since he was a boy. Its scaled body was green and gold.

More recently, a bigger beast has been at large. A fifteen foot long reptile was reported in 1969 near Forli, northeast of Florence. The terrified witness said: *"It was a huge scaly thing at least 15 feet long. It walked on thick legs and its breath was searing hot. I ran for my life and it followed me for a couple of hundred yards."*

In the Alpine mountains of Austria, Bavaria, and Switzerland a strange reptilian animal is occasionally reported. It is described as a cylindrical, scaly animal with a blunt head and powerful jaws. Its legs are greatly reduced and some say it sports only a front pair of limbs.

It grows to some 90 cm (three feet) in length and is greatly feared on account of its aggressive nature. It is believed to have a bite so venomous that it can kill a cow, and can even breath out poisonous gas. It is known variously as the *Tatzelwurm* (worm with feet), the *Springwurm* (jumping worm), and the *Stollerwurm* (tunnel worm). For clarity I shall stick with the former name.

In 1723 naturalist Johann Jakob Scheuchzer published his book *Itinera per Hevetiae*. In it he records the killing of a strange monster by one Jean Tinner. Who came upon the creature on Frumensburg mountain in Switzerland. The animal had a coiled, snake like body two-metres (seven-feet) long, with a black and grey colouration. It reared up its neck, revealing a cat-like head. Tinner shot and wounded it with his musket. Together with his Father, he managed to kill the monster, but sadly its remains were not retained.

Local farmers believed that the odd animal had been suckling milk from their cows. This seems like an odd habit for a reptile, but it is a theme that is often repeated in dragon lore.

The creature's existence was accepted as fact in the Alps, and it appeared in several books on Alpine natural-history and hunting along side more familiar animals. Swiss naturalist Friedrich von Tschundi was convinced of the reality of the creature, and wrote in 1861:

In the Bernese Oberland and the Jura the belief is widespread that there exists a sort of "cave worm" which is thick, 30 to 90 cm long, and has two short legs; it appears at the approach of storms after a long dry spell...

"In 1828 a peasant in the Solothurn canton found one in a dried-up marsh, and put it aside intending to take it to Professor Hugi. But in the meantime the crows ate half of it.

The skeleton was taken to the town of Solothurn, where they could not decide what it was and sent it to Heidelburg - where all trace of it was lost.

Cryptozoological evidence has a habit of going awry during transportation.

In 1903, the Austrian Privy Councillor, A. von Drasenovich, was told by a close friend of an attack by the Tatzelwurm. The man - a professional hunter - was at an altitude of 1,500 metres near Murau in Steiermark, when he encountered the beast. It resembled a grotesque worm 50 cm long by 8 cm thick, with four stubby legs. As he approached, the monster leapt at his face. He slashed at it with his knife in self-defence, but the blade could not penetrate its thick scales. The brute made six of these spectacular leaps at the man, before retreating into a crack in some rocks and disappearing.

A poacher and herdsman was hunting on Hochfilzenalm mountain in the south of Austria, when he saw a Tatzelwurm 90cm (three feet) long, as thick as a man's arm, and with two short legs, basking on some rocks. The hunter raised his rifle to shoot it, but the animal made a huge arching leap at him. At this point he took to his heels.

Three years later, two travellers in the Mur valley came upon a singular carcass. It seemed to be a partial skeleton of a huge lizard around 120 cm (four feet) long. The pair had the presence of mind to show the corpse to a local veterinary student. The student identified it as the remains of a roe deer (*Capreolus capreolus*). The finders were not convinced by his conclusions, but once again the bones went missing.

Two years later - in exactly the same spot - a young shepherd saw a giant lizard that so scared him he refused to work there for the whole summer.

In the 1930s, Dr Gerhard Venzmer and Hans Fulcher collected the evidence of 60 witnesses. All agreed that the tatzelwurm was 30 to 60 cm (one to two-feet) long, cylindrical in shape, with the tail ending abruptly. It had a large blunt head that grew directly into the body with no narrowing in the neck area. The eyes were large, and the body scaled. It hissed like a snake.

There have been sightings further south in Europe as well. Similar creatures have been reported from France. In Ossum a woman encountered one whilst picking berries in 1939. The late Roger Hutchings – a much missed member of the CFZ - heard talk of such reptiles whilst living in Provence in the mid '60s. The older people referred to the creature as "Arasas" others called it "Le Gros" (the big one). Most people claim to have seen it. Those with a rural existence such as shepherds and truffle gatherers were very familiar with it. They reported that is was seen basking close to holes or clefts in rocks. If disturbed it would quickly retreat into its lair. The descriptions fit exactly to those given by witnesses further north.

Farmers in Palermo, Sicily, reported a snake-like creature with a cat-like head and two short legs, attacking pigs in 1954. The cat's head seems at odds with other reports, but perhaps this was in reference to its large eyes. Maybe the Siracuse animal and Jean Tiller's cat-headed horror mentioned earlier were of the same species.

Strangely, there is a report of what sounds very like a Tatzelwurm from Denmark in June 1973! A strange "snake" was reported from the Ulushale forest on Mon Island. It was described as four and a half feet long, with a dark back, light underside and a "nasty" head. A description fitting our monster.

So, if it exists, what is the Tatzelwurm? There are several candidates. The ones that spring to mind most readily are the skinks. These are a group of elongated lizards. Most are tubular in shape and some resembling animated salamis! Many have greatly reduced or even vestigial limbs. One type - *Chalcides striatus* - dwells in the French maritime Alps and can reach 60 cm (two-feet). This species is, however, quite slender in build.

The largest species is the monkey tailed skink (*Corucia zebrata*) of the Soloman Islands. It can grow to around 75 cm (two and a half feet), and with is heavy scales and blunt head it resembles the Tatzelwurm in passing. Could an even larger skink with much reduced limbs exist in the Alps?

Another possibility is that the Tatzelwurm is related to the European legless lizard (*Opisaurus apodus*) - a large powerful legless lizard closely related to the well-known slow worm (*Anguis fragilis*). It can grow to almost 90 cm (four feet) long, and can inflict a mighty (but not venomous) bite. Most become hand tame in captivity, but a wild specimen will - if annoyed - hiss, rear, thrash, and savagely bite. This aggressive behaviour is reminiscent of the Tatzelwurm. The glass snake's range is south east Europe and south-west Asia. Perhaps our beast could be a stouter north European relative of the legless lizard.

The deadly venom attributed to the Tatzelwurm may very well be folkloric - much like the capabilities attributed to the salamander. But there are *genuine* venomous lizards.

The Mexican beaded lizard (*Heloderma horridum*), and the gila monster (*Heloderma suspectum*) both have a poisonous bite. The venom is painful, but not usually fatal to humans. The Alpine horror may indeed be a giant lizard with a toxic bite - probably the continent's largest reptile.

The Tatzelwurm may be something other than a reptile. An Austrian schoolmaster who came across one in 1929 whilst exploring a cave on the Tempelmauer believed it to be a giant salamander.

I started to look for the entrance to the cave. Suddenly I saw a snake like animal sprawled on the rotting foliage that covered the ground.. Its skin was almost white, not covered by scales but smooth. The head was flat and two very short feet on the fore part of the body were visible. It did not move but kept staring at me with its remarkably large eyes. I know every one of our animals at first glance and knew that I faced one that is unknown to science the Tatzelwurm. Excited, joyful, but at the same time somewhat fearful, I tried to grab the animal but I was too late. With the agility of a lizard the animal disappeared into a hole and all my efforts to find it were in vain. I am certain that it was not my imagination that let me see the animal but that I observed with a clear head.

"My" Tatzelwurm did not have large claws but short and atrophied looking feet; his length did not exceed 40 or 45 centimetres. Most probably the Tatzelwurm is a rare variety of salamander living in moist caves and only rarely coming to the light of day.

There are aquatic amphibians with only two legs. The siren (*Siren lcertina*) of the south east United States is one such creature. Others have a pallid hue, such as the blind cave dwelling olm (*Proteus anguinus*) of south-eastern Europe. Both of these animals sport feathery external gills, a feature notably lacking in the schoolmaster's description. The white skin and troglodyte existence does suggest that what this man saw was some unknown cave dwelling salamander. The large eyes are somewhat out of character. Creatures evolved for a cave existence usually have atrophied or even absent eyes. Perhaps the milky hide was due to albinism.

There is another (admittedly somewhat remote) possibility as to the Tatzelwurm's identity. This theory all hinges around a remarkable photograph taken in 1924 by a Swiss Photographer called Balkin. He was photographing scenery around the Meiringen area when he took a snap of what he thought was a rotten log. As he pressed the shutter, the stump sprang into life and revealed itself to be a large angry lizard. The alarmed man fled but later had the snap developed. It showed a blunt headed heavy scaled animal head on to the camera. A soon as I saw the picture, it immediately brought to mind the Australian lungfish (*Neoceratodus forsteri*). Of course the photo may be a fake - nothing more than a carved model. But if it is genuine, the resemblance to the lungfish is very striking.

Lungfish (*dipnoans*) are a bizarre group of fish. Their swim-bladders are modified to act as lungs that allow them to gulp air. This is a distinct advantage in times of drought. The South American and African species can also aestivate in periods of hardship. The former burrows into mud tunnels, whereas the latter builds a "cocoon" of mud about itself. There are six species; four from Africa, one from South America, and one from Australia. The latter species bares a strong resemblance to the archaic lobe-finned fish, which first crawled onto land in the late Devonian era (408 to 360 million years ago) to give rise to the amphibians.

All known lungfish are tropical, but could there be a distant relative adapted for temperate climes? An amphibious, bulky fish with a powerful bite. Hibernating in winter and inhabiting remote pools and caves. The tubular body and thick scales giving it a reptilian appearance. Perhaps this kind spends more time on land like a mudskipper (*Periophthalmus spp*), and with better-developed eyes. We will never know for sure, until someone takes up the challenge of solving this cryptozoological mystery on our doorstep.

Thousands of miles away from the Alps lives another worm-like reptilian monster, one so strange and deadly it could have slithered straight out of an episode of *Doctor Who*. It is said to lurk beneath the ancient sands of the

Gobi desert in Mongolia and is known to the desert nomads as *Allghoi khorkhoi*. This translates as 'intestine worm', due to its resemblance to a length of cow's intestine. The creature is described as 90 to 150cm (three to five feet) long, blood-red in colour, and as thick around as a man's arm. It is apparently very hard to tell the animal's head apart from its tail. In the West, this horror has been given the name "Mongolian death-worm" and with good reason. Mongolians go in great fear of the monster on account of its death-dealing capabilities. The death-worm can spit a corrosive venom that acts like acid, searing through the victim's flesh and into the veins. Those killed by the death-worm's venom, are said to turn yellow - the *Allghoi khorkhoi's* grotesque calling card. As if this were not enough, the death-worm is believed to generate a deadly electrical charge that can strike down victims from several metres away.

The death-worm first came to the attention of the West in the 1926 book *On the Trail of Ancient Man* by the legendary palaeontologist, (and real life inspiration for Indiana Jones), Prof. Roy Chapman Andrews. Andrews had led the 1922 Central Asiatic Expedition from the American Museum of Natural History. His main aim was to find fossil evidence of ancient man, but instead he found some of the most important dinosaur fossils ever discovered. These included the first dinosaur nest sites - complete with eggs - and some of the earliest fossil birds.

Before he embarked on this epic journey, Andrews met the Mongolian cabinet in order to obtain the necessary permits - Mongolia having previously been closed to outsiders. He was amazed to find no less a personage than the Mongolian Premier in attendance. The Premier had an unusual request for Andrews - to capture a death-worm should he come across one. He was even given forceps and dark glasses to protect him, (presumably from it spitting venom). Andrews commented on the death worm:

To the Mongols it seems to be what the dragon is to the Chinese.

Perhaps he is closer to the truth than he realises in this comment. He seemed, however, to doubt its existence.

This is probably an entirely mythical animal, but it may have some little basis in fact, for every northern Mongol firmly believes in it and gives essentially the same description. It is said to be about two feet long, the body shaped like a sausage, and to have no head or legs; it is so poisonous that even to touch it means instant death. It is reported to live in the most arid, sandy regions of the western Gobi. What reptile could have furnished the basis for the description is a mystery!

The monster is mentioned in Ivan Antonovich Efremov's 1958 book *The Wind's Path*. (Efremov was a palaeontologist on a Soviet expedition to Mongolia in 1946). Danzang - a geologist fluent in Mongolian - enquired about the death-worm, to an old man called Tseveng. The Mongol told him that its lair was a desolate wasteland called Khald-zan-dzakh - 80 miles to the south east of Dalandzadgad. It lurked beneath the sands, surfacing only in June and July. Upon hearing of the worm's deadly powers, Danzang thought the whole tale was a joke. The old man replied in anger:

You laugh only because you know nothing and understand nothing. The allghoi khorkhoi-it is a terrible thing!

The men were impressed by the real fear displayed by Mongols in relation to the death-worm. Efremov himself, believed the animal to be some kind of living-fossil perpetuating its line from prehistory into historic times.

Czech explorer Jaroslav Mares heard an account of just how lethal the worm can be, in 1967 whilst searching for dinosaur bones in Nemeght.

My brother - living in Oboto Chajun aimak - knew a man who encountered an allghoi khorkhoi", one herdsman told me. His name was Atlan. Once he returned with a friend from a neighbouring camp. They were riding their horses, and it was just after noon, one day in July. The sun was shining...

Suddenly Altan's friend's horse fell down. The rider stood up and went to the horse, but suddenly cried out and fell again. Atlan was five metres behind, and saw a big, fat worm slowly crawling away. Atlan stood in horror and then ran to his friend. But he was dead and so too was his horse.

The first Westerner to have embarked on organised expeditions to specifically look for the death-worm, was the Czech cryptozoologist Ivan Mackerle whom we met in chapter nine, and who believed that he had come under psychic attack from the monster. Mackerle was told the story that we read in Chapter One, and, to date, has made two treks into the hostile sands of the Gobi hunting his deadly quarry.

The first took place in June and July of 1990, and concentrated on the desert - south-west of Dlandzadgad – which was mentioned earlier. This area is so remote that not even Mongolian explorers have visited it. They used a low-tech method of attempting to attract the worms by driving a wooden log repeatedly into the ground. The worms were not impressed and did not appear.

Some interesting anecdotal evidence *was* turned up however. The expedition's interpreter, Sugi, told them of a dramatic incident from his childhood. A party of geologists had been visiting Sugi's home region. One of them was poking into the sand with an iron rod when he suddenly collapsed as if poleaxed. His colleagues rushed to his aid only to find him dead. As they examined the ground into which he had shoved, they saw the sand begin to churn violently. Out of the dune came a huge bloated death-worm.

An even more spectacular demonstration of the electrical potency of the death-worm came from no less an authority than a nature-ranger. The man, Yanzhingin Malhgalzahav (who hailed from Dalans.zadgad), told the team that in the 1960s - just north of Noylon - a single death-worm had electrocuted a whole herd of camels, when one of the luckless creatures had stepped on it.

The second outing occurred in 1992, and was based to the west of Dalanszadgad. They interviewed lamas, shamans, and nomads close to the Chinese border. They also tried to force the worms to surface using controlled detonations - a little like fishing with dynamite but less wet. Once more the worms remained elusive. Perhaps the shock-waves just frightened them deeper beneath the sands. The trip was filmed for Czech television as a documentary entitled "The Sand Monster Mystery"

Despite the stars of the show failing to put in an appearance, more information was gathered on the beast. One old woman named Puret, claimed that when on the attack, the worm rears up half its body like a cobra. A bubble of venom is formed at one end as the worm inflates itself. The bubble ultimately squirts forth at its victim. Anything struck by this noxious emission turns yellow and is corroded.

Another interesting snippet of information was that the death worm seemed to frequent areas where a plant known as the goyo (*Cynomorium songaricum*) grew. This is a cigar-shaped parasitic plant found growing on the root of the saxaul plant. Both the goyo and the saxaul are poisonous, and it has been postulated that the worm gains its venom by feeding off these plants. Oddly the venom is said to lose its potency in July.

The death worm seems to have a close relative - or perhaps a colour morph. Mongolian author Dondogijn Tsevegmid was told by a herdsman in Oemnoegov Aimak, of creatures known as *shar khorkhoi* or yellow worms:

I was riding my camel along the Tost mountains. Suddenly I spotted a long yellow animal in front of me. It looked like neither fox nor wolf....My camel started to cry out in fear, and its cry attracted others of the same creature, which began to crawl out of their holes in the ground and approach me. So I took flight with fear. When I turned my head while riding away I saw about 50 of the creatures following me. I met some nomads riding against me. They told me they were shar khorkohis, living underground. Lately they are rare.

Apart from the off-beat colour, this report is interesting for a several of reasons.

- Firstly the camel's fear of the worm - suggesting perhaps an instinctive fear of an animal, that its wild relatives once lived cheek by jowl with.
- Secondly this is the only known report of a whole group of these beasts. Some reptiles - such as garter

snakes and rattlesnakes - hibernate in huge colonies and emerge *en-masse* in the spring. It would be interesting to find out at just what time of year this encounter occurred.

- Thirdly the camel's cry seemed to attract the worms. Snakes are deaf and can only hear via vibrations carried through the ground. If the worms were attracted by the distressed animal's vocalisations then they cannot be a kind of snake, one of the major candidates for their identity.

Another colour difference was reported by A. D. Simukov, a Soviet scientist, in 1930. He wrote that the death worm was white in hue. Unfortunately Simukov died whilst being transported to the Gulag, and his archives destroyed. What more he could have told us about this elusive monster is sadly lost forever.

The death worm (or some related species) has been reported from elsewhere in the arid regions of Asia. Ivan Mackerle found reference to such an animal whilst reading a Mongolian-Kazakh dictionary. He found that in Kazakhstan, the death worm is known as *Bujenzhylan*. In addition the horrors may even range west of this area into the north of Chechnya and Dagestan in Russia. The renowned zoologist and investigator into the *almas* (the mid-Asian wild man, possibly a form of surviving Neanderthal), was told of a sand worm by the Kalmyks - a people inhabiting the Kalmykia deserts. The thing resembled a short, grey snake some 50 cm (20 inches) long by 20 cm (eight inches) in diameter. The worms possess a smooth, grey skin and are rounded at one end, and abruptly end in a short tail at the other. The oddest thing about the grey worms is that they are not supposed to possess any bones. If struck with a stick upon the back, they explode, showering slime over a metre all around. If this is a defence mechanism, it is a damn poor one, as it seems just as fatal to the worm as any would-be attacker (an inversion of the death-worm's behaviour!) Whether this desert firework is related to the death-worm is uncertain, as both are obscure by anyone's standards.

The question of the death-worm's identity is just as thorny as that of the Tatzelwurm. Some of the candidates of the former - true worms (*Annelids*) - require moist conditions in which to live. They quickly become desiccated in hot dry climates. It is far more probable that the creature is a vertebrate. A huge limbless skink would make an excellent death-worm. Many of the desert dwelling species have much reduced limbs and effectively swim through the sand like fish.

Another group of reptiles that match the worm's description even more closely are the amphisbaenas. Though they somewhat resemble primitive snakes or legless lizards they are in fact neither. Amphisbaenas form a sub-order of *squamata* - the group of reptiles that include snakes and lizards. Their exact relationship to the other sub-orders is far from clear. As the sharp-witted reader will have noticed, these queer creatures derive their name from the amphisbaena of legend - the snake with a head at each end. Indeed at first glance, it is hard to tell these animal's heads from their tails. They dwell in substrate awaiting prey (mainly invertebrates), that they detect through vibrations, being virtually blind. The head is blunt and bullet-shaped, for pushing its way through the earth. The tail is almost identical in shape. When threatened the amphisbaena will wave its tail complete with this "false head" aloft. This diverts the attacker's attention from its true head. In some species the tail can be shed allowing its owner to make an escape. Many are pink or reddish in colour and match the death-worm's description.

In colour and shape amphisbaenas are dead-ringers for our beast. The raising of the tail to enemies may explain the way the worm is said to rear up when spouting venom. But what of the venom? No known species of amphisbaenas are poisonous, but it is feasible that one could have evolved. Alternatively it has been suggested that the "venom" is in fact excrement if the creature's tail-end, rather than its head being raised. This sounds odd, but several species of animal defecate upon attackers. These include the grass snake (*Natrix natrix*) that squirts a yellowish white foul smelling excreta onto those who harass it.

The largest known amphisbaenas grow to a length of around 60 cm (two feet) - far short of some of the death worm's reported lengths. The worm's reported size and bulk would mean that if it was an amphisbaena it would be by far the largest worm lizard in the world.

Alternatively, the Gobi's most dangerous resident *could* be a snake. One group of snakes - known as sand boas

(*Eryx* spp) - fit the bill nicely as far as shape is concerned, but are totally harmless. Some unknown venomous species would surely make a better model. Some snakes - such as the spitting cobras or rinkhals - can spray their venom over two metres (seven feet). The fangs have smaller apertures than those of non-spitting cobras. The venom is forced through them like water out of a hypodermic needle. Spitting cobras aim at the eyes of their enemies, and the venom can cause blindness. All cobras have the elongated body-plan of an average snake, unlike the squat, sausage shaped death-worm. Perhaps the brute is more closely related to the Australian death adder (*Acanthophis antarcticus*). This snake is not a true adder (*Viperidae*) - as none of these snakes inhabit Australia. Rather, it is a relative of the cobras, coral snakes, and kraits (*Elapidae*). With no true adders or vipers in the picture a squat viper-like Elaphid snake evolved. This is known as convergent or parallel-evolution, where two unrelated species in different parts of the world evolve to resemble each other because they inhabit similar ecological niches. Perhaps the death worm is a spitting Elaphid that has become short and squat in shape - much like the death adder.

The most problematic aspect of the death-worm is its alleged electrical generating abilities. The only known animals that can generate electricity at voltages high enough to kill humans are fish. Several species employ electricity mainly to find and kill prey. The most infamous of these is the electric eel (*Electrophorus electricus*) of tropical South America. This is not a true eel but a colossal knife fish (*Gymnotidae*). The electric eel can discharge a shock of up to 650 volts - enough to kill a horse! The charge is generated via highly modified cells called electroplaques that are flattened and arranged in columns. There are up to 10,000 of these cells in an electric eel.

If the death worm has such a power, it would be truly unique, as this apparatus is known only in aquatic creatures. Water is an excellent conductor of electricity, whereas sand is a poor one. It is possible that the 'worm' generates electricity via friction as it slithers through the sands, and can transmit this over short distances like a living spark plug. As a zoologist I find myself wondering why any creature would evolve two such formidable and specialised weapons? This would be evolutionary overkill. Either the venom *or* the electricity should be enough to capture prey and deter any predators. One thing is sure. The answers to this most deadly of cryptozoological riddles will not be easy to come by. The Mongolian Gobi is one of the least explored, remote and inhospitable places on Earth, and the death-worm the most lethal of quarries.

In an arid area on the other side of the world from the Gobi Desert, the death-worm may have a larger and even more obscure relative. For around an hour on the afternoon of Friday 13th of July 1984 something disturbed the surface of a street in Fort Worth Texas. At six metre (20 foot) long bulge, 2 feet high, rose up and move back and forth as if alive. Charlie McCaffery of the fire department said…

It seemed almost alive. What spooked me was there wasn't even a crack in the road.

Street crews employed jackhammers to smash through two inches of asphalt and four inches of concrete. They found no indication of a gas build-up.

Shortly afterwards, the three children of Calvin Lang spotted a similar disturbance on their homestead on the outskirts of Fort Worth. On telling their father, he prodded the spreading mound with a rake. The bizarre shape disappeared beneath the ground. Looking around, Lang noticed buildings had been ripped apart, fences torn down, and trees and shrubs uprooted.

Later - and about two miles away - Jeremy Boiter reported a thing shaped like a giant tentacle erupting up from the earth in a shower of gravel and dirt. Boiter watched in horror as the thing devoured a cat and her litter. Two dogs attacked the creature, but were engulfed in its slick, dripping mouth and swallowed. Screaming, Boiter fled the three miles to the house of his friend Phil Dewar. When the pair returned to the site they found the remains of birds, rabbits and other animals amongst the rubble of a destroyed hut.

For now let us leave the shackles of earth, and examine modern reports of that most quintessential of monsters; the winged dragon.

Picture a ghostly, ethereal globe of light bobbing and flitting in the inky night sky. In the west this would doubtless be called a U.F.O, and some would even deem it to be an alien spacecraft. To the Namaqua people of Namibia, however, this light would mean something infinitely more terrifying - a latter-day dragon. The Namaqua have been reporting such creatures for decades. Their flying-snake is described as being the size of a large python, yellow in colour and speckled with brown. From its cranium two horns sprout, and a pair of bat-like wings grow from behind the head. Strangest of all, a glowing ball of light is said to shine on its forehead. This is strikingly reminiscent of the magickal pearls or jewels that were said to be embedded in the heads of Asian dragons. It would be easy to dismiss this as native folklore, but European settlers have seen them as well. In January 1942, 16 year old Michael Esteruise was tending sheep when something emerged from a cave on top of a nearby hill and launched an attack.

I heard a sound like wind blowing through a pipe, and suddenly the snake came flying through the air at me....it landed with a thud and I threw myself out of its path. The snake skidded, throwing gravel in all directions. Then it shot up in the air again, passing right over a small tree, and returned to a hill top close by.

Michael had been sent out by his father - the owner of a vast farm in Keetmanshoop - to dispel the native mumbo-jumbo that had been costing him both men and money. All of his farm workers had left after he ignored their stories of a giant flying-snake that laired in the mountains where his sheep grazed. He finally deputised his boy to show the ignorant savages the folly of such beliefs. The boy did not return. He was later found unconscious and when he came to, related his dramatic tale. Oddly he related that the snake smelt of "burned brass". Police and farmer investigated in time to see the winged serpent crawl back into its cave. Lighted sticks of dynamite were hurled in after it. After the explosions they heard a low moaning for a while, that gradually died away.

This incident was investigated by no less an authority than Dr Marjorie Courtenay-Latimer, a woman forever immortalised in the annals of cryptozoology as the discoverer of the coelacanth *(Latimeria chalumnae)* - an archaic fish believed extinct for 65 million years. She interviewed the boy who took her to the spot of the attack. She did not see the beast, but observed the great furrow that it had made in the dust. She also noticed the lack of small animals such as birds and rats.

Another witness was Michael Oarum who observed the creatures "night light".

I saw a light coming out of the mountains, and just wondered whether it could be an aeroplane or something like that, but after a couple of minutes I thought; ' but aeroplanes do have sounds. What kind of thing is this that doesn't make any sounds?' That's when I saw a big light in the clouds...It was kind of blinding me, so I turned my back on it. Shortly afterwards something told me' it's a big snake. Run for your life'. So I ran away.

Allegedly, a flying snake was filmed in a swampy region of Namibia by an expedition in 1975. The film - if it ever existed - never made it to the hands of scientists or the media.

In 1988 Professor Roy Mackal - better known for his Congo excursions - investigated fantastic claims on a remote property owned by German settlers. Locals described a massive featherless creature, with a nine metre (thirty foot) wing-span, that glided between two hills about a mile apart at dusk. The thing seemed to have lairs in crevices in the hills. Team members discovered the remains of ostrich carcasses in highly inaccessible areas, and believed that the creatures had preyed on them, before taking their kills back to the nest area. Mackal returned to the U.S.A without having spied the animal, but shortly afterwards, one of his team members got lucky. James Kosi - who had stayed on in Namibia for a while - saw the monster from a distance of around a thousand feet. He described it as a giant glider, black with white markings.

Namibia was once a German colony. In German folklore there is a creature known as 'The Lightning Snake'. This too is a flying snake with a light in its head. Did the native Namibians pick this up from the Germans? or was there a pre-existing dragon-lore in the country prior to colonial times? No one seems to know for sure, but determining the age of the native legends would be an interesting avenue of inquiry.

Whether the Germans passed this legend on or not is really irrelevant, as the idea of giant winged reptiles in Africa goes back far longer than colonial times. In 1745 the book *The Harleian Collection of Travels* quoted Mr E Lopes -

a Portuguese man who travelled in what is now Zambia, in the province of Bemba near the river Ambrize.

There are also certain other creatures which, being as big as rams, have wings like dragons, with long tails, and long chaps, and divers rows of teeth, and feed upon raw flesh. Their colour is blue and green, their skin painted like scales, and they have two feet but no more. The pagan Negroes used to worship them as gods, and at this day you may see divers of them that are kept as a marvel. And because they are very rare, the chief lords there curiously preserve them, and suffer the people to worship them, which tendeth greatly to their profits by reason of the gifts and obligations which the people offer unto them.

John Barbot, Agent-General or the Royal Company of Africa spoke of winged monsters inhabiting the coasts of South Guinea in the 1749 book *Collection of Voyages.*

Some blacks assuring me that they (i.e. snakes) were thirty feet long. They also told me there are winged serpents or dragons having a forked tail and prodigious wide mouth, full of sharp teeth, extremely mischievous to mankind, and more particularly to small children. If we may credit this account of the blacks, they are the same sort of winged serpents which some authors tell us are to be found in Abyssinia, being great enemies to elephants. Some such serpents have been seen around the river Senegal, and they are adorned and worshiped as snakes are at Wida or Fida, that is, in a most religious manner.

There is, in fact, a flying snake (*Chrysoplea ornata*). This mildly venomous snake does not fly, but glides by means of longitudinal ridges that run along each side of the belly. The snake can leap from tree tops and acts like a living ribbon, gliding for up to twenty metres (67 feet). This species only reaches around 1.5 metres in length - far short of Namibia's giant. Also the flying snake only inhabits South East Asia. Despite this, legends of flying snakes abound in Africa. The author was told, matter of factly, that flying snakes inhabited an island in a small river just outside of Mombasa in Kenya. As I was only fifteen at the time and *en route* to somewhere else, I did not have the opportunity to investigate.

Other accounts are not so vague, and far more dramatic. In his book, *In Witchbound Africa,* Frank H. Melland describes the beliefs of the Bokaonde and Kaode people of the swamps of northern Zimbabwe (Rhodesia back then in the 1920s). They told of a frightening winged beast called the *kongamato,* or overwhelmer of boats. It was said to swoop down, and overturn boats as they tried to cross rivers in the swamps. In 1911 two women were killed in a flash flood. This was said to be the work of the *kongamato.*

The natives had charms to ward the monster off. The *kongamato* - they said - had the power to cause the waters to rise, swamping the vessels. Others claimed that it actually dived into the water, and turned the boats over. Once more we can note the association of dragons with the control of water - a factor that the reader will by now be familiar with.

The charm consisted of the root of the mulendi tree, ground up and mixed with water until it becomes a paste. This is then put into a cup and carried on their canoes. When crossing a ford on foot, strips of the root are carried in a bundle. The bundle was dipped in the water should the monster appear. Some said that even to look upon the *kongamato* meant death. The horror was thought to be flesh and blood rather than a spirit, but nonetheless it was deemed both immortal and unkillable. Victims of the *kongamato* would have their little-toes and fingers eaten, together with their eyes, nose and ear lobes.

As a zoologist, I must confess that this seems like a wasteful feeding pattern for such a large creature. It is more likely that corpses believed to have been mauled by the *kongamato,* have merely been attacked by small scavenging animals. Eyes nose and ears would be among the first things to rot or be eaten in a rainforest environment.

The natives described it as a sort of bird without feathers, and possessing a beak with teeth. Melland, realising the implications, questioned them further. The kongamato had a wingspan of 2.15 metres, leathery red skin and bat-like wings. It lived in the Jiundu swamps - a 50 square mile morass of marsh, fern, tree, and creeper. When showing them a picture of a pterosaur in a book, the natives excitedly identified it as the kongamato. Melland considered that it might be a surviving *Pterodactyl* and searched for the monster without success. No native would be his guide in the feared Jinudu.

The Marquis of Chatteleux was a traveller and adventurer who circled the world several times in his wanderings. He entertained listeners to Radio Luxembourg with tales of his travels, and won fame in the 1920s in Belgium under the name of "Chalux", due to a series of articles on the Congo published in *Nation Belge*. His most widely used pseudonym however was "Stany".

In the fourth of his books, *Far From the Beaten Paths*, he relates how he heard of the *kongamato* from a British writer and traveller, (almost certainly Melland). He travelled to the Jinudu, and interviewed natives along the way. He was given much the same information as Melland, but he too found no trace of the creature itself.

In a village beyond the Congolese frontier, he spoke to an elderly native matriarch called Nzake. She was the wife of the now infirm Chief Tshipeshi, and effectively ruled in his place. She related how before sinking into alcoholism, her husband had been a great hunter. She was present when he killed the last three *kongamato* with arrows. The bodies were not saved as the creatures were so detested. The tale seems to have been an idle boast as reports continued long after the 1920s.

Colonel Charles R S Pitman mentions hearing of the animal in his book *A Game Warden Takes Stock* in 1942. He too wonders if the creature could be a *Pterodactyl*.

Melland, Stany, and Pitman where not the only ones to hear such stories. English newspaper correspondent G. Ward Price was accompanying the - soon to be - Duke of Windsor on an official trip to Rhodesia in 1925. They visited a local civil servant. A foolhardy native had braved the cursed swamps and later reappeared with a gaping wound in his chest. He was taken to the house of the civil servant and told his uncanny tale. Whilst in the swamps, he attacked by a huge bird-like creature that stabbed at him with a long, murderous beak. The civil servant (who, it seems had heard similar accounts), showed him a book on prehistoric animals. On seeing pictures of pterosaurs the native ran from the house screaming.

A similar event occurred in 1957. A native was admitted to the hospital at Fort Rosebery with a severe chest wound. When asked about its cause the man told doctors he had been attacked in the Bangweulu swamps by some kind of huge bird. He was furnished with a crayon and paper, and asked to draw his attacker. The rendition matched a pterosaur.

In 1956 engineer called J. P. F. Brown was driving just west of Lake Bangweulu. At around six p.m he decided to stop for a drink and went to fetch a thermos flask from his car boot. He saw two strange winged creatures fly directly overhead. He described them as having long narrow tails, long heads like those of a dog, with elongate muzzles, and possessing wingspans of three and a half feet. One creature opened its mouth, and Brown saw it had pointed teeth. He estimated they had an overall length of four and a half feet, beak-tip to tail-tip.

Soon after, a Mr and Mrs D. Gregor came forward, claming to have seen two and a half foot long flying-lizards in the southern part of Rhodesia, between Livingstone and Bulawayo.

Moving east, the eerie and magnificent Mount Kilimanjaro in Tanzania may play host to latter-day dragons. Professor J.L.B. Smith - the scientist who first described the coelacanth - describes beliefs in such brutes.

The descendants of a missionary who had been living near Mount Kilimanjaro, wrote from Germany giving a good deal of information about flying dragons they believed still to live in those parts. The family had repeatedly heard of them from natives, and one man had actually seen such a creature at night. I did not and do not dispute at least the possibility that some such creature may still exist.

As someone who has visited this strange mountain, I must second the good Professor's view. Kilimanjaro - an extinct volcano - literally consumes the horizon from miles away. Whilst taking tea in a mountaineer's lodge (an odd colonial building looking something like a Victorian manor house and looking anachronistic amidst the jungle wreathed lower slopes), I perceived what I at first thought was a snow storm - an impossible occurrence in the blistering tropical heat. On further investigation, I found that the "snow flakes" were in fact tiny white butterflies swarming in hundreds of thousands. If dragons can live anywhere today, Kilimanjaro must rank near top of the list.

A. Blayney Percival - in his 1928 book *A Game Ranger on Safari* - tells of identical beasts inhabiting the slopes of Mount Kenya:

The Kitiui Wakamba tell of a huge flying beast which comes down from Mount Kenya at night; they only see it against the sky, but they have seen its tracks; more they have shown these to an old white man, who told me about them, saying he could make nothing of the spoor, which betrayed two feet, and an, apparently, heavy tail.

The pterosaurs in question were a group of flying reptiles contemporary with, (but not closely related to), the dinosaurs. They are often wrongly referred to as pterodactyls whereas *Pterodactylus* was merely one type of pterosaur. Their wingspans ranged from around thirty cm (one foot) up to twelve metres (forty feet) in *Quetzalcoatlus*. Unlike bats, their wings were not braced by elongated fingers webbed with skin. In pterosaurs, only the "little" finger was elongate - the others were free for manipulation. The skin stretched down, and attached to the body or legs. The wing-membrane was strengthened via bands of cartilage running through them. Pterosaurs became extinct 65 million years ago, along with most of the other Mesozoic reptiles. The same objections to pterosaur survival can be raised as those to non-avian dinosaurs. However, consistent reports from around the globe, suggest the some kind of unknown flying creatures of considerable size do exist, even if they are not *true* pterosaurs.

Now it is time to leave the primal jungles and deserts of Africa, and cross the Atlantic to The New World, and a host of living dragons. The wild jungles of the Amazon seem a good hiding place for our winged weirdoes, and indeed such rumours have filtered out from there.

J. Harrison, a Liverpool man was navigating the Manuos tributary of the Amazon in 1947, when he and several of the hands on his boat's deck observed a flight of five huge creatures passing overhead in a V-formation.

The wingspan must have been at least twelve feet from tip to tip. They were brown in colour like brown leather, with no visible signs of feathers. The head was flat on top with a long beak and a long neck. The wings were ribbed just like those of large prehistoric birds.

By the last sentence, I presume he means pterosaurs. If so, he is wrong. As we have seen, pterosaurs did not have bat-like ribbed wings. Whatever Mr Harrison saw, they were not pterosaurs.

An Australian weekly magazine called *People*, ran a story about a close encounter between a small commuter aircraft and a giant flying-lizard over the jungles of Brazil. One of the twenty-four passengers was US anthropologist Dr George Biles who was quoted as saying:

This was a classic case of a white pterodactyl with a giant wingspan. Of course I have heard the rumours for many years that these prehistoric creatures still roamed the Amazon. But I was sceptical like everyone else. But it wasn't an aeroplane or a U.F.O flying beside us. It was a pterodactyl.

The magazine goes on to recount how the giant reptile had buzzed the plane as it was about to land forcing the pilot to veer in order to avoid collision. Maya Cabon a stewardess is quoted :

Here was this giant monster flying right next to the plane. He was only a few feet away from the window - and he looked right at me. I thought I was going to die.

So, a "classic case of a white pterodactyl"? I'm a cryptozoologist and I've not heard of any. These do not seem like the words of a scientist. He makes it sound like a common event. Are we also to believe no one on board had a camera? U.F.O.s have been photographed several times from passenger planes. This whole story sounds like a

172

tabloid fabrication.

Moving north to Central America, the island of Puerto Rico has a tradition of a dragon-like monster haunting La-guna Cartagena, a body of water on the south western edge. A resident of a community close to the lake, reported seeing a hideous creature perched on a metal fence. Four feet tall it possessed leathery, barbed wings, scales, and a horned head. The monster looked at the man before taking to the wing and flying off. The witness drew a sketch of the creature. His drawing looked remarkably like a *Pteranodon*.

Strangely it is not the trackless jungles of the neo-tropics that produce the majority of New World dragon reports but Northern Mexico and the southern United States. In 1962, Thomas Penfield wrote a book on lost mines and buried treasure hidden around the Mexican/U.S borders. South west of Tombstone, Arizona, in the Pajarito range around Nogales on the Arizona/Mexico border, one such mine was said to lie, with at least thirty tons of high grade silver ore in sacks. The treasure has never been recovered due to the dread that the Mexicans have of the range. It is said to be inhabited by flying lizards. In particular, one mountain, Cerro Ruido was particularly feared. The early mission padres, travelling from their station in Sonora to those in southern Arizona, took a short cut close to the "evil mountain". As well as the mine, a horde of treasure - hidden from the Spanish crown by Jesuits - is said to lie here. Once again we see this link between dragons and treasure!

Shortly after the First World War, two army veterans from Tucson began prospecting in the area. They found an area of dirt and rock piled up at the base of a ledge, apparently by human hand. One man travelled to Nogales for extra supplies, whilst his partner began excavation.

When the first man returned, he found his partner unconscious at the base of a tree. His clothes had been ripped and his face and arms badly scratched. Once he awoke he told a queer story to his friend. He had been excavating the site with pick and shovel, when he exposed a small opening in the rock face. He crawled through and into a tunnel. Finding his way with a carbide light, he finally came across a pile of crude rawhide sacks. He opened one and found that it was full of silver ore. On examining the whole pile of sacks he estimated there to be thirty tons. He explored further and found the tunnel ran for some 1,200 metres (four-hundred feet) and had several shafts running off either side.

The next day he climbed the canyon wall into another canyon. He followed this up until he came upon a small opening obscured by dry grass and shrubs. On entering he discovered the ruins of an ancient church surrounded by trees. It was obvious he had discovered the Jesuit mission, and that their treasure and the silver ore were one in the same.

As night was approaching he made camp by the old ruin. But as darkness fell a nameless dread crawled over him. He had a mounting feeling of impending danger. Suddenly an awful scream broke the silence and looking up the man saw its originator. It was a giant winged bat-like creature, perched on the mission's crumbling walls. Fleeing in abject terror, the man crashed through thorn bushes, and stumbled over boulders. Finally, he collapsed under a tree where his friend found him.

The first man managed to convince his partner that he had suffered a nightmare, and that his ore samples should be taken to Tucson for analysis. They split up again. The first man leaving the mountains and heading for Tucson. Unfortunately, whilst he was gone a massive storm struck and flash floods swept the entire region. The first pros-pector returned and searched for two days for his friend, before travelling to Nogales for horses and help. No trace of the second man, the mine entrance, or the church, were ever found. The riddle of the hidden treasure, the lost chapel, and its horrific guardian remained unsolved.

David Hatcher Childress - an American author - was told a modern day analogue of this story by some friends at a co-operative venture called the Atrstone Collective in Tucson. The father of one of the collective's members went out to look for an old Spanish mine in the desert south of Tucson. The had acquired an old map of the area, and were hauling a dune buggy on a trailer behind their camper-truck. Whilst sleeping one night, they awoke when something smashed their wind screen. They could find no culprit, and the desert seemed empty so they went back to sleep.

A short time later they were awakened by what sounded like the flapping of gargantuan wings. It appeared that some large winged animal was standing on the dune buggy, flapping its wings as if trying to lift the vehicle off the ground. The pair cowered in the camper as it turned its attention to them. It seemed as if it were trying to get them out of the truck. Wisely, the terrified friends stayed put, and the creature eventually flew away. In the morning they abandoned their venture and returned home.

These modern day treasure guardians are just as conscientious as their medieval ancestors!!

Tall tales you might think? But not nearly so tall as the next account, that has become one of the most contentious modern dragon stories of all. On April 26th 1890, *The Tombstone Epitaph* published a fantastic story said to have occurred in the desert between Huachua and the Whetstone mountains six days earlier. Two ranchers had been riding through the desert when they came upon a colossal monster apparently in some distress. It had leathery wings, a crocodile-like head with massive teeth, and two small legs at the front of its body. It seemed ill or injured as it was flapping wildly in vain attempts to get air borne. The men opened fire with their Winchester rifles and finally killed the beast. The then took its startling measurements. It proved to be 92 feet (over 27 metres) long and had a wingspan of 160 feet (48 metres). The men, fearing ridicule, cut of a wing tip to bring back to Tombstone.

The whole story sounds about as convincing as a *Star Trek* alien, and would be completely written off if it were not for a couple of odd sequels to the saga. In 1969, after reading about the story in a magazine, a man called Harry McClure came forward, claiming to have known both the ranchers involved. It seems that in 1910 he was living in Lordsurg New Mexico some ninety-seven miles north east of Tombstone. Both the ranchers also lived there, and were well respected citizens. McClure heard the story straight from their mouths. He wrote to *Old West Magazine* in 1970.

The men did indeed meet a dragon-like animal in the desert, but its wingspan was closer to thirty feet than 160! It had large saucer-like eyes, and a pair of horse-like hind legs. It twice became airborne in its attempts to fly away. The men shot at it with their Winchesters, but it seemed unharmed, so they wisely let it be. The *Epitaph* story therefore had a grain of massively exaggerated truth behind it.

The convoluted story doesn't end here, for there is a *third* version of the adventure. In this scenario, the creature is killed and later brought back to town. It is hung against a barn and photographed with a group of men standing with their arms outstretched to give an indication of the animal's massive wingspan. A search through the Epitaph's archives shows that it was not printed there. Many people claim to have seen the photograph, but cannot remember exactly where. Often they were engaged in looking for some other information, and disregarded the picture, not realising its importance until much later. Even more confusingly, some claim the picture shows a featherless reptilian beast, whilst others recall what looks like a giant vulture!

Renowned Fortean investigator John Keel says that more then 20 people have written to him claiming to have seen this picture. Robert Lyman, a writer, believes that the photo was published in *True Western magazine* sometime between 1940 and 1960. Ivan T. Sanderson - one of the original cryptozoologists - was given a photocopy of the picture in 1966. He described it as:

An immense bird was shown nailed to the wall of a large barn. Before it were six grown men wearing Western clothing with their arms outstretched fingertip to fingertip. By this measure the bird appeared to have a wingspan of 36 feet (11 metres).

Sanderson loaned the photocopy to two men who were travelling through north Pennsylvania researching the Indian thunderbird legends. Stupidly they lost it and it has not been seen since.

Sasquatch researcher Mark Opasnick says he came across the legendary snap whilst looking for material on Bigfoot.

While visiting Arcturus Book Service in Albany, New York in May of 1986 I was leafing through a number of old magazines in a box on the bookshelves, when I saw the infamous Thunderbird photo. I distinctly recall the creature was either pinned up or being held up against the barn by what appeared to be a group of cowboy-type individuals. However, not having an interest in Thunderbirds I failed to make note of the publication or any other pertinent data. At the time I didn't realise that it was a controversial topic since Bigfoot was my main interest then. However, later descriptions of the photograph seem to confirm that I did see the legendary Thunderbird photograph.

Another witness, and one who seems to recall a reptilian creature, is Peter F. Johnson of Boulder, Colorado.

When I was about 9 or 10 years old - 1966 or so - a group of us would ride our bikes down to our local fire station and read the 'adult' magazines in the firehouse men's room. While Police Gazette was an obvious favourite - remember those nudes with black rectangles over their eyes? - there were also copies of True, Argosy, and Saga. It was in one of these that I saw the picture of the pteranodon (?) nailed up to a huge barn door, with these bearded miner types in front. It was tinted brown or blue and was a 2-page spread with white writing, beginning an article or story obscuring some of it.

W. Ritche Benidict, a researcher from Alberta, Canada, believes he has narrowed the search down to one magazine and three years. From the descriptions of the typeset, print, layout and the ages of the witnesses he thinks the thunderbird photograph appeared in *Saga* between 1965 and 1967. If any readers come across this long defunct publication in a car boot sale, second hand bookshop, or flea market I urge you to take a look. You may solve one of cryptozoology's most vexing puzzles!

The Tombstone story and the picture, may in fact be two totally different events, that have somehow become muddled together. But there are plenty more accounts of these desert dragons on file.

David Hatcher Childress - whom we met earlier this chapter - was told a story by friends, of something that had terrorised night-watchmen at an opencast mine south of Tucson. One night the watchman, who was staying at the mine's dump, radioed his supervisor in distress. When the supervisor arrived he found the watchman shaking with terror. He refused to say what had frightened him so, but demanded to be driven away from the mine immediately. He would not stay on site any longer, and quit his job.

A replacement was soon found. This second watchman reported hearing a strange flapping sound one night, and investigated. He claimed to have seen a "gargoyle" in the desert night. It had scaly skin, a beak, and bat-like wings arched up above its shoulders. It stood perched upon a boulder. This was what had put paid to the man's predecessor.

In the mid 1970s, one of the most intense spate of modern dragon sightings reached its peak. The stage was the Rio Grande Valley, and its principle star a reptilian horror that the press dubbed "Big Bird". The area was no desolate wasteland but a cosmopolitan are of the state of Texas. Hosts of gun-toting teenagers roamed the streets hoping to cash in on the money prize on offer for the monster's capture. Ornithologists tried desperately to explain the beast away as some mundane, known species. Pelicans, herons, and owls were some of the lamer theories. Those who had seen the thing knew it was no bird of normal pedigree.

What may have been a precursor to the main event happened on December 26 1975. Joe Suarez of Raymondville tethered his goat in a coral behind his barn. During the night something killed it. The 'something' ripped open the goat's whole right side. The 'something' ate the goat's heart and lungs. The 'something' bit off the goat's snout. The 'something' left no footprints despite the pools of blood and gore splattered everywhere. Blood and gore that was still warm when the police arrived.

The first sighting seemed to occur on January 1st 1976. Eleven year old Tracey Lawson and her cousin Jackie Davies (aged fourteen), were playing in Tracy's back yard when they noticed something standing in a ploughed field some 100 yards away. Tracey retrieved some binoculars from the house and the children took a closer look. The thing stood five feet tall and had a gorilla-like face with large red eyes and a thick beak around six inches long. The head was featherless with grey skin. The wings were bunched up on thick shoulders three feet wide. It made an strange *"eeeee"* sound at one point.

The monster - that had been standing next to an irrigation canal - vanished only to swiftly reappear on the north east corner of the Lawson property, peering at them over some bushes. The children took fright and ran indoors. Tracy's parents did not believe their story, but Jackie's stepfather decided to take a look at the field in question. He was amazed at what he discovered. Three toed tracks, eight inches across and pressing down an inch and a half into the dirt. The first three were found behind the fence close to the house. The fourth was discovered twenty yards out into the field, and a fifth twenty yards beyond it.

Waldon realised there was something to the story, and contacted Mrs Lawson at work. She phoned the County Sheriff and her husband. When they were assembled, Mr Lawson pressed his own foot down next to the creature's print. The 170 pound man hardly made any impression. Whatever had made the prints was very heavy. Mr Lawson also recalled with growing unease that the previous night his dog had seemed scared for some reason, and at about ten p.m he had heard something that sounded like flapping wings, scraping across his bedroom window screen. He saw nothing, but in the morning found a large tear in the screen.

After the incident was publicised on local television, others came forward with strange stories about the night of the first of January. Sergeant Sam Esparza of the San Benito police force contacted the Lawsons. He had left his house at around ten p.m and returned an hour later. Glancing into his back-yard, he was horrified to see that the clothes out on his clothesline were darkly stained with what seemed to be blood. His wife told him that their usually ferocious Doberman had seemed frightened all night. Esparza recalled that the night before something had slammed into his trailer home.

The thing seemed to have an unhealthy interest in trailers (perhaps in search of canned food!) On January 7th something big and heavy struck the trailer of Alvercio Guajardo. He investigated immediately. Not owning a torch, he climbed into his station wagon, and turned on the headlights to illuminate - in his words - "a creature from another planet". The thing rose up from the ground and stood about four feet tall. Its bat-like wings were folded about its shoulders. It had a beak between two and four feet long, and made horrible noises from its pulsating throat. The man sat, gazing in terror at the creatures glowing red eyes, the size of silver dollars. Just as Guajardo was plucking up courage to bolt for a neighbour's house, the monster vanished into the night.

Exactly one week later, the creature attacked a human. The attack on Armando Grimaldo was described in Chapter One.

On January the 11th, Jesse Garciea and Vancacio Rodriguez saw the thing whist inspecting the stock tank on a fish ranch north of Poteet. The five foot creature was standing in the water. It took off silently and without beating its wings.

In mid January two sisters - Libby and Deany Ford - saw a big black bird as large as they were skulking near a pond near Brownsville. Upon looking through a book later, they identified it as a Pteranodon - a giant, crested pterosaur believed extinct for 65 million years.

The next sighting was not only a multiple witness sighting, but it involved three elementary school teachers. On February the 24th, Patricia Bryant, Marsha Dahlberg and David Rendon were driving to work along an isolated road south west of San Antonio. They were frightened as a huge winged animal flew low over the road, casting an enormous shadow with its wings. The trio estimated its wingspan to be over six metres (twenty feet). All said it had strange bony wings. Rendon was particularly struck by this.

...it had huge wings, but the wings were very peculiar like. It had a bony structure, you know, like when you hold a bat by the wing tips, like it has bones at the top and inbetween.

The beast was only as high as a telegraph pole and displayed a prominent breast.

Upon reaching the school, they looked through a stack of encyclopaedias until they found a match - the pteranodon.

This seemed to be the last sighting in this particular "big bird flap". Gradually, the hysteria died down, and life returned to normal.

The monster reared its crested head again in 1982. At 3.55 am on September 14th, James Thompson, an ambulance technician was driving along Highway 100, four miles east of the Texas town of Los Fresnos. He was returning from an inspection on South Padre Island. He was startled by a large bird-like creature that swooped across the road 150 feet in front of him. The creature's long tail almost struck his car, as he slammed on the brakes and pulled over.

I expected him to land like a model aeroplane. He flapped his wings to get above the grass. It had a black or greyish rough texture. It wasn't feathers. I'm quite sure it was a hide type covering. Its thin body ended with a fin stretched over eight feet; its wingspan was five to six feet. The wings had indentations on their tops and possibly their bottoms as well. At the back of the head it had a hump like a Brahama bull's. There was almost no neck at all.

Like others before him, Thompson consulted books and identified what he had seen as a pterosaur.

This case is far from unique. Every so often it seems that some bizarre creature appears terrorises a community then vanishes back to wherever it came from. Medieval records tell us that this has been happening since time immemorial. Our ancestors seemed unsatisfied with mere "disappearances", and invented heroes who slew the beast and freed the community. Thousands of miles north of Los Fresnos, and over half a century earlier in New Jersey's Pine Barrens, another such saga was played out.

The American Indians were aware that something was "wrong" with the Pine Barrens. The named one particular area, a creek near the boundary line with Philadelphia, "Popuessing" which translates as "place of the dragon". When Swedish explorers discovered the area in 1677, they found strange tracks, and called the place "Drake Kill". Drake or firedrake is another term for dragon.

The white men who settled the Pine Barrens soon encountered the thing that had left those footprints. They lost no time in christening the monstrosity "The Jersey Devil". They even came up with a story to explain the creature. In 1735 a local woman named Mrs Leeds fell pregnant for the 13th time. At the prospect of another mouth to feed, she said that the child might as well be The Devil's. As in all good fairy-tales, her rash words were punished. When the Leeds sprog was born it had a horse's head, bat's wings, cloven hooves, and a long forked tail. The screaming horror promptly exited by flying up the chimney, and has haunted the surrounding forests ever since.

The creature has been the state's official daemon since the 1930s, and the name "Jersey Devil" has become a kind of catch-all for every strange creature seen in the Pine Barrens. Sasquatch type creatures, black panthers, ghosts and even strange balls of light seen in the woods have all been called the Jersey Devil. The term is now used much like bunyip in Australia.

The original Jersey Devil seems to have been a dragon-like creature, and the main spate of 20th century reports seem to support this.

On January the 17th 1909, a police officer named Sackville was on foot patrol in the vicinity of Buckley Street, Bristol, New Jersey. It was two a.m, and he had been alerted to a constant wild barking among the local dogs. Following the trail of noise, he found himself near a bridge over the Delaware River. He saw something moving in the shadows by the towpath. The officer illuminated the gloom with his lantern, and got the shock of his life. In the glow stood a scrawny creature - humanoid but with huge bat's wings. It was hopping up and down just yards away from the man. The redoubtable officer drew his revolver, and approached the thing. It gave an eerie cry and began to hop away. Sackville gave chase, shooting at the creature with no visible effect. Suddenly it began to beat its monster wings, and rose up into the night. It flew away over the river and was lost in the darkness.

The Jersey Devil's shenanigans on this particular night were far from over. Close by, Bristol's postmaster E.W. Minster was having a sleepless night. Plagued by a bout of insomnia, he was planning to soak his head in cold water. What he saw as he rose from his bed, made him forget his sleeplessness.

As I got up I heard an eerie, almost supernatural sound from the direction of the river. I looked out upon the Delaware and saw flying diagonally across what appeared to be a large crane, but which was emitting a glow like a fire-fly.

Its head resembled that of a ram, with curled horns, and its long thick neck was thrust forward in flight. It had long thin wings and short legs, the front legs shorter than the hind. Again, it uttered its mournful and awful call- a combination of a swquark and a whistle, the beginning very high and piercing and ending very low and horse.

The busy monster then went on to frighten John McOwen of Bath Street. McOwen's house backed onto the river. He was awoken by strange sounds that he described as a cross between a factory whistle, and the scratching of a phonograph before the music begins. Peering out of his window he saw an eagle-like creature hopping along the towpath.

The creature's meanderings took it further down river to Trenton. E. P. Weedon - a Trenton City councilman - was rudely awakened by the sound of something trying to smash down his front door. Scrambling to a second story window he looked down. The intruder had gone, but it had left a series of hoofprints in the snow.

Another Trenton resident - John Hatman - saw a flying creature with huge wings circle his yard, and then fly off into the night.

The sightings continued. A group of workers at the Hilltown clay bank in Camden threw down their shovels and ran for their lives as the Jersey Devil swooped down at them.

On the 19th of January the nocturnal horror turned up on the shed roof of Mr and Mrs Nelson Evens in Gloucester City. They described it as..

...about three and a half feet high, with a head like a collie dog and a face like a horse. It had a long neck, wings about two feet long, and its back legs were like those of a crane, and it had horses hooves. It walked on its back legs and held up its two short front legs with paws on them. It didn't use its front legs all the time we were watching. My wife and I were scared, I tell you, but I managed to open the window and say 'Shoo!', and it turned around, barked at me, and flew away.

On the 21st of January, William Wasso - a track-walker on the electric railway between Clayton and Newfield - saw the Jersey Devil sniff a section of rail. The monster's long tail touched the track, and the ensuing explosion melted six metres (twenty feet) of track, and the Devil had vanished. As any scholar of dragonlore could tell you, dragons don't die easily, and sure enough this particular one lost no time in returning.

The Devil turned up in Philadelphia, just over the border with Pennsylvania. It appeared in the yard of a Mrs J. H. White, and spat a jet of flame at the unfortunate woman as she was fetching in her washing. Next evening it had returned to New Jersey and seized a pet dog.

If the dragon was immune to electricity, it seemed also to be immune to bullets. The *Philadelphia Record* describes how Theodore D. Hackett, a telephone company lineman, rescued from the clutches of the Jersey Devil shortly after the above event.

In an isolated spot in the Jersey Pines, about five miles from Pleasantville, at a place known as Beaver Pond, one of the linemen, Howard Campbell, was detailed on a piece of work a little distance from the rest of the men on duty. After walking a little way into the woods, his attention was attracted by something coming down the path to wards him. He became so frightened by the unusual appearance of the thing that he made straightway for the nearest telegraph pole. Letting out several yells for help and losing his wits entirely by the time he reached the top of the pole, Campbell threw himself out on the mass of wires between the two poles and was lying there helpless by the time the rest of the gang, including myself, had arrived

Seeing the "Terror" on the pole, I raised my gun and fired. One shot broke a wing, and it fell to the ground, uttering hideous screams; but before anyone could collect his wits the thing was up and off with long strides and a sort of hop, dragging one wing, and then disappearing into the pine thicket.

We got ropes and tackle and helped Campbell down from his precarious position. As nearly as I can describe the terror, it had the head of a horse, the wings of a bat and a tail like a rat's only longer.

No body was ever found, and the devil re-appeared again. You cannot kill a dragon with a gun. In 1930 two men from Erial saw a creature with the body of a man, a cow's head, giant bat wings and big feet. It tore the tops off trees as it flew. Two girls saw the same thing at the same spot a while later.

The most fantastical episode in the history of the Jersey Devil occurred in the early 1920s. A farmer's wife - Mrs J. H. Hopkins - had run into the devil crouching behind a barn. The creature had bounded away but left a trail of long prints in the ground. An expert from the Smithsonian Institute surfaced to announce his theory that the Jersey Devil legend was based on a surviving population of pterosaurs inhabiting the Pine Barrens.

The husband of Mrs Hopkins had formed a posse to capture the creature. The group had managed to corner the monster and took it alive. At this point a Mr Norman Jeffries of Arch Street Museum Philadelphia appeared on the scene and persuaded the men to turn the devil over to the museum. With a great media circus, Jeffries shipped the monster to his museum (being careful to conceal it). Then he opened the establishment's doors to the world with a live monster on show. Hundreds flocked to Arch Street in the hope of seeing a living legend. They were greeted by a weird bipedal, winged beast lurking behind a heavily barred cage.

In 1929 Jeffries admitted the whole affair was a huge hoax. This particular "devil" was in fact a kangaroo purchased from a dealer in Buffalo. Jeffries had attached large bronze wings to the poor marsupial and painted black stripes down its back. He turned it loose where he knew that it would be seen, then brought it back from the farmers who caught it. Displaying it at the museum, he must have made an enormous amount of money.

Elsewhere and elswhen, other airborne, reptilian monsters have been seen over America.

In a letter to the *Fredrick News* - a paper in Maryland - a man who signed himself "R.B" claimed he had seen a dragon. At 6.30 one morning in 1883, whilst standing on a hilltop, he saw a monstrous dragon with glaring eyeballs, a wide mouth, and a tongue that hung like flame from the jaws. The creature was rearing and plunging above Catocin Mountain.

In 1873 the skies over Bonham, Texas, a flying serpent manifested itself. Men working on a farm saw a yellow striped snake, the size of a telegraph pole, floating in the sky. The creature would coil itself up, then lunge forwards as if striking at something. Shortly after, the beast was seen over Fort Scott, Kansas. This may have been the same animal that western historian Mari Sandoz recorded earlier:

Back in the hard times of 1857-58 there were stories of a flying serpent that hovered over a Missouri river steamboat slowing for a landing.. In the late dusk it was like a great undulating serpent, in and out of the lowering clouds, breathing fire, it seemed, with lighted streaks along the sides.

A remarkably similar animal is described in a letter printed in *Occult Review* of December 1917, by a man who called himself a "philosophical aviator". The writer had been told of an encounter between a First World War air pilot, and a dragon. Whilst at a considerable height, the pilot had seen a dragon rapidly approaching him. He rapidly descended to avoid the colourful reptile. On reaching earth he said nothing to his colleagues for fear they would think him drunk. This account is suspect because the details are so scant. The narrator and the witness are nameless, and the location is not mentioned. The sighting may have been caused by oxygen depravation at a great height. Even so another account that is so alike to this may lay weight to the pilot's story.

Again the *Occult Review* took up the story with a letter from Georges Lajuzan-Vigneau printed in April of 1918. He claims to have seen a letter in a French newspaper in 1909 (a good year for dragons it seems). The story involved three aviators who encountered a huge bluish coloured dragon, that caught up with their plane, and kept pace with it easily. The men panicked, and began to descend, whereupon the dragon seized one of the trio, and flew away with him. A grim story but one with little evidence to back it up.

In October 2001 Stevenson Fisher of Camden, Minnesota claimed to have seen a flying monster with a twenty-four foot wingspan. The grey creature had leather wings of skin. Fisher said he could see light through them. It flew close to telegraph wires and the roof of his house. He use these to gauge the monster's size. He saw the same creature (or another of the same species) that winter.

The skies above Europe have also been filled with bizarre reptilian entities. In the April 1798 edition of the periodical *The Gentleman's Magazine* a story of a diminutive dragon appeared.

In the beginning of the month of August, 1776, a phenomenon was seen in a parish a few miles west of London, which much excited the curiosity of the few persons that were so fortunate to behold it. The strange object was of the serpent kind; its size that of the largest common snake and as well as could be discovered from so transient a view of it, resembled it by its grey, mottled skin. The head of this extraordinary animal appeared about the same size as a small woman's hand. It had a pair of short wings very forward on the body, near its head; and the length of the whole body was about two feet. Its flight was very gentle; it seemed too heavy to fly either fast or high, and its manner of flying was not in a horizontal attitude, but with its head considerably higher than the tail, so that it seemed continually labouring to ascend without ever being able to raise itself much higher than seven or eight feet from the ground.

The same publication printed a second account of a winged serpent. A reader signing him/herself "J.R" wrote in with an account that allegedly happened to a friend between Hammersmith and Hyde Park Corner on June 15th 1797 at 10.30 p.m.

The body was of a dark colour, about the thickness of the lower part of a man's arm, about two feet long.. The wings were very short, and placed near the head. The head was raised above the body. It was not seven or eight feet above the ground. Being an animal of such uncommon description, I was particular in noticing the day of the month, and likewise being the day preceding a most dreadful storm of thunder and lightning.

Again we see this link between dragons and thunderstorms. This seems to occur everywhere from South America to the Orient. A dwarf storm bringing a dragon to inner London is strange enough, but the next account is truly fantastic.

If there is any thing to the reports, as already briefly alluded to in chapter one a colony of small gaudily coloured dragons nested close to Penllyne Castle, Glamorgan, Wales, early last century and some were even shot! These incredible events were uncovered by folklorist Marie Trevelyan whilst researching her book *Folk and Folk Stories of Wales*. A detailed description of these fantastic beasts was given to her by an eyewitness who died around 1900.

The woods around Penllyne Castle, had a reputation for being frequented by winged serpents, and these were the terror of young and old alike. An aged inhabitant of Penllyne, who died a few years ago, said that in his boy hood the winged serpents were described as very beautiful. They were coiled when in repose, and "looked as if they were covered with jewels of all sorts. Some of them had crests sparkling with all the colours of the rainbow". When disturbed, they glided swiftly, "sparkling all over" to their hiding place. When angry, they "flew over people1s heads with outspread wings bright, and sometimes with eyes too, like the feathers of a peacock's tail".

He said it was "no old story invented to frighten children", but a real fact. His father and uncle had killed some of them, for they were "as bad as foxes for poultry". The old man attributed the extinction of the winged serpents to the fact that they were "terrors in farmyards and coverts.

Unlike the Jersey Devil, these creatures seem flesh and blood. Indeed many were said to have been shot. Indeed they may well have, like so many other "inconvenient" creatures which suffered extinction at mankind's brutal hand. We see this in the next account and also the association between dragons and buried treasure. This link, like the storms mentioned above seems to be widespread in dragon lore.

An old woman, whose parents in her early childhood took her to visit Penmark Place, Glamorgan, said she often heard the people talking about the ravages of the winged serpents in that neighbourhood. She described them in the same way as the man of Penllyne. There was a "king and queen" of the winged serpents, she said, in the woods around Bewper. The old people in the early days said that wherever winged serpents were seen "there was sure to be buried money or something of value" near at hand. Her grandfather told her of an encounter with a winged serpent in the woods near Porthkerry Park, not far from Penmark. He and his brother " made up their minds to catch one, and watched the whole day for the serpent to rise. Then they shot at it, and the creature fell wounded, only to rise and attack my uncle, beating him around the head with its wings" She said a fierce fight ensued between the men and the serpent, which was at last killed. She had seen its skin and feathers, but after the grandfather's death they were thrown away. The serpent was as notorious "as any fox" in the farmyards and coverts around Penmark.

It is truly frustrating that this priceless skin was discarded - it could well have been the most important zoological specimen of all time! This said, the very fact it was thrown out shows that the populace did not consider the winged serpents anything out of the ordinary. True, they were pretty, but also a pest to farmers and looked on in the same way as a fox or buzzard. It has been theorised that the serpents were some kind of tropical birds set free from captivity, but no birds that could prey on farm stock remotely resemble these Welsh wonders. Perhaps in some cellar or stock room of a museum, or in the attic of an old Welsh farm, some remains of these remarkable beasts still lie in wait for an incredulous scientific community to discover them.

If they are extinct in Wales, could they - or a related species - survive in other parts of the world? In 1947, colourful flying snakes were reported in Bulgaria. Izzet Goksu of Bursa recounted his mother's sighting of the monsters.

I used to go and fetch fresh water from the spring 200 metres from our house. One lovely summer evening, I picked up two buckets and started to walk towards the spring. After about 40 metres, I noticed what looked like branches on the path, but as I got closer I saw them moving. They were black, grey, and white, thin and one or two metres long. I stopped, thinking they might be snakes, but they were moving in a straight line ,not like snakes at all.

As I got closer, something alarmed them and they noticed me. They gave the weirdest cry I have ever heard, before taking off and flying two or three metres above the ground straight as arrows. They flew all the way to the spring about 150 metres away and disappeared behind the trees. I don't remember seeing any wings on them. Whenever I remember that cry my hair stands on end.

There's a world of difference between rural Wales in the 1800s, Bulgaria in the 1940s, and west London in 1984, but that's where our next account comes from. It is the outlandish case of what became known as the "Brentford Griffin". The case began when Kevin Chippendale was walking along Braemar road, Brentford, west London at around 5.00 p.m. He noticed a creature flying level with a block of towers, remarkably enough named 'Green Dragon Towers'! He described it as the size of a large dog, with four legs, wings, a long muzzle and a tail. Some six months later he saw the same beast at the same block of flats at the same time of the afternoon. He realised that the animal resembled the griffin on the sign of a local pub. Kevin told some colleagues, the story got to the media and the "Brentford griffin" was born.

Another witness, a psychologist (of all people!), saw the griffin whilst out jogging on the banks of the Thames.

181

Some believed that the creature was nesting on a small island in the river close by.

Andrew Collins later interviewed Kevin Chippendale. Some of the descriptions seem to point to a small dragon, rather than the eagle/lion hybrid that is a griffin. He said that it had no beak. Its skin seemed smooth and not feathery. Kevin drew the creature and produced leathery, bat-like wings with ribs rather than the traditional bird wings of a griffin. The creature seemed to have small wings in relation to its body size, and according to Kevin seemed to flap them in "slow motion." Despite this, the creature flew very swiftly, and seemed highly manoeuvrable. The slow-motion movement has turned up several times in accounts of other monsters such as Bigfoot, and may well be a pointer to its *real* nature, as we discussed in an earlier chapter.

Brentford is not the only place in Britain that seems to have been visited by flying dragons in modern times. In September 1982, a freakish animal was appearing in the skies above the Aire Valley in West Yorkshire. It was first spotted in a wooded area known as the devil's punchbowl on the 12th of September. It flew low and erratically, on large, bat-like wings and according to the anonymous witness, resembled a *Pterodactyl*. The witness was interviewed by a friend of the author and expert on the occult history of Ilkley Moor, Paul Bennett. It was also seen by a resident of nearby Eldwick, who described it as being grey with a pointed beak and short legs.

It returned on the night of the 15th, and was spotted by a man walking his dog in Pudsey. On hearing a loud scream, followed by a low groan, the man - fearing a mugging was taking place - investigated. The sounds were repeated from rooftop level, and he looked up to see a bat-winged, bird-like creature perched upon a neighbours roof and towering over the chimney pots. He said:

It was making a screaming call with its beak open, the grunt with its beak closed. It launched itself from the roof, its weight causing it to drop below roof level, before its slow wing beat carried it off into the darkness.

The witness estimated the monsters wingspan to be eight feet.

It was seen again in Yeadon, flying towards the airport. Then the sightings trailed off until June 7th of the following year. A woman living in Thackley, Bradford, saw it flying with laborious strokes down her street towards a wooded, disused railway. The massive size astonished her.

Mike Priestly, features editor on *The Telegraph & Argus* and twice 'Yorkshire Reporter of The Year', decided to track the mystery down and photograph it. His patience was rewarded when he snapped a large flying creature in the skies above Bradford. His 300mm telescopic lens was unable to get a clear picture due to the extreme distance of the subject. The thing in Priestly's photograph however is clearly a bird and not a *Pterodactyl*. Perhaps he captured a large bird of prey such as a buzzard on film.

Reports of the beast continued from Basildon, Shipley, Crossflats, Pudsey, Yeadon, and Thackley. The last recorded sighting occurred in November 1985. Journalist Malcom Hodds described a black beast with a five foot wingspan and finger like feathers.

The Yorkshire *Pterodactyl* flap was over, but on the other side of the Pennines a remarkably similar monster reared its head in 1999. Ian Wharton told the author of the strange encounters of two of his colleagues in the Parks Department working at Hesketh Park, Southport. One man, Clive Everson, approached Wharton one morning in having claimed to have just seen what looked like a *pterodactyl*. A grey skinned, bat-winged creature, with a long beak and massive wingspan, had risen up out of the bushes in front of Everson, and flown away leaving him dazed and alarmed.

A second man - Percy Whaterton - had seen two beasts answering the same description in the woods that backed onto his house. They strange creatures were badly frightening the birds in the park, and Whaterton thought that they may be nesting in the forest. To date, nothing further has been heard from this area.

Further north, winged dragons have made their presence felt. Damien Smith and his two uncles were walking one evening in the north-west Highlands of Scotland. They were in a remote part of Sutherland, and stopping in a cabin. The surrounding area was uninhabited and consisted of miles of bleak, open moorland. The nearest town was 50 kilometres away. It was 10.30 at night and the men were returning to the cabin. As they walked up the driveway they all heard a flapping sound. Their torches revealed a huge flying creature with a wingspan of between twelve and twenty feet. It had a long beak, and was grey in colour. They were certain that it was not a heron or eagle both of which they had seen many times before.

In 1996, Neil Mitchelson was camping in the Lake District, between Little Longdale and Coniston. There was a full moon, and he and his friends had a large fire burning. He noticed a shape beneath the clouds, moving left to right. As it drew closer he alerted his companions, and all ten campers watched a manta ray-shaped object, with a 35 foot wingspan flying in the night sky. They could clearly see the wings flapping.

As late as 1986 winged dragons manifested in the skies of Southern Europe. In the summer of that year, three youths - Nickolaos Sfakianakis, Nikolaos Chalkiadakis and Manolis Calaitzis - were hunting along a small river in the Asterousia Mountains in western Crete. At around 8.30 a.m, the trio were alerted by the sound of huge wings flapping. Looking up, they saw a huge creature soaring above them. They described its wings as grey and bat-like, but with protrusions akin to fingers. It possessed massive sharp talons, and a beak like a pelican's. The dragon flew away into the mountains. Upon reaching home the men consulted several books. It will come as no surprise now that they identified the monster as a *pterodactyl*.

On the other side of the world, amazing Australia has winged dragon reports too. A woman who wishes to be known only as "Penny", was out walking with her husband one night near Perth, Western Australia. It was December 1997, and the couple were between the suburbs of Heathtidge and Ocean Reef. They saw a creature with a thirty to fifty foot wingspan, and a long tail. It seemed to glide rather than fly. The skin was leathery and reddish brown. They were baffled, until they found pictures of pterosaurs in a book. Penny was scared by the encounter

Some of the latest modern winged dragons to come to the attention of the "civilized world" have filtered out in strange tales from the ill explored island of New Guinea. The *Duah* is said to be a flying reptile with a six metre (twenty foot) wingspan and a crested head. In 1995 villagers from Gum-along reported seeing a *Duah* swoop down from Mount Bel, soar over a jungle valley, and then head out to sea. The monster's underbelly was allegedly bioluminescent.

The *Duah* has a smaller relative on the island of Rambunzu, off New Guinea's east coast. It is known as the *Ropen,* and has a wingspan of around four feet. It trails a long tail terminating in a diamond-shaped fin. The *Ropen* is allegedly an aggressive beast like its African counterparts. It is attracted by the smell of decaying flesh and is said to attack funeral gatherings. Western Missionaries have observed this, and attacks on fishing boats where the *Ropen* has snatched fish from the nets. These mini-dragons are believed to roost in caves like bats.

Stories of giant winged monsters in New Guinea are nothing new. On page 76 of *Nature* Volume 13 in November 1875, there is an account of an encounter with such a beast. A Mr Smithurst - an engineer on a steamer that travelled up the then recently discovered Baxter River - saw a gigantic "bird". It was brown, with a white breast, long neck, and straight beak. The wingspan was sixteen to eighteen feet. Natives told him that it could carry off turtles, kangaroos, and dugongs.

In May of 2003, David Nardiello was working teaching English in Nigshimozu high school in the town of Watagh Shinke-Cho, Osaka, Japan. He was cycling home late one night through heavy rain. The torrent had formed a pool in some nearby rice fields. Nardiello saw a white animal emerge from the water and turn to look at him. It had a long neck and snake like head with black "shark eyes" and fangs. The body and tail were akin to a lizard whilst the four legs resembled a cat. The animal had leathery, featherless wings. It flew into the air to a height of thirty metres (100 feet), and Nardiello - increasingly scared - cycled home as fast as he could.

Later that night, he saw it flying through the night sky from his third story flat. He asked his neighbours if they had seen it but none had. Some however said they had heard weird cries from the fields for the past few nights. His co-worker Kato Sensi dubbed it *Nekohebitori* or 'cat, snake, bird'. Nardiello felt strongly that the animal was a predator and was dangerous.

Back in The New World, three boys called Jonathan, Carlos, and Diego, had a scary encounter with a winged dragon on July 23rd 2003. The boys were spending the night in Diego's grandfather's shack near San Pedro de Atacama in northern Chile. Shortly after nine pm, all the neighbourhood dogs began barking, and something started to scratch at the door of the shanty.

As their only source of light was a candle, the boys were too scared to move, and huddled beneath their blankets. After the noises ceased, the trio plucked up enough courage to investigate. To their horror, they saw a monstrous creature standing fifteen metres (fifty feet) away among some pear trees.. It was one and a half metres (five feet) tall, and had a three and a half metre (eleven foot) wingspan. Its wings were leathery and bat-like. The skin was hairless, black, and glistened. It had a beak and a crest like that of a rooster. Its huge eyes were black and glimmered. The monster beat its wings, shaking the trees around it, and rose effortlessly up into the night. As it took off, the boys noticed that it had bird-like talons.

As I was putting the finishing touches to this book an amazing discovery was made in Oxford. I believe that the story – taken from the Russian newspaper *Pravda* - is a fitting way to round off this chapter.

Are Dragons for real?

Are Dragons for real? The greatest mystery of all times can finally be fully revealed.

Up until recently, science has been rejecting the existence of dragons. Nevertheless, one of such interesting specimens preserved in alcohol has been discovered not so long ago by David Heart from Oxfordshire in his own garage.

The dragon appears to be quite cute. The creature does not fit the common description of dragons. He is only 1 meter long and judging by the present umbilical cord, the baby creature has ended up in the bottle straight from an egg or from his mother's womb. His back however is decorated with a pair of tiny wings.

The find might not reveal the "greatest mystery of all times" after all. However, it may surely reveal the methods used by scientists in previous centuries in order to discredit their competitors. The bottle discovered by Mr. Heart contains a note in old German. The note is characteristic of 1890s. Apparently, it had been stored in his garage in a metal container for all these years.

The following scenario comes to mind: "the dragon preserved in alcohol" is a mere skillful forgery made by German scientists in times of fierce competition between Germany and the UK. The find can be interpreted as a mere joke. It can also possess a rather offensive character.

As it follows from a document, at first, the little dragon has been offered to the United Kingdom's National Museum of Natural History. However, they immediately spotted the falsification and threw the poor fellow in a dumpster. David Heart's grandfather was able to preserve the can with the mysterious creature. He picked it up from trash and brought it home.

The dragon looks exceptionally realistic. It is difficult to tell whether he is real or fake. The intrigue remains. It was decided to send the find for a thorough analysis.

Mr. Mitchell, who received the can from Mr. Heart is today's proud possessor of the find. He claims, "The winged pangolin is absolutely perfect. His tiny teeth, his face, the umbilical cord, everything appears stunning. I am inclined to believe that it is a fake made from natural rubber, since Germany had been one of the world's largest manufacturers of this product at the time. It can also be made of wax. Anyone who sees it exclaims with passion: 'He is real!'"

Sadly, however, several weeks later it emerged that the whole affair had been a publicity stunt to launch a novel about dragons. I wish I'd thought of that!

However, fakes aside, whatever their true nature, we cannot ignore the fact that dragons are still being seen today. They crawl across the land, flap through the skies and swim in our lakes and seas. It is in the latter element that modern dragons are most frequently reported and its there we will be going in the next chapter.

CHAPTER SEVEN

Dragons of Rivers and Lakes

"Ride the snake, to the lake, the ancient lake, baby
The snake is long, seven miles
Ride the snake
He is old, and his skin is cold.

Jim Morrison *"The End"* (*The Doors* LP 1967)

t is only natural that we fear deep water. It is an alien environment in which even the finest divers and swimmers are out of their element. We cannot breath in it. We are slow in it. It restricts our vision. But most of all, it harbours terrifying creatures.

Ever since man developed abstract thought, he has peopled the seas and lakes of the world with monsters. Originally the dragon seems to have been an aquatic beast relating more to water than fire. Little wonder, as the seas take up most of the surface of this planet that humans arrogantly call "Earth".

Some of these ancient monsters have proven to be far more than just legend. That multi-armed bane of ships - the *Kraken* - long dismissed as Scandinavian maritime folklore began to wash ashore alive, kicking, and highly dangerous, off the coast of Newfoundland in the 1870s. It has now been graced with the scientific name *Architeuthis dux* - the giant squid. Growing to over eighteen metres (sixty feet) long, this Lovecraftian creature has eyes the size of dinner plates. A veritable monster indeed!

In 1938 a naturalist came across a large blue fish at the bottom of the catch of a South African fisherman. The specimen finally found its way into the hands of an ichthyologist. It turned out to belong to a group of fishes believed to be extinct for 65 million years - the coelacanths. This neo-coelacanth was called *Latimeria chalumnae* and remains the most celebrated case of a "prehistoric survivor".

More recently, the vasty deeps have given up creatures equally as strange. In 1976 a truly bizarre species of shark unknown to science, was accidentally scooped up in a parachute used as a sea anchor. The creature was unlike any other shark. A plankton feeder, it attracted tiny organisms into its mouth via its huge luminous lips! Unsurprisingly it was called the megamouth shark (*Megachasma pelagiso*).

As recently as 1998, scientists discovered three metre long carnivorous worms and fifteen centimetre long isopod crustaceans resembling a giant woodlouse. These were part of a community of giant invertebrates living in the Antarctic seas. What else is down there?

We shall begin our hunt for aquatic dragons not in the deep oceans, but in fresh water, and what better place to start than at Loch Ness?

Gouged out by glaciers in the ice age, Loch Ness runs like a livid scar across the Great Glen of Scotland. Twenty three miles long, a mile wide, and over 800 feet deep, the loch is a fitting abode for a dragon. It is said that the entire population of the world - every man, woman, and child - could fit into the loch three times over, and *still* there would be room for more. The waters are stained inky black by masses of peat washed down from the surrounding hills. This reduces underwater visibility to only a few feet. The cool temperature (42 degrees centigrade), and treacherous undercurrents, add to the loch's dark reputation.

Legends of something odd in the waters date back to at least 565 AD when the oft-repeated story of Saint Columba was said to have occurred. The Irish saint was in Scotland converting the Picts to Christianity, when he met a water monster said to have bitten a man to death in the River Ness (not the loch). He overcame the brute with his holy powers and since then, according to legend, it has been harmless.

In medieval times the creatures were known as water horses or *kelpies*, and were believed to drag down and devour humans. It seems that Saint Columba had as little luck in exorcising the monster as Donald Ormand did centuries later. Many locals saw some massive creature in the waters over the years, but few reports travelled far. All this aside, the monster did not achieve true fame in the outside world until 1933 - shortly after a lochside road had been built, making the remote area more accessible. A young couple - called the Mackays - were motoring along the northern shore, when they saw a churning of the water, and observed the two humped back of a huge animal disporting itself in the water. Shortly afterwards, the *Inverness Courier* dubbed it a monster, and the phrase "Loch Ness Monster" was born.

From then until now the monster has had more written about it than any other mystery creature. Enough volumes to fill a library have been penned on the subject, and the Loch Ness Monster is now surely the most famous monster in the world. An identikit picture from witness descriptions creates a large bodied animal with a long neck terminating in a small head. A somewhat shorter tail, and four turtle-like flippers. The average length seems to be nine to twelve metres (thirty to forty feet), and the colour an "elephant" grey. I will not spend time and space repeating sightings that have been discussed *ad-nauseam* elsewhere although there are several eyewitness accounts in other chapters of this book. Instead I will briefly discuss some of the evidence gathered for the creature's existence.

With the loch being such a tourist attraction, and hordes of camera-wielding holidaymakers thronging to its banks each year, it is no wonder that most of our evidence takes the form of still photography. If anything, it is surprising that there are not more photos of the creature. Sadly, none can be seen as conclusive proof of the monster's existence.

The first photograph of the monster was snapped on November 12th 1933 by Hugh Grey, a worker at the British Aluminium Company at Foyers. At the time he was walking along a natural promontory built up by the Foyers river and looking down at the loch from about nine metres (thirty feet) above. About ninety metres (300 feet) out, the still waters were broken by a huge animal thrashing up large amounts of foam. Grey saw a rounded back and lashing tail. Grey estimated the creature to be twelve metres (forty feet) long. He snapped five shots before the animal disappeared.

Only one of the photographs came out and was subsequently published in the *Daily Record* and the *Daily Mail*. The negative was examined at the *Daily Record* office by M. C. Howard of Kodak and C.L. Clark of *Kodak* magazine. No faults or tampering could be found.

The picture itself is blurry and appears to show a serpentine animal thrashing on the surface of the loch. No head or neck seem to be visible. Some have likened it to a dog swimming towards the camera with a stick in its mouth. This is almost certainly simulacra; the human mind assembling random shapes and objects into a form that we know such as seeing "faces" in rock formations. There is no indication of size. The picture remains a fuzzy enigma.

The second photograph purporting to be the creature is without doubt the most famous image ever to be associated with Loch Ness. Indeed in the mind of the public this is *the* picture of the monster. It was shot on April 1st (yes!) by a London surgeon R. K. Wilson F.R.C.S.

Wilson was on holiday, and had been driving all night. He parked his car two to three miles from Invermoriston at an elevation of some thirty metres (100 feet) above the surface of the loch. Noticing a disturbance some 180 metres (600 feet) from shore he retrieved his camera - a quarterplate with telephoto lens - from the car.

Wilson observed a head and neck emerge from the water and reeled off four shots before the object sank from sight. He had the pictures developed immediately by a pharmacist in Inverness. One showed what has become the classic head and neck shot against a vista of water. The other apparently shows the animal submerging.

The two decent photos and their negatives were obtained by the *Daily Mail.* They were subsequently examined by the Linnaean Society in London. Most students of the phenomena were convinced that these pictures showed the head and neck of the Loch Ness Monster, but there were some problems. Wilson said that he believed the head to have been held some four feet above the water. Looking at the wave formations around the object it would seem to be much smaller. I must confess that I always believed this picture to show some kind of water bird like a grebe, but a genuine mistake on the part of Wilson.

However, on the 13th of March 1993, the story exploded in the faces of cryptozoologists everywhere.

Two researchers - David Martin and Alastair Boyd - claimed that they had discovered the whole story was a hoax. The hoax itself was a complex web. The pair claimed to have interviewed Christian Spurling before his death in November 1992. Spurling was the step-son of film producer and big game hunter Marmaduke Weatherall.

Shortly after the Loch Ness Monster had grabbed Fleet Street's attention in the early 1930s, Weatherall had been called in by the *Daily Mail* to hunt the beast. Weatherall was also a fellow of the Royal Geographical Society and the Zoological Society of London. Soon Weatherall's investigations bore fruit as he discovered large tracks on the lochside.

The 21st December edition of the *Daily Mail* ran the dramatic headline: *"Monster of Loch Ness is not a legend but a Fact"* Weatherall is quoted:

It is a four-fingered beast and it has feet or pads about eight inches across. I should judge it to be a very powerful soft-footed animal about 20 feet long. The spoor I have found clearly shows the undulations of the pads and the outlines of the claws and nails...

I am convinced that it can breath like a hippopotamus or crocodile with just one nostril out of the water. The spoor I found was only a few hours old, clearly demonstrating that the animal is in the neighbourhood where I expected to find it.

A subsequent examination of the tracks by Dr W. T. Calman and M.C.A Hinton of the Natural History Museum showed that the tracks were all made by *one* foot, the right hind foot of a stuffed hippopotamus, probably an umbrella stand! The great white hunter had been duped.

According to Spurling, Wetherall was out for revenge, and asked *him* to produce a monster picture. Spurling created his monster by moulding a head and neck with plastic wood onto a clockwork submarine. Wilson was a respectable front man for the whole scam. The conspirators were overwhelmed by the stir the pictures created, and decided to keep quiet, until Spurling's death bed confession.

Now there are counterclaims that purport the hoax to be a hoax itself! Suspicious of "death bed " confessions, some think that Wilson's story was on the level after all. Either way the 'surgeon's photo' has been tainted, and is now useless as a piece of evidence.

The picture allegedly taken by a woman tourist on June 10th 1934 and published in the *Scottish Daily Express* is said to show a low hump on the Loch's surface. I have never seen this photograph published anywhere, and little data on it. Therefore it remains inconclusive.

Sir Edward Mountain mounted an expedition to the Loch in 1934. Twenty one pictures were taken on the trip. All except one have been identified as waveforms. The remaining shot shows what appears to be a hump some twelve feet long and 300 feet from the shore. It seems to be throwing up spray. The shot is not clear enough for proper identification.

1934 was a prolific year in monster photography. Yet another shot was taken on August 24th by F.C Adams. The picture shows the back of an animal, and a projecting fin. Some have suggested that this may be a flipper of one of the Loch Ness animals as it rolls to one side on the surface. In fact it's morphology closely resembles the dorsal fin of a cetacean. I believe that this picture shows a dolphin or porpoise that has strayed into the Loch. This has been recorded on several occasions.

On July 14th 1951 Lachlan Stuart, a woodsman who lived in a croft cottage 90 feet above the southern side of the Loch, had risen early to milk his cow. He noticed what he at first thought to be a motor boat out on the water. As it approached he saw it was three humps. Each was some five feet long at the water line. The first protruded two feet from the water, the second four feet, and the third three feet. The humps were separated by about eight feet each. In front of these was a sheep-like head on a six foot neck. He shouted to three others, including his wife and retrieved a box camera from the cottage.

Lachlan managed to take one picture, before the object turned about and swam to the centre of the Loch submerging as it went.

The picture shows three dark triangular humps on the surface with the north shore in the background. Constance Whyte, author of *More than a Legend* - the first book on the Loch Ness Monster - saw the picture that afternoon after it had been developed by John MacPherson of Drumcharrel. She believed it genuine. Lachlan was interviewed two months later by Dr. Maurice Burton, another Loch Ness pioneer. Burton too concluded the photograph to be genuine. It seemed that so far this was the most impressive picture and it would be if that was what had *really* happened.

A couple of weeks later Lachlan took a friend down to a beach near his abode and showed him the monster; - several bales of hay and some tarpaulin. It had been a joke that got out of hand with the press, and authors of Loch Ness books. He made his friend promise to keep silent about the affair, which he did until 1974, when he confessed to Nicholas Witchell in his book *The Loch Ness Story*.

The next snapshot of the monster provides us with a puzzle almost as perplexing as that of the monster itself. Peter A. McNab - an Ayrshire councillor - photographed the monster off Urquhart Castle on July 29th 1955. Standing on the road above the castle, he saw a movement in the water, and took a shot with an Exacta127 camera. Within seconds he took a second snap with a Kodak fixed focus camera.

The original negative was printed in Constance Whyte's 1957 book *More than a Legend*. The same negative was loaned by McNab to cryptozoologist Roy Mackal, who noticed several important differences from the Whyte version. These included trees in the foreground, and a greater expanse of visible shore near the castle on the Whyte picture. These things were missing on Mackal's copy.

McNab countered that there may have been confusion after such a length of time (Mackal was writing in 1976) and that he sent off the negative of the second shot. But here we encounter problems as well. McNab said that the 50-foot animal he photographed was moving at around fourteen miles per hour. He also stated that it took two seconds to change cameras for the second shot. In that time the monster should have moved 30 feet. In fact it is in the same position in both pictures. The supposedly undulating humps look static. Many now believe the photos are fakes, the humps being superimposed over a boat.

Equally as controversial is the Peter O'Connor picture allegedly taken on 27th May 1960. O'Connor, a 26 year old fireman from Gateshead, had been camping by the loch near Foyers. He awoke needing to relieve himself in the small hours, and walked around 100 metres (300 feet), from his camp. He then saw the monster swimming round a headland. The creature was some twenty five metres (75 feet) away from him. The visible part of the monster consisted of small sheep like head on a ten foot (three metre) neck and a sixteen foot (five metre) body. A three and a half foot (one metre) expanse of water lay between the neck and body. The creature was greyish black. Wading waist deep into the loch, O'Connor took a picture with a flash before shouting to his companion. He took a second shot without a flash. The second shot did not come out. His companion arrived in time to see the beast submerge.

There are a number of problems encountered when trying to square O'Connor's story with his picture. The angle and lighting on the creature visible in the picture suggest that it was taken from a height of twelve feet rather than waist high in the loch. The size and clarity of the image is also incompatible at the range of twenty-five yards with O'Connor's camera (a Brownie flash 20).

O'Connor never made the negative available for scrutiny and his past antics throw a dim pall of the picture. Previously he had gathered sixty volunteers from the Northern Naturalists Society for an expedition that intended to destroy the monster with Bren guns and a bomb. Luckily for all involved, this stupid idea did not see fruit. O'Connor went on to claim that his organization had named the photo *Nessiesaurus O'Connori.*

Most people believe O'Connor faked the shot with plastic bags and sticks. I am inclined to agree.

A greater contrast between the last photographer and the next could hardly be asked for. Dr Maurice Burton was deputy keeper of zoology at the British Museum (Natural History). In June 1960 he led an expedition to the loch. On the 22nd Burton and his family observed a series of transverse ripples appearing some half a mile from their vantage point. The ripples formed a V shape in the water and began to move towards them. Some of the ripples were out of line, and Burton interpreted this as a long neck moving from side to side in the water.

A small, dark, oval object broke the surface, and travelled at some eleven miles per hour. This later submerged, and was replaced by two small humps. These objects were surrounded by concentric ripples. Burton photographed the phenomenon. The shots were later analysed, and showed that something was indeed swimming just below the surface. The transverse ripples were caused by its nearness to the surface. The ripples could also have been produced by something swimming at a regular rate but raising and lowering a small head on a long neck. Burton claimed that the object could not have been an otter due to the speed and style of its swimming. However he later recanted (under pressure from his paymasters at the museum?), and said that he had photographed an otter.

The next shot is interesting in so much as it was independently witnessed by four people (excluding the photographer and his family). R H Lowrie and his brood were aboard the forty foot motor yacht *Finola* at around 4.15 pm on August the 7th 1960. They saw a strange shape rise up about four or five metres (twelve – fifteen feet) astern. At first they thought it was a couple of ducks, but it soon became apparent that this was something more substantial. They changed course in order to avoid a collision, and observed a greeny brown neck breaking the surface, and then sinking again. The whole creature seemed to be about the same length as their yacht. It swung away towards Aldourie Point, and they snapped some shots of the beast. The pictures show something very substantial making a large wake. It is strikingly akin to the film taken by Richard Raynor in 1967.

As this was occurring Torquill McLeod, his wife and an Australian couple, Mr and Mrs Seddon-Smith were watching with binoculars from the bank. They observed rhythmic splashes of something moving at about 8-10 knots.

On August the 8th 1972, the first underwater photograph of what may have been the Loch Ness monster was taken. Dr Robert Rines, - of the Academy of Applied Sciences in Boston, working with the Loch Ness Investigation Bureau - set up underwater cameras whereby sonar contact with large moving objects would set off the strobe camera taking pictures every fifty-five seconds whilst the target remained in range. The set-up was deployed off Temple Pier in Urquhart bay. The result was an underwater photograph of a large flipper like object. Diamond in shape, it has been estimated to be between five and eight feet long. H. Lyman of the New England Aquarium, stated that it did not look mammalian and did not conform to any known species.

The important thing in this case is that an object was detected by the sonar and photographed by the camera. Two machines independently recorded an anomaly in the Loch at the same time. Machines do not care if the Loch Ness Monster exists or not. They have no agenda, they just record.

The team returned to the Loch in 1975 and produced more photographs. One shows what appears to be the front half of a long necked animal with a much thicker body. Two appendages, possibly flippers, are visible. The neck has been estimated to be seven feet long. This photo has never been adequately explained and may well show one of the Loch Ness animals.

The other photograph has been dubbed "the gargoyle head". Some say it shows a close up of the creature's face. It appears almost spherical with horn like projections. Most people nowadays believe this shot is of a decayed tree stump. Scuba diver and Loch Ness investigator Dick Raynor dredged up a stump that looks remarkably like the image in the photo during Operation Deepscan in 1987.

On the 18th of July 1975 Alan Wilkins, a school teacher from Annan, and his son Ian, saw and photographed something in the Loch. Beginning as a black line, the object revealed itself as a bulky mass causing a disturbance in the water. It then moved at a leisurely pace across the Loch. The pictures were sent to a laboratory in the Pasadena, California for development. They show a distant, dark hump protruding from the water. Other holidaymakers in the caravan next to Mr Wilkins said that they saw the creature as well.

1977 saw the famous colour shots of the creature's head and neck taken by Tony "Doc" Sheils. We had dealt with these remarkable images in the "esoteric theories" chapter. Though no tomfoolery could be found with the photos, the negatives have vanished, and "Doc" is a self-confessed trickster. Some think that they are double exposures or superimpositions. Others think that the pictures are close ups of a very life-like painting done by a highly competent artist; someone like Doc himself.

The story had a baffling sequel. In September 1983 an anonymous woman took a photo of the head and neck of the monster near Achnahannet. The image is startlingly like Doc's photo. If it is on the level then it shows the same species. It could be argued that Doc faked this second images to bolster up his first picture. Anonymous witnesses must always be treated with suspicion. But the flip-side to this argument is that the 1983 photo looks like the Sheils picture because it is indeed the same creature. We may never know.

In 1982 Jennifer Bruce took a photo of the Loch from Urquhart Bay. At the time she saw nothing unusual, but when the photos were developed the shot of the bay showed what appeared to be a snake-like head and neck in an S-shaped curve. The object was dark above and lighter below. Analysis of the picture in 1987 showed water ripples visible through the object suggesting that it was two dimensional. It may have been a camera fault, or more likely a sea bird flying past that was caught in the shot. The motion of the wings may have blurred making the water behind it visible as the camera's shutter was not fast enough to catch a static image.

In June of 1986 Alan Greig was walking around the Loch at 4.12 am. He saw an animal over six metres (twenty foot) long, surface about 150 metres (450 feet) from the shore. Despite being badly shaken, he took a snap of the creature before it submerged. The resulting picture was blurry even by Nessie standards. Little can be made out except water, a background of hills and an upright object in the water. The head and neck of the monster? Sadly the picture quality is far too poor to say.

In August 1992 the *Daily Mail* reproduced one of three photographs purporting to be the monster. They were taken by an anonymous man who claimed to have seen a six foot long head and neck at 6.30-7 a.m. The animal opened its mouth and slid underwater only to reappear 200 metres away. The picture looks like a very crude fake. It resembles nothing so much as an image of a loon or some other member of the grebe family superimposed onto the background. The *Daily Mail* claimed to have had the pictures examined by Kodak and The RAF's photographic laboratory.

A Flight Lieutenant, Caroline Smith, said *"We would say they would not have been tampered with or touched up."*

Kodak scientist Roger Flint said *"It is a genuine photograph of something, though we have no comment about the image."* Very bloody useful, I'm sure.

The *Daily Mail* picture desk later admitted that the neck had been enhanced for publication. This taints all subsequent pictures reproduced in that newspaper. I stand by my comments. I believe this is a fake using the image of a waterbird.

On June 17th 1993 Edna MacInnes and her boyfriend David Mackay saw a 7.5 metre (25 foot) animal with a giraffe-like neck. It was dark brown in colour and sent a great wash inshore as it swam. The couple had no camera and the beast submerged. The pair went to a relative's house to borrow a camera and returned. Forty minutes after the initial sighting they saw the creature again some 200 metres from the shore. They began taking pictures but sadly the results were less than impressive. A white wake is visible but the creature itself is not.

 School teacher Austin Hepburn snapped a solid black object making a large wake. It was 4 pm on Sunday August 11th 1996 .The object was about three-quarters of a mile away and moving up the Loch towards the town of Dores. A boat is visible in the back ground giving scale and showing the impressive size of the wake. Hepburn noticed a camper-van of tourists pointing at the object.

A week later, fisherman Frank Wilson, was fishing with his two sons and his friend - Willie McLean. The group was alerted to a whooshing sound and looked up to see a twelve metre (forty foot) creature ploughing through the water. Wilson said it bore two grey-black humps and resembled a giant snake. As he began to photograph the creature it seemed to be on a collision course with a boy in a dinghy. Then it submerged showing a huge fin. The pictures show a white wake with what appears to be two low-lying protrusions.

On the 21st of March 1997 Richard White, a pet-food salesman, was driving along the Lochside towards Foyers. It was 11.30 in the morning when he saw something disturbing the water halfway across the Loch from Urquhart Castle at a distance of about 200 metres. Stopping his car for a closer look, he took a small Olympus camera from his glove-compartment and took ten photographs in quick succession. The object dived then re-emerged as a series of humps. Unfortunately he was out of film by then.

The combination of distance and small camera makes identification of the object in the resulting pictures hard. The negatives were passed on to NASA, but the results - to my knowledge - have never been published.

In 1998, Chris Rivett and his girlfriend Melissa Bavister, stopped in a lay-by beside the Loch when they saw something rise up from the waters. Melissa - a veterinary nurse - took a photograph of two black objects with her £30 Kodak camera..

The picture was examined by Jim Cordiner, senior lecturer in photography at Glasgow's School of Building and Printing. He had the following to say:

This was certainly one of the most interesting monster photographs I have ever seen. Objects planted to look like humps are almost impossible to fake in deep water. A boat would not appear so dense in the photo. The outline of the object is too defined for it to be a wave or a trick of the light. There is no shadow or reflection that could result in this shape in on the water.

On June 20th of the same year a Canadian man named Gavin Joth may have seen the beast, whilst still in Canada! A now sadly defunct webcam had been set up beside the Loch for 24/7 surveillance. Gavin usually logged onto the cam site in his lunch-break. On this particular occasion he saw something odd:

I was carrying out my usual watch on Nessiecam when I saw a dark, oval head moving across the water away from the camera. It was larger than a human head but much smaller than a boat and at one point raised out of the water to reveal what I think was a stocky neck.

193

The film was examined by John Kirk, president of the British Columbia Scientific Cryptozoology Club. Kirk himself has seen the legendary Canadian lake monster 'Ogopogo' several times. But more of that later. Kirk said: *We have been studying Loch Ness pictures for twenty years now and these are the best in a long time. All the usual explanations such as seals and boats were discounted.*

It should be noted that the equally well-respected researcher Dick Raynor has said he thinks the image shows a diminutive boat.

In 2000 James Grey was fishing from a rowing boat in the Loch. Something caught his eye, and he looked up to see a black object protruding from the water. He took two photographs as it fell back into the Loch. One shows an upright, neck-like shape with what appears to be a distinct head. The second shot shows the same shape falling down to the surface. A third shows it lying flat in the water. On close examination the objects seems exactly the same shape in each shot. Only the angle has changed. This suggests that the object in the photograph is inanimate. It is likely to be a piece of debris such as a branch or log. Some have even likened it to the bumper from a Morris Minor! The pictures were shown on the front page of the *Daily Mail*. We cannot ignore the smear left on this publication by the dubious 1993 photographs.

Roy Johnson from Loughton in Essex was holidaying in the Highlands in August 2002. On the 7th he drew his car into a layby near Inchnacardoch, on the A82 over looking the Loch. Shortly before 9 am he saw a long neck like object rise several metres out of the water. The neck then splashed gracefully back into the water. Johnson took four snaps. One shows a thin neck with a snaky head yellowish brown in colour. The second shows it arching down into the water. A third shows it lying flat. And the final picture is a large splash of water as it submerges. Johnson said that he thought it was an eel until he realized that it was too big. In fact he may actually have been right in his first, assessment as we shall see later.

On close inspection there appears to be a light outline around the objects in the Johnson pictures. Some have suggested that these are superimpositions. Once again they appeared in that trustworthy stalwart of Grubb Street; the *Daily Mail*. Draw your own conclusions.

None of these photographs can prove the existence of a large unknown animal in Loch Ness. The best, as pieces of evidence, are the Rines underwater pictures of 1972 and 1975, mainly because of the corroborative evidence of two machines independently recording something. Moving pictures are another matter and are less easy to fake or be mistaken about. Let us examine some of the cine-film and video footage taken at Loch Ness.

The first sequence of film alleged to be of the monster is almost as much a mystery as the monster itself. It was supposedly taken in the mid 1930s by a Dr Farquar McRae - a Bachelor of Medicine and a Master of Surgery born in 1855. The film is said to show the monster at a range of 300 feet. It is over three metres (ten feet) long. The head is conical, with two horn-like appendages and slit eyes. The neck has a stiff - but flexible - bristly mane running along it. The beast rolled over in the water showing a flipper.

The Doctor took a second sequence of film at nearby Loch Duich showing a similar creature rubbing its neck over some seaweed.

The good Doctor was apparently worried about being taken seriously, and placed the films in a London bank vault until in his own words *"mankind took the subject of the Loch Ness Monster more seriously."* He showed the films to only three other people; his trustees Colonel Sir Donald Cameron, Alistair Dallas, and an un-named third person. The Doctor and the two known trustees are now dead. Researchers Mike Dash and Paul Harrison have tried to track these sequences down. On the 21st May 1998 they interviewed Alistair Dallas junior - son of one of the trustees. The interview raised more questions than it answered. Dallas Jr. had never seen the film, though he had heard of it. He said that it was family knowledge that Dr McRae did not know exactly where the films were kept. He had no idea who the third trustee had been, but heard that he was dead.

If the films are indeed being kept in a vault, then someone must be paying for it. The known trustees are dead. If the third trustee is alive then he must be very old. Moreover, one would have thought that in the day of high tech searches for the monster involving respected scientists, he would have released the films. Checks on the records of banks in the 1930s reveal no record of such an item being kept in any vault. It seems that the McRae films may have less chance of existing than the monster.

Just as frustratingly, some early films, known positively to have existed, have been lost.

Malcolm Irving, Stanley Clinton, and Scott Hay filmed something on December 12, 1933. The film, taken near Inverfarigaig at a distance of 300 feet shows an elongated, dark, object approximately five metres long. It lay still initially then more of its body protruded causing some spray. The object then swam off out of camera range.

The two-minute sequence was taken on 16 mm film. We know it existed because it was shown to the Linnaean Society. Their consensus was that it showed a living animal. However, the film has since been lost, though a pair of drawings based on stills have been published in Dr. Maurice Burton's book *The Elusive Monster*. These show a log-like object lying low in the water. The second sketch shows spray at one end.

As noted above, in July 1934 Sir Edward Mountain employed twenty men and posted them at various sites around the Loch, setting them to watch between 9 am and 6 pm five days a week for five weeks. The outcome was disappointing with the few photos taken now being almost universally identified as boat-wakes. However, the man put in direct command of the expedition, was Captain James Fraiser. Later that year he filmed something himself. On September 15th just outside Urquhart Bay, he filmed what he described as looking like an upturned boat fifteen feet long. He was using a 16 mm Kodak cine camera, with a six inch telephoto lens. The distance of the object was about three quarters of a mile.

It was again put before the Linnaean Society who said it resembled a whale. This film too has now been lost.

In 1936 Malcolm Irving took his second sequence of film. Taken on 22nd September at 3.30 pm it showed a long, dark, irregular, nine metre object moving fast through the water, and causing much foam and turbulence. Its speed was put at around thirty knots (34 miles per hour). This film was lost for sixty-five years, until it dramatically re-surfaced in 2001.

Janet McBain, curator of the Scottish Screen Archive found it in a rusty tin - one of 20,000 passed on to them by the former Scottish Film Council. I have viewed the film and was impressed. It shows an animate object of considerable size and power ploughing fast through the water. The creature appears to be just below the surface but two portions of the body breech. It puts one in mind of a basking shark *sans* the large dorsal and tail fins. All in all it is a convincing piece of film. One can only hope that the other lost films will be rediscovered in this manner.

G. E. Taylor was a South African man touring the Highlands in May 1938. Whilst opposite Foyers, he noticed a dark hump six feet long and tapering to a neck that it raised periodically. It was some 900 feet from shore. Taylor shot some three minutes of 16 mm colour film in two segments. The first was 1000 frames, the second 1500 frames. Taylor filmed the first sequence then moved on. He returned some 45 minutes later with an old lady who wanted to see where the creature was. The beast reappeared around 450 feet off the opposite shore, and Taylor filmed it again. The object is a light chestnut in colour, and is seen to submerge and rise again in the film.

Sadly, the general public have not seen this film. Taylor gave it to Dr. Burton who showed it to only a handful of people. Burton inexplicably refused to let anyone else see the film and died in 1992. The whereabouts of the film is currently unknown.

The most famous sequence of Nessie film was taken by Tim Dinsdale an aeronautical engineer who became full time monster hunter and is still remembered as the phenomena's greatest champion. On the 28th April 1960 he took what is still the most compelling piece of footage on something weird in the Loch. Using a small 16 mm Bolex camera with a telephoto lens, he filmed a large hump zigzagging across the water in Foyers bay at a distance of 3900 feet.

He first saw the object when it was lying still on the surface, and observed it through binoculars. He stated that it was a mahogany colour with a dark blotch. He filmed it as it swam away in a curve partially submerging. Later he filmed a boat in the same area for reference. The film was analysed by the RAF's Joint Airforce Reconnaisance Intelligence Centre (JARIC), who interpreted film of enemy bases and weapons in WW2.

JARIC's conclusion was that the object was probably, animate and rose 3-3.7 feet above the surface. The length of the hump was 5.5 feet. JARIC's estimates are impressive. They put the boat Dinsdale later filmed at 13.3 feet and moving at six mph. Its actual length was fifteen feet and it was moving at seven mph.

During 1993's Project Urquhart - an expedition involving *Yorkshire Television* and the *Discovery Channel* - the Dinsdale film was examined once again. This revealed the distinct shape of a body beneath the object. This adds more weight to Dinsdale's already impressive film.

James David was a Conservative Member of Parliament, and leader of the Loch Ness Investigation Bureau. He put an astounding amount of his own time and money into the Bureau and was rewarded by filming something odd in the Loch on several occasions. On October 18th 1962 he filmed half a minute of footage using 35 mm black and with camera with a 6 inch lens. The object therein appears as a black shape swimming close to but never breaking the surface. The film was analysed by JARIC. Their analysis was impressive. They put the height of the camera above the water at 8.5 to 11.5 feet. The actual height was ten feet. The range was between 450 to 600 feet. The visible part of the object was about eight feet and moving at ten m.p.h. It seemed solid and glistened.

The second film was taken on June 6th 1963. A dark, cylindrical object emerged from the water and lay for half an hour in the shallows on a beach. Witnesses reported a serpentine head and neck. Once again JARIC examined the film. They said that as far as could be made out, the film corresponded with eyewitness descriptions, but the distance made definite conclusions impossible.

The third film was obtained in Borlum Bay on June 13th 1963. A hump was seen moving through a heat haze, trailing some kind of slick. It was examined by a panel of experts including Dr. Maurice Burton. Distinct movement across the Loch's surface was noted, as was turbulence.

JARIC also looked at the film, but the poor quality and lack of frames of reference made it impossible to guess the dimensions of the hump.

Mr and Mrs Peter Hodge were searching for the monster on 2nd May 1964. It was 8.15 am when Peter saw a pole-like neck. Running for his camera he slammed the door of his car causing the four foot neck to submerge. His wife Pauline filmed a wake with an 8mm camera but the film is from too great a distance to be of much use. A group of nearby students witnessed the events as well.

Elizabeth Hall was taking part in a 1965 Loch Ness expedition, when she filmed something from the Achanhannet expedition site. Using a main rig camera combination, she filmed nine seconds, showing two wakes - one about seven feet behind the other. No solid objects are visible in the film. However it was processed by JARIC (where would Nessie hunters be without them?) The wakes were 3,846 feet from the camera. The wakes were substantial and had a width of over six feet. They concluded that it was unlikely that the wakes were made by any of the Loch's known fauna.

Long-time Loch Ness investigator Dick Raynor filmed something weird on June 13th 1967. Whilst on a Loch Ness expedition camera watch at the north end of the Loch, Raynor filmed a 35mm sequence at a range of 900 feet and an elevation of 20 feet. He used a Newman Sinclair cine camera with a seventeen inch lens. The film shows a long wake with a large object breaking the surface. The tourist boat *Scott II* is in shot, and this helped those good people at JARIC to judge that the object is moving at five m.p.h and the portion that breaks the surface is five feet long. In many ways it looks very like the Dinsdale film.

On May 4th 1968 Lindsay Irving filmed a long, dark, log-shaped object that broke the surface with two humps. Once again the film is of little use due to the inadequate camera (8mm) and the distance (half a mile).

Similar faults plague the film taken by scoutmaster Harvey Barsky on 27 May 1969. Barsky filmed and his scouts watched as a long, low lying object moved erratically across the Loch and changed direction rapidly. The film is too unclear to tell us any more.

Schoolmaster Alan Wilkins claimed to have seen the monster on several occasions. On 18th July 1975, he and his son saw a hump that emerged and sank several times. He filmed the latter part of the sighting. The author has never seen this film or stills from it, and it is unclear if it was ever made public.

Gwen and Peter Smith were at the shore near Urquhart Castle at 5.05 pm on 22nd August 1977. They saw something rise vertically from the water about 160 metres out. It was a periscope shaped object, a foot thick and leathery brown in colour. It had a thick rectangular head and stood the height of a man out of the water. Gwen filmed it with an 8mm Printz T3 Zoom camera. The film shows the object rising and submerging three times, and moving it's head from side to side. No features are visible on the head.

On 21st of July 1992 an anonymous witness saw a commotion in Urquhart Bay. The subsequent film was shown on a BBC news broadcast and seemed to show some animal rolling and plunging in a dolphin-like fashion.

In the summer of 2003 the CFZ were shown a sequence of video footage taken by a man who has asked us not to reveal his name. It shows two pale objects moving across the surface of the Loch near Urquhart. At first glance they seem like two water birds, but as they dive it becomes obvious that the two objects are in fact portions of one larger object. They rise and fall together in a sequence last for several minutes.

Mark Martin – The CFZ's South Yorkshire representative, and a trusted and respected researcher - knows the area and is familiar with the small beach visible in the background. Using this frame of reference he estimates the object to be 30 feet long. The sequence was put up on the CFZ website and caused much controversy. Many dismissed it as waterbirds. Some thought it was a scuba-diver. Others still thought it showed seals (who do enter the Loch from time to time). A giant eel swimming near the surface was also suggested. This film more than any other encapsulates the Loch Ness riddle. Like the story of the elephant and the blind men, everyone is interpreting the images differently.

Another source of evidence at Loch Ness is sonar signals. We have already seen the impressive evidence Robert Rines got in the 1970s. Now let us examine some other sonar experiments at the Loch. From 1954 onwards a number of vessels using depth finders recorded anomalous readings of large objects in deep water. Though none of these were conclusive they caused enough interest to warrant the use of sonar in scientific expeditions.

In 1968 Professor D G Tucker of the University of Birmingham conducted some sonar experiments at the Loch. The Professor employed digital sonar machines that fed acoustic returns into a computer that in turn sorted the data and displayed it on an oscilloscope screen. A 16 mm cine camera was synchronised with the equipment, so that every pulse of energy was filmed as a permanent record. The set up was fixed at Temple Pier. A cross-section of the Loch was kept under constant surveillance for 19,960 minutes.

Pre-expedition trials in the spring had interesting results. Two moving objects with a minimum length of 12.5 feet were recorded. One close to the bottom of the Loch, the other rising vertically. This was *nothing* to the results obtained that summer.

On August 28th eight large objects were recorded rising from the bottom at a distance of fifty metres and moving at speeds of up to seventeen m.p.h. The objects were around six metres (twenty feet) long. There is nothing of that size and shape among the known fauna of the Loch.

In 1969 Robert E Love carried out a sonar sweep of the Loch on the motor boat *Rangitea,* fitted with a Honeywell

Scanna II-F sonar. He tracked a target north east of Foyers, 190 metres ahead of the boat, and 67 metres down. He estimated that it was of comparable size to a pilot whale at around six metres (twenty feet).

Also in 1969, the six man submarine *Pisces* was used to tow a five ton model of the monster around the Loch for the shooting of the film *The Private Life of Sherlock Holmes*. The tow-cable broke and the model was lost. The sub also helped in a search for the real monster using a side-mounted sonar. On one occasion they tracked an object fifty feet from the Loch's bottom and 600 feet away. As they closed in to 400 feet, the object moved away.

Using the same equipment as Love, Jeffery Blonder obtained similar readings to Love's on October 22nd at a range of 900 feet and a depth of 130 feet off Invermoriston.

In 1987 Adrian Shine led Operation Deepscan. A flotilla of 24 motor cruisers all fitted with Lawrence X-16 echo sounders swept the length and breath of the Loch. A number of strong contacts were made with objects at about 150 feet deep. One contact stands out above the others. Made at 606 feet it was subsequently independently recorded by another boat that was not one of Shine's flotilla. This eliminates interference from other boats in the Deepscan group, and suggests that the object had move away then returned after the Deepscan vessels had moved on.

During Project Urquhart in 1993, Dr Colin Bean monitored an underwater storm caused by atmospheric conditions on his boat-mounted sonar. The next day whilst examining the sonar charts he noticed two large underwater contacts followed by a wake. It was confirmed from the readings that they were not shoals of fish, as these do not leave wakes.

In 2003 BBC presenter Steve Leonard took part in a sonar sweep of the Loch as part of a poorly researched and executed "documentary". The programme took the frankly ridiculous premise that the Loch Ness animals could not be anything other than *plesiosaurs,* then wasted time and money with computer animations of them. After explaining why these creatures could not live in Loch Ness, (setting up a straw-man to make themselves look clever), they took part in a sonar search with no results whatsoever. Their conclusion; the monster is a myth.

In fact, the type of sonar they used does not record solid objects - only pockets of air that one would find in an air-breathing animal's lungs. They did not acknowledge that the Loch Ness animals might not be air breathers, nor indeed anything except prehistoric marine reptiles. This was pseudo-science at its worst, and a shameful waste of the licence payer's fee.

So what is living in Loch Ness? Theories have included long-necked seals, giant otters, huge amphibians, and even prehistoric invertebrates. The most popular theory is that Nessie is a surviving form of plesiosaur or something descended from them. These were long-necked sea dwelling aquatic reptiles of the mid to late Mesozoic era. Loch Ness with its fresh water, cold temperature, and poor fish stocks could not be a much more inhospitable place for them.

If air-breathing animals were behind the Loch Ness riddle, then they would be seen at the surface more often. The sonar readings suggest the creatures are benthic or bottom dwelling, and that they derive their oxygen directly from the water. Some sort of fish would seem the obvious choice. A titanic eel would seem the best candidate. With its sinuous form it can rear up to resemble a long neck and head. Though they flex themselves in the horizontal plane, eels *can* swim at the surface on their sides, and resemble a series of humps moving in the vertical plane. Ergo a stout bodied eel in the 6-9 metre range would make a very fitting 'Nessie'.

We must not forget the odder aspects of the Loch that we examined in the chapter on esoteric theories. A good fortean keeps an open mind. Many Loch Ness sightings have very weird aspects and may be something more complex than an unknown animal. The Loch may be the home to gigantic eels and dragon-like beasts of a more nebulous character.

Most people wrongly assume that Loch Ness is the world's only monster-haunted lake. They could not be more wrong. Many lakes in many countries have reports of anomalous animals attached to them. In fact in Scotland *alone* there are around 34 such bodies of water. After Loch Ness, Loch Morar is the most famous. Morar is a deep glacial loch much like Loch Ness. At eleven miles long it is smaller, but its depth of 1,000 feet makes it the deepest lake in the UK. Its resident monsters have been named 'Morag' - a derivative of the Gaelic *mordhobhar* meaning 'big water'. In centuries past it was believed that Morag would only show itself if a member of a certain Scottish clan was about to die. Morag could appear as a fair maiden or a great serpent.

So much for folklore, but in the age of enlightenment may people claim to have seen a monstrous creature in Loch Morar. In fact the Loch is second only to Loch Ness in reported sightings. Sightings like that of John MacVarish barman at the Morar Hotel on August 27 1968.

I saw this thing coming. I thought it was a man standing in a boat but as it got nearer I saw it was something coming out of the water. I tried to get up close to it with the outboard out of the water and what I saw was a long neck five or six feet out of the water with a small head on it, dark in colour, coming quite slowly down the loch. When I got to about 300 yards of it, it turned off into the deep and just settled down slowly into the loch out of sight.

The neck was about one and a half feet in diameter, and tapered up to between ten inches and a foot. I never saw any features, no eyes or anything like that. It was a snake like head, very small compared to the size of the neck-flattish, a flat type of head. It seemed to have very smooth skin, but at 300 yards it's difficult to tell. It was very dark, nearly black.

It was 10am, dead calm, no wind, brilliant sunshine. I saw it for about ten minutes travelling very slowly: it didn't alter it's angle to the water. It looked as if it was paddling itself along. There was very little movement from the water, just a small streak from the neck. I couldn't really see what was propelling it but I think it was something at the sides rather than behind it.

Earlier the same year, Robert Duff got a clearer look at the creature. Duff - joiner from Edinburgh was fishing in Meoble Bay on the Loch's south shore. It was July 8th. The water was about sixteen feet deep and very clear. The bottom was pale, almost white with leaves on it. Lying on the bottom was what Duff described as a giant lizard over six metres (twenty feet) long. The skin was a dirty brown colour, and he saw three digits on the beast's front limbs. It was motionless and looking up at him with slit-like eyes. Terrified he revved up his motor boat and made his escape.

The most dramatic encounter took place on August 16th 1969. Duncan McDonnell and William Simpson were returning from a trip up the loch. It was around 9.00 pm but still light. McDonnell was at the wheel and the boat was doing seven knots. He writes:

I heard a splash or disturbance in the water astern of us. I looked up and saw about twenty yards behind us this creature coming directly after us in our wake. It only took a matter of seconds to catch up with us. It grazed the side of the boat, I am quite certain this was unintentional. When it struck the boat seemed to come to a halt or at least slow down. I grabbed the oar and was attempting to fend it off, my one fear being that if it got under the boat it might capsize it.

Simpson wrote…

As we were sailing down the loch in my boat, we were suddenly disturbed and frightened by a thing that surfaced behind us. We watched it catch us up then bump into the side of the boat, the impact sent a kettle of water I was heating onto the floor. I ran into the cabin to turn the gas off as the water had put the flame out. Then I came out of the cabin to see my mate trying to fend the beast off with an oar, to me he was wasting his time. Then when I seen the oar break I grabbed my rifle and quickly putting a bullet in it fired in the direction of the beast. Then I watched it slowly sink away from the boat and that was the last I seed of it.

Neither of the men seemed to think that the bullet had any effect on the monster. They estimated it to be nine metres (thirty feet). The skin was rough and dirty-brown in colour. It had three humps that protruded eighteen inches out of the water. McDonnell thought they may have been undulations rather than humps. McDonnell reported seeing a snake-like head, a foot across, held eighteen inches out of the water.

Loch Shiel is seventeen miles long, a mile wide and 420 feet deep. Its monster has been unsurprisingly named 'Sheila'. Father Cyril Dieckhoff of the Benedictine Abbey at Fort Augustus collected many accounts of the creature and was planning to write a book. Sadly he died in 1970 leaving his work unpublished.

One of the earliest reports is from 1905. An old man called Ian Crookback, and two boys watched through a telescope at a three humped creature as they crossed the loch opposite Gasgan in a mail-steamer.

Another report is of a long-necked monster with a wide mouth and seven humps. It was observed through a telescope by Ronald McLeod as it emerged from the water near Sandy Point in 1926.

Loch Oich lies directly below Loch Ness. In 1936 a headmaster and member of the Camberwell Borough Council, his son, and two friends, saw the Loch's monster whilst boating in fairly shallow water. Two humps - like the coils of a snake - emerged only a few metres from the boat. The coils were three feet long, three feet high, and three feet apart from each other. Then a dog-like head emerged. They watched the creature rise and dive several times.

Loch Lochy lies below Loch Oich and is Scotland's third deepest after Morar and Ness. On September 30th 1975, at 2.00 pm, Mr and Mrs Sargent and their two children were driving along the south shore road. As they turned the corner by the Corriegour hotel they saw a six metre (20 foot) black hump gliding through the water, creating a wave. Mr Sargent slowed his and his wife fumbled with her camera as the great wash hit the shore. Sadly the hump submerged before she could get a shot. Meanwhile, Mr Sargent stopped the van further up the road, and saw a smaller hump following the first. Mrs Sargent did not notice this second hump. The whole sighting lasted about two minutes. Mrs Sargent noticed his wife was visibly shaking, and that the children were shouting excitedly.

In 1996 a 3.6 metre (twelve foot) dark-coloured animal, was seen swimming in the loch. It had a curved head and three humps. The creature swam in circles whilst being observed by staff and guests at the Corriegour hotel. One witness - Catronia Allen, an Aberdeen University Psychology student - who observed it through binoculars, said that it was not an otter, a dolphin, a porpoise, or seal.

The following year, a six man expedition including Loch Ness witness and researcher Garry Campbell, and diver Cameron Turner, conducted a sonar sweep of Lochy. Near the centre of the Loch they picked up a unidentified reading indicating a six metre (twenty foot) object swimming in the water.

Loch Treig lies beneath Britain's tallest mountain, Ben Nevis. Back in 1933 a hydro-electric scheme was started in the Loch. B. N. Peach, the man in charge of the scheme, reported that many divers left their jobs after encountering monsters underwater. Sadly, little more detail on this case is available.

At Easter 1980, Mr and Mrs Maltman and their daughter, were camping at Loch Lomond. They were terrified to see a five foot long head and neck with a bulky body behind it, rear up from the water 900 feet from were they sat. The beast was visible for 30 seconds. The Maltmans were so scared that they fled, leaving their belongings at the lochside.

If few people have heard of lake monsters other than Nessie in Scotland, fewer still can have heard of the strange creatures sighted in Welsh lakes.

Llyn-y-Gadair is a small round lake near to Snowdon. In the 18th century a man decided to swim across it. His friends who were waiting for him on the bank were horrified to see a long trailing object winding after him. As he approached the shore it reared up and seized him. Winding about him like a python, it dragged him down into the lake.

At Glaslyn, another lake in the Snowdon range, a monster was spotted in the 1930s. Two climbers looking down on the lake saw a long grey body with a pale head rise to the surface then dive again. It was unlike any other creature either of them had seen before.

But it is Llyn Tegid (or Lake Bala) that has gained the most fame. At four miles long and 150 feet deep Lake Bala is a puddle compared to Loch Ness. It lies in Gwynedd in north Wales. Legend has it that the lake was created by a water spirit who dwelt in a well. He provided water for the surrounding villages. One night a local man forgot to replace the wooden boards that cover the well every evening. In the morning the people awoke to see a lake.

Mrs Ann Jones saw the now familiar hump aspect moving across the lake in October 1979. Mr John Melville was fishing on the lake with cousin in the same year and got a more detailed look.

It had a large head, like a football and rather big eyes. We could see the body which was 8 feet long. It wasn't aggressive at all. It swam to within a few yards of us then turned and disappeared. I wouldn't say I had seen a monster, just a large being. But I have caught some rather big pike in the lake before now and it was bigger than any of those.

In March 1995 Paul and Andrew Delaney from London were fishing on the lake, when they noticed something about 260 feet from their boat. The brothers initially thought it was a tree trunk until it rose up three metres (ten feet) out of the water. It was an elongate neck with a small head. The brothers said it reminded them of pictures of the Loch Ness monster.

Veteran Australian cryptozoologist and author of the excellent book *Out of the Shadows; the Mystery animals of Australia*, Tony Healy told the author of his trip to Lake Bala in the 1980s. He interviewed two men who had been out fishing on a boat. Something that resembled the back of a cow; large, rounded, and brown, surfaced close to their boat. The men were so frightened that they never went back onto the lake.

Some manner of death dealing serpent may have been abroad in Rhayader, mid Wales in the late 1980s. It seemed to make it's home in a river, and crawl out leaving trails of flattened grass. The animal killed sheep by biting them close to the sternum (breast-bone). By October 1988 the animal had killed thirty five sheep on the 2,000 acre farm of Bodalong owned by the Pugh family. Foxhounds picked up its scent, and trailed it back and forth to the river, but it was never seen. The sheep carcasses were examined by a local vet who believed they had been bitten by something venomous. Universities examined the bodies as well, but were baffled. Just what kind of venom was involved was never made clear, and the vet in question has moved away from the area, as researcher Mike Hallowell found out when he tried to investigate the case. The killings stopped as abruptly as they had started, leaving everyone involved perplexed. Needless to say, Britain's only venomous snake, the adder (*Vipera berus*), is far too small to have killed all these sheep. This case begs many odd questions. Why would an animal go to all the trouble of wasting venom and energy killing so many sheep then not eat any? If it was a large, exotic, venomous snake that had escaped from captivity how did it cope with October in Wales? We shall probably never know.

Saint Patrick supposedly cast all serpents out of Ireland. It seems he did a particularly shoddy job. The waterways of the Emerald Isle are seething with serpents. We have already heard Georgina Carberry, account of the Lough Fadda wyrm, but now let us hear some more.

In the west of Ireland is a network of interconnected lakes. It is truly amazing that such a wilderness - like something from the Siberian wastes - exists in western Europe. The watery labyrinth is connected to the sea and is the sight of many lake monster encounters. Stories of creatures known as peistes or horse eels reach far back into Irish folklore and legend. The anonymous author of the tenth century *Book of Lismore* writes:

When the monster heard them, it shook its head, and its bristles and its rough hair stood up on it, and it looked at them unlovingly and recklessly. Not calm, friendly, or gentle was the look that it gave them, for it was astonished that anyone should come to it's island. It marched toward them, then, firmly and impetuously, so that the ground shook under it's feet. Repulsive, outlandish, fierce, and very terrifying was the beast that arose there. It's front end was like a horse, with a glowing, blazing eye in its head, sharp, bitter, furious, angry, keen, crimson, bloody, very harsh, rapidly rolling. Anyone would think that it's eye would go through him, as it looked at him. It had two hideous thick legs under it at front. Iron claws on it which struck showers of fire from the stony rocks were it trod across them. It had a fiery breath which burned like embers. It had a belly like a pair of bellows. The tail fins of a whale on it behind, with iron nails on them pointing backwards; that laid bare the surface of the ground wherever they went, behind the monster.. It could travel over sea or land alike when it wished. Now the sea would boil with the extent of it's heat and venomousness as it rushed into it. .Boats could not catch it; no one escaped to tell the tale of it, from then till now.

The picture of horror that passage paints is quite comparable to the fear that gripped Georgina Carberry at Lough Fadda.

Lough Mask has had a monster tradition for centuries. The very name reflects this. 'Mask' is derived from the Swedish for worm. A member of the venerable O'Flaherty family was said to have encountered a dragon in the lough. A carving depicting the beast survives today on the O'Flaherty tomb in Oughterad church. On 16th June, 1963, at 9.15 am Mr A R Lawrence of Tullamore County Offaly saw the creature. He had his sighting from Inishdura Island at a range of 750 feet.

As I stood on the boat-slip looking north-west across the bay, I suddenly saw what appeared to be the head and tail rise of a large fish close to the rocks. A second or so later, the movement was repeated in about the same place. Then there occurred another head and tail rise ahead (north-east) of the first two, followed by the same movement some yards further north-east.

I then realized I was watching two humps, one behind the other, moving forward slowly and regularly across the mouth of the bay. It seemed to me like the back of a very large eel-like fish. I never saw the head or tail, but I would guess the humps were about five or six feet in length, and the distance between them eight to ten feet. The water through which the object travelled was only three or four feet deep. It disappeared from my sight when a point on the island blocked my view.

Irish lake monsters have been seen slithering across the land on several occasions. In the 1890s a vast eel like creature was trapped in a culvert between Lough Crolan and Lough Derrylea in County Galway. The creature was said to have rotted away into a foul smelling slime. F. W. Holiday and Roy Mackal visited the sight in 1968. Measuring the culvert they deduced the creature must have been eighteen inches in diameter.

An almost identical event occurred shortly after, at Ballynahich Lake four miles to the north. A thirty-foot creature - as thick as a horse - became jammed in under a bridge that spans the Ballynahich river close to the castle. A local blacksmith - Patrick Connelly from Cashel - forged a huge barbed spear to slay the beast. This specimen was more fortunate than its comrade. A flood washed it clear of the bridge.

At the turn of the 19th century, a Connermara woman was terrified by a horse-eel she met on land. Whilst tending to her turf on a bog next to Lough Auna she heard a commotion in the water. To her horror, a horse eel slithered out of the water and came right up next to her. The thing was only a few feet away and the woman ran for her life. She said it looked like horse in front and tailed of to an elongate eel-like rear.

Sometime later, a boy and his mother were stacking peat by Lough Auna when they both saw the monster. It looked like a huge eel with a bristly mane and sported three or four humps. It was between nine and twelve metres (thirty-forty) feet long.

On Mat 14th 1980 a retired Netherlands Royal Air Force officer, Commander Kort, was holding a barbecue at his loughside cottage. He and several of his guests watched a five foot long black hump one foot tall, glide across the lough.

In her book, *The Smile and the Tear*, Violet Martin describes a monster seen in Lough Abisdealy. The witnesses were a bride and groom, and their kitchen maid who were driving to church.

Suddenly they beheld a long black creature propelling itself rapidly across the lake. It's flat head, on a long neck was held high, two great loops of it's length bucked in and out of the water as it progressed.. Obviously a snake and a huge one. The three witnesses stared, doubtful of their own eyes at this amazing sight. The avenue is within a few yards of the water, so they were able to have a clear view of the mysterious monster. For how long they gazed at it I don't know. Unfortunately a virtuous anxiety not to keep her scholars waiting, induced the principal witnesses to proceed on their way to church before the snake submerged.

On another occasion a man saw a huge animal slithering out of the same lough at night. He reckoned it to be 7.5 metres (25 feet) long.

Lady Augusta Gregory - the author of *Visions and Beliefs in the West of Ireland*, friend of the poet W. B. Yates and founder of the Abbey Theatre in Dublin - saw a monster in the small lake, Dhulough.

I was coming home with my two brothers from Tirneevin school, and there as we passed Dhulough we hear a great splashing, and we saw some creature put it's head up, with the head and mane like a horse. And we didn't stop but ran.

Lady Gregory was told a story by a County Clare man that bares a remarkable resemblance to the 18th century story from Llyn-y-Gadar in Wales. Sometime in the 19th century a man had gone swimming in Lough Garney. Observers from the bank were appalled to see a gigantic eel-like monster appear and start to swim towards him. As not to make him panic they shouted, *"If you ever were a great swimmer show us now how you can swim to the shore."* When he reached the shore, the thing was in the place he had originally been. If it were not for his companions' quick wit, then he may have ended up like the hapless Welshman.

In 1963 or 1964, farmer Tommy Joyce was looking out of his window at Lough Shanakeever, when he saw a huge back seven or eight feet long heave up two feet out of the water. It moved away crushing a path through some weeds.

Patrick Walsh was on a boat when he saw the Shanakeeva monster. A head and neck emerged from the lough close to his vessel. He rowed quickly for shore fearing the beast, which he reckoned to be sixteen feet long, would capsize him.

Lough Nahooin in County Galway is more of a pool than a lough. It is 300 feet long 240 feet wide and only 20 feet deep. Nevertheless a monster has been reported in it. The Nahooin wyrm was seen by a whole family - the Coynes - in July 1968 At 7.00 pm Stephen Coyne went down to the loughside to bring up some dried peat. He was accompanied by his eight year old son and his dog. Although it was sunset it was still light. The trio saw a weird animal swimming in the lough. It was about twelve feet long and a foot in diameter, with black, smooth skin. It would occasionally put its head underwater and as it did this two humps would rise. A flat tail also surfaced. The dog began to bark at the monster and it seemed to become angry. It swam towards the shore with its mouth open. Inside the mouth was white. As Mr Coyne ran to his dog the monster turned back. The boy ran to fetch his mother and the four other Coyne children. All seven of them continued to watch the monster. They noticed it had small horns on its head. The thing came as close as 12 feet to the shore. As night fell the family returned home leaving the monster still swimming round the tiny lough.

The following year, sheep farmer Thomas Connelly saw the Nahooin monster lying on the turf, fourteen feet from the lough. It slid forwards in a rolling motion and slipped into the water sending up spray. Connelly described it as being bigger than a donkey's foal, two and a half feet thick, and black. He noticed four stubby legs. The monster's overall appearance was eel-like.

A very similar-sounding creature was reported in 1940 from Lough Bran in County Kerry. A fourteen year old boy saw a black creature with four short legs basking on the shore.

In 1954 the Bran monster was seen on Christmas Eve by a Mr Timothy O'Sullivan. Whilst taking his cows to be milked he saw two humps two feet long, and protruding two feet proud of the surface. The distance between the humps was twelve feet. O'Sullavan ran home and returned with his wife and a shotgun, but the animal had vanished.

In 1979 two brothers who farmed the area saw a beast that they described as a cross between a seal and a dragon, and as black as soot, swim the length of the Lough, some 1800 feet before submerging. Their father had seen the beast several years previously.

Lough Ree on the River Shannon has been the sight of several monster encounters. In his book *Thanks for the Memory,* Colonel Harry Rice wrote that a friend of his had seen the Lough Ree monster and described it as like a dozen barrels of porter strung together. Doubtless this refers to a row of humps. We shall see descriptions like this again in the sea monster section of the book.

Two Englishmen fishing in Lough Ree were towed around the lough by some immensely strong animal in 1958. They were forced to cut their lines. Then in 1960 Patrick Ganley and Joseph Quigley caught a huge creature in their nets whilst fishing for pike. The men tried to haul it ashore but it tore the nets. They commented that whatever it was must have been as strong as a horse.

Moving away from the British Isles we find a mass of lake monsters in Scandinavia. We have met the lindorm, Scandinavia's legendary serpent dragon already. It was believed that they started life as ordinary snakes but over the years grew massive in size. As they grew bigger, they entered deep lakes to become lake monsters. Eventually they became so massive that they headed out to sea and became sea monsters.

In 1555 the exiled Archbishop of Upplasa, Olaus Magnus, the residing in Rome, published his book *Historia de gentibus sertentrionalibus.* This dealt with the serpentine monsters of Scandinavian waters. He writes:

There is also another serpent of incredible magnitude in a town called Moos (ie Lake Mjosa), of the Diocess of Hammer, which as a comet portends change in all the world, so, that portends a change in the kingdom of Norway, as was seen Anno 1522, that lifts himself high above the waters, and rolls himself round like a sphere. This serpent was thought to be fifty cubits long by conjecture, by sight afar off: there followed the banishment of King Christiernus, and the great persecution of the Bishops; and it shew'd also the destruction of the Country.

We can see from this passage that the Scandinavians held their dragons in as much awe as their Viking ancestors did. The rising himself high, and rolling into a sphere, sounds like the head and neck aspect, and hump aspect of sea and lake monsters.

In 1636, the cleric Nicolas Gramis recorded that a serpent that dwelt in the Mjos and Branz river in Norway had left its home, and crawled across the surrounding fields. It was said to look like the long mast of a ship, and it knocked over trees and huts that stood in its way.

The most famous of these north European beasts lives in Lake Storjsson in Sweden. This is Scandinavia's answer to Loch Ness. On Forson Island there is a huge megalith upon which a lindorm, swallowing its own tail like the orobourus, is carved. Along it's coils are written Viking runes. A legend tell that a lindorm is bound to the lake until the runes are deciphered. Deciphered or not a lindorm is resident in Lake Storjsson.

Its first appearance in modern times was in 1820 when a farmer fishing on the lake claimed to have been followed by a huge animal. Another man Aron Anderson saw the beast sunning itself on land. It was grey in colour with a white mane on the neck. It returned casually to the water.

Circa 1855 it was spotted by Paul Anderson and four other men. It moved so fast that it overtook the boat they were rowing. In the same year a young man from Ostersund said it pursued his vessel and that it looked like an upturned boat.

In 1863 Jan Brumee and his family observed a dozen blackish humps whilst crossing the lake. They followed the family's boat closely. Thy attempted to catch the monster but it proved too swift. Jan saw it again eight years later.

I was out on the lake with my family and some friends. A rainstorm came up and we headed to shore. That's when the animal moved right past us. It was swimming at an incredible speed. The creature left a very large wake. I didn't give chase that last time, realising this thing had to be strong to swim that fast. With that sort of power it could have overturned our boat.

Towards the end of July, 1878, Eric Olsson and some colleagues, were fishing on Storjsson when they saw what looked like a log in the path of their boat. Alarmed when the "log" resolved itself into a serpentine animal with a dog-like head, they made for a small island and pulled up until the creature vanished.

Another man had a better look at the Storjsson lindorm one year later. Martin Olsson, a mechanic at the Ostersund sawmills, lived in a cabin beside the lake.

I was fishing near Forson island when I got a strange feeling someone was watching me. I looked behind me and the lake creature was not more than forty metres behind my boat. I dropped my pole and line in the lake when I saw it. The weather was bright and sunny and I got a good view of the animal The neck was long, about as round as a man's body at the base where it came up out of the water. It tapered up about six feet to a snake-like head that was larger than what I figured the neck could support. There was a hairy fringe just back of the neck, hanging down the back. This 'ribbon' was stuck close to the neck, possibly because of the wetness. The colour was greyish brown. The thing had two distinct eyes that were reddish in appearance. The body was not exactly black-but a sort of blackish rust colour in appearance. There were a couple of dark humps visible beyond the neck. Both of these humps, and the part that was out of the water, glistened in the sunlight. I did not see scales. There was a skin on the animal that resembled the skin of a fish.

I didn't want to alarm the animal, but I did want to get away as quickly as possible. Moving very cautiously, I took my oars and pulled slowly away from the spot. I became even more frightened when I had rowed about ten metres distance and the animal began to swim towards me. I stopped rowing, and the thing just lay there in the water staring at me. This must have gone on for about five minutes. I'm uncertain because my mind was on anything but the passage of time. There was no doubt in my mind that this thing could have overturned my little boat. I thanked god when he dropped beneath the water and I saw a blackish hump move out in the opposite direction.

1893 was a busy year for the monster. After badly frightening two girls, a whaler from Norway was called in to hunt it. A local man also constructed a huge steel trap that he baited with a pig. The monster avoided both trap and whaler. But in the winter he was back. The monster terrified skaters when three metres of its head and neck smashed through the ice between Froson island and Ostersund.

A newspaper reporter told his friends how he rowed up to the monster to get a better view of it in 1896.

At first we thought the dark mass in the water was a boat that had turned over. We observed the mass for a few moments, then realised it was the infamous monster of Lake Storjsson. I had just read about the sea-orm mentioned in olden times. I thought this creature could be a throwback to something that once lived in olden days. I talked my companions into rowing out onto the lake where the serpent was making a lot of threshing manoeuvres, raising waves, and disturbing the calmness of the lake.

The group observed a smooth-bodied, cinnamon-coloured creature, showing several humps above the surface.

The Storjsson lindorms terrorised a couple, Rolf Larson and Irene Magnusson, on a fishing trip in 1976.

We were about 500 metres from land and going home when we passed a buoy. Suddenly some waves rocked the boat. 50 or 60 metres from us' between the land and the boat, something moved under the surface. Then it came up to the surface, not with a splash but with smooth waves. The part of the body we saw above the water was not more than 20-30 cms high and about 1 metre long, but from the amount of water it displaced we could see it was a large object beneath the surface. I would compare it with an upside down boat. You only saw the keel of it. We had shut off the motor because we were fishing. The thing was swimming in half circles around our boat.

From the beginning I stood completely still without really understanding what was going on. After some minutes I started the motor, but then Irene, who had been quiet all the time, shouted that I should immediately return to land. She was pale as a corpse. We made off shore and the animal followed for a time. We were doing perhaps 10 knots, but the animal kept up with us. We returned to land, and we could see the wake of the creature for four or five minutes the water was so calm.

Storjsson is not the only Scandinavian lake that has a monster. Lake Seljord in Norway is another hot-spot for sightings. According to legend, the monster - known as the 'Seljordsorm' - once inhabited a smaller mountain lake. It outgrew this abode and moved overland to Lake Seljord. Eivind Fjodstuft saw it whilst fishing in 1920. He described it as black, fifty to sixty feet long, with a head like a crocodile.

In the summer of 1975, dentist Rolf Langeland started a practice in a small hamlet called Sandnes close to the lake. Three days after his arrival he was driving near the lake with his three children when they saw Seljordsorm. He brought his car to a halt, as five humps broke the surface churning the water, and moving at an amazing speed. Langeland estimated the monster to be 30 to 50 metres in length. The size sounds excessive but he may have seen several specimens swimming in line together.

On Easter Monday 1977 Ivar Hesmyr and his daughter Solveig were fishing from a small boat with a neighbour's son. Suddenly three glistening humps rose from the water 300 feet away. Hesmyr estimated the beast was nine metres (30 feet) long. A serpentine head and neck rose up, and the creature began to swim away at a speed that caused the boat to rock. Solveig began screaming and her father attempted to calm her. When he looked up again the Seljordsorm was gone. Solveig said that the humps disappeared first followed by the head and neck. When they reached shore Hesmyr swore he would never go back out on the lake again.

Another, smaller Norwegian lake with a lindorm in residence is Rommen in south-western Norway, close to the Swedish border.

In 1929 Astrid Myrvold was fetching water for her mother when she saw something on the shore. In later life she likened it to a big, black, plastic pipe (though these did not exist then). It had a horse-like head and a fin on the tail. Disturbed by her presence, it slithered into the lake drawing a large wake behind it. Astrid noticed it had protruding ears (or horns). She told her mother but was not believed. Hence she did not speak about it again until 1976 when a local man said he had also seen the monster.

On 30th September 1976, at 1.30 pm Asbjorn Holmedal was driving a school bus near the lake. He noticed large waves coming ashore between Bjornoya island and the mainland. He thought it might have been caused by a swimming moose. However when he stopped the bus and got off to take a closer look he saw a massive animal in the water. He and fifteen children (aged 8-15), saw it rising out of the water and causing great commotion. It was seven to ten metres (23-30 feet) long. It had four, metre long humps, around one to two metres apart. They protruded a foot above the water. The beast submerged leaving the lake mirror calm.

In July 1992 Bjord Bohn was holidaying beside Rommen with her husband and daughter. Looking out of her window she saw, fifteen metres (fifty feet) from shore, a hump resembling an upturned boat. She made a drawing of the creature, which she said was patterned like a crocodile. Both her husband and daughter observed the animal before it dove beneath the waters leaving a commotion in the shallows.

Well over forty other Scandinavian lakes are said to have monsters in them. A whole library could be written on the subject, but for now we must move on elsewhere in our worldwide tour of lake monsters.

The Middle-East is not an area that leaps to mind when thinking about lake monsters, but these creatures have been recorded here. It is Lake Van in eastern Turkey that has gained the most fame in this area. Lake Van is a huge, highly alkaline lake close to the border with Iran. An ancient church close to its shores has carvings of aquatic dragons devouring humans, but it was not until the mid 1990s that the Van dragon made its first modern day appearance. It was seen by the deputy provincial governor, who said it was ten to fifteen metres (thirty three to fifty feet) long. He said it looked like a dinosaur with triangular spines along its back. It was black with a white underside. The great undersea explorer Jacques Cousteau was planning to investigate the monster, but sadly died before he could embark on his expedition.

In 1997 the monster was filmed by Unal Kozak, a Van University teaching assistant. His film shows a crocodile like head surfacing close to shore. It is brown and a large cow like eye is visible. Kozak wrote a book on the monster, and claims that 1,000 people have seen it. Quite a number since it only appeared in the mid 1990s.

Many have said that the monster in Kozak's film look stiff and inanimate, like a carved wooden model. It has been suggested that he faked the film to promote his book. A model monster was indeed found in the nearby village of Citoren, but it is unknown if it was used to fake the Van footage or for that matter if the Van footage *is* fake.

Further east, Lake Kol-Kol lies in the Dzambul area of Kazakhstan and is said to be home to a fifteen metre (fifty foot) serpentine creature, with a six foot long head, known as 'Aidakar'.

The massive continent of Asia, spiritual home of the dragon is riddled with lake monsters. We have already met the monsters of tropical Asian lakes as well as those in China and Tibet. So now we will move further east to look at the latter-day dragons of Russia's far east and those of Japan.

The world's mightiest forest is not the Amazon rainforest. Neither is it the jungles of the Congo. It is found far north of the tropics, a cold verdant wilderness consisting mainly of pine and Siberian larch (the most numerous tree on the planet). The Russian Taiga is a forest of almost unconceivable dimensions. It stretches from the borders of Europe in the west, across Mother Russia to the Bering Sea in the east. Shot through with freezing swamps and huge lakes it is almost uninhabited. The Taiga covers an astounding seven million square kilometres.

The Taiga is at its wildest and most ill-explored in that icy, abandoned region known as Siberia. Here in winter temperatures can drop so low that they can shatter steel. The brief summers are haunted by clouds of blood-hungry mosquitoes that swarm around any warm blooded animal. Siberia not only consists of forest, but miles of boggy tundra and frozen mountains and plateaus where no man has ever set foot.

Giant reptiles seem to be the last creatures you would associate with such a cold place, but there are reports of giant snakes and snake-like creatures. And in Siberia's lakes we have some of the most dramatic encounters with modern dragons on record.

An amazing story came to light in 1873, when the *New York World* published an interview between one of its correspondents and a Russian convict called Cheriton Batchmatchnick, who had been pardoned by his government because of his remarkable discoveries. He had been banished to Siberia for smuggling, and set to work in the mines at Nartchinsk. He escaped and reached the mountains, where he struck southwards heading for the Amur river in the hope of reaching China. After meeting Cossacks, he turned north and entered what seemed to be a pass in the Altai range. Turning eastward he entered the gorges of the Aldan mountains. Here winter overtook him.

He followed vast herds of migrating animals to the summit of the range. Here he found a lost valley, hemmed in by cliffs on all sides. He estimated it to be fifty miles wide, and one hundred and fifty miles long. As he descended he found it to be warm and fertile. The place was filled with animals and contained a blue lake.

During the night he heard some very large animals moving around and the sound of trees being broken. In the morning he found the spoor of massive creatures beside the lake. He decided to seek a safer spot for the next night.

He discovered a cave and on entering heard a deep breathing. There standing in the cave was a full grown mammoth. He described the beast as being twelve feet tall and eighteen feet long. It was covered in reddish wool and black hair. The curving tusks were eight to ten feet long.

In the coming days Batchmatchnik saw about twenty mammoths in the valley. They were peaceable animals who were never aggressive and took little notice of him. There was however, a much more dangerous animal in the valley. He only saw it once. It was a dragon-like monster that dwelt in the lake and preyed on the animals that came there to drink. It was nine metres (thirty feet) long and armed with savage fangs. Its scaly body was serpentine and its head like that of a crocodile. He dubbed it a "saurophidian". He saw it attack a mammoth. The reptile seized its victim and enfolded it in its coils. After an hour-long struggle the mammoth managed to pull itself free, and limp off to safety. (Antagonism between elephants and dragons again!)

Batchmatchnik finally managed to find his way back to civilization, but what are we to make of his story? It seems worthy of Conan-Doyle or Edgar Rice Burroughs. It may seem fantastic, but the Russian officials seemed to believe it, as they pardoned him due to his services for science. But why no follow up expeditions? Why have we heard no more of this lost valley in 130 years? Can't the Russians locate it: or is the whole thing a newspaper hoax?

Hoax or not, many others have encountered the Siberian dragons.

The best known 20th century case was reported in the November 21st 1964 issue of the newspaper *Komsomol'skaya Pravada.*

Moscow University mounted a geological expedition to explore the mineral deposits of the Kula range and the surrounding districts. The expedition lasted from June until October, and was led by A. Kharchenkov, an engineer. The team consisted of seven other scientists. The team hear rumours of a monster inhabiting Lake Khaiyr. The lake is not large, being some 600 metres by 500 metres, but we have learnt from the monster-haunted lakes of the Republic of Ireland, that a lake does not have to be big to hold a monster. It is however connected to many other small lakes in the basin of the Omoleya river. It is an area of recent disruption of the Earth's crust, and is a thermal lake, freezing later than its peers. After trekking miles over freezing tundra, the scientists were told by the local inhabitants of the small Khaiyr village that no-one dared fish on the lake, and that no waterfowl would alight there. The lake's depth had never been measured, but was said to be very deep.

The team's biologist, and a member of the Yakut branch of the Academy of Sciences, Dr Nikolai Gladkika, was the first to see the creature. He had gone to the lake to draw water one morning. He saw a massive animal that had crawled out onto the shore. It had a small snake like head on a long neck, a large body with four short legs and a dorsal fin running down it's back, and a long tail. Its scaly body was bluish black in colour. He thought it was browsing on the grass; a strange diet for such a creature.

Dr Gladkika ran to fetch his team-mates and they returned with cameras. Unfortunately the dragon was gone but there was a large area of flattened grass. There was no indication of the grass being eaten. Indeed we shall see evidence shortly that these beasts are flesh-eaters. Perhaps the animal had just been rubbing its snout among the vegetation. Gladkika produced a drawing of the monster that could have come straight out of a medieval bestiary. The creature strongly resembles a dragon, with slit-like eyes, scaly skin, finned back, and long neck.

Fortunately the dragon put in a second appearance. This time the expedition leader and two members of the biology group were looking across the lake. The monster broke the surface, its head and dorsal fin clearly visible. It lashed the water with its long tail sending waves across the lake.

The expedition leader postulated that it could be some kind of prehistoric reptile. He intended to return the following year and set up camp by the lake. If he did, no reports have ever reached the West of a second expedition.

This was not the first time monsters had been seen in the lake by non-locals. In 1942 two pilots reported seeing a pair of strange creatures in the water. They likened the monsters to giant newts due to the crests on their backs.

Russian geologists seem to have a lot of luck monster hunting! In July 1953 a prospecting party led by V. A. Tver-dokhelbov travelled to the Sorongnakh Plateau. The party arrived at Lake Vorota on a bright sunny morning. Tver-dokhelbov and his assistant Boris Baskator observed an object some 300 metres out on the lake.

At first they thought it was a floating oil-drum, but soon realised that this was not the case as the object swam closer to shore. The pair climbed a cliff to get a better view. In Tverdokhelbov's own words...

The animal came closer, and it was possible to see those parts of it that emerged from the water. The breadth of the foreparts of the creature's torso, evidently the head, was as much as two metres. The eyes were set wide apart. The body was approximately ten metres. It was enormous and of a dark grey colour. On the sides of the head could be seen two light coloured patches. On its back was sticking up, to a height of half a metre or so, was what seemed to be some kind of dorsal fin which was narrow and bent backwards. The animal was moving itself forward in leaps, its upper part appearing at times above the water and then disappearing. When at a distance of 100 metres from the shore it stopped; it then began to beat the water vigorously, raising a cascade of spray; then it plunged out of sight.

Was this the same kind of beast that haunts Lake Khaiyr? The dorsal fin and water thrashing behaviour are alike, but no mention is made of a long neck. The head of this animal seems broad. Perhaps the what the witnesses took to be the head was part of a bulky body, or perhaps this is a totally different creature. Only further expeditions can answer that question.

Lake Labynkyr lies on the same plateau. It is a big lake nine miles long and 800 feet deep, and also has an evil reputation. Locals are convinced that The Devil inhabits the lake. Gun dogs that have leapt into the water to re-trieve shot ducks have been eaten by the monster. One man told of how the brute pursued his raft. He described a dark grey beast with an enormous mouth. Some reindeer hunters observed the monster coil up out of the water to snatch a passing bird.

In 1963 a small expedition visited both of these lakes. Four members observed an object 800 metres out on Lake Labynkyr. It emerged and submerged several times. They could not take photographs as the sun was setting. The following year three teams, each replacing the other in shifts visited the lakes. The third and final group saw the Labynkyr monster in the latter half of August.

Two expedition members saw a row of three humps 100 metres from shore. They ran after the humps trying (unsuccessfully) to photograph them. The humps dived and rose together. It was not clear if they were separate animals or parts of one creature.

In 1964 two journalists from the Italian magazine *Epoca* visited Lake Labynkyr whilst travelling to Oymyakon. They were told that some time before a party of men saw a reindeer swim into the lake. The deer vanished and did not resurface. Then a dog swam on and vanished as well. Suddenly, and shrouded in a mist, a vast black monster rose snorting from the lake. One of the observers, apparently a scholar, was convinced that the beast was a dino-saur. The locals flatly refused to take the journalists out onto the lake.

Another story concerns a hunter's dog who swam out into the lake and was eaten by the monster. The grieving hunter constructed a raft out of reindeer skin and filled it with hot coals. He floated the smouldering raft out onto the lake. The monster snatched it and dived. It reappeared shortly making terrible sounds.

In the 1970s a lame horse belonging to some geologists was attacked in the night by some unknown predator. Alerted by the horses screams the geologists got up out of their sleeping bags to investigate. They were too late. Something large and powerful had already dragged the horse down into the lake. Locals said that they often found holes in the ice with strange tracks around them.

In a letter published in *Komosomol'skaya Pravad* on January 21st 2000 Vladimir Osadchy from Moscow stated that he and a group of tourists had visited the lake in November 1979. The tourists made their way out onto the frozen lake heading for a reservoir two kilometres from the shore. Halfway there they, stopped for a rest. An object like a black pillar was seen to rise up in the distance. A number of the tourists ran to investigate.

They reached the spot fifteen minutes later and ascended a bank two metres high. They discovered a patch of un-frozen water a metre across. The edges looked like they had been licked. It looked as if some aquatic animal had created a breathing hole. Upon returning, they were told, by those who stayed behind, that they had observed the "pillar" rise several times again whilst they were gone. In the morning, they searched the area and found another breathing hole with licked edges.

In August 2000 a group of journalists from *Komosomol'skaya Pravad* travelled to the lake. Using sonar, they detected two large moving objects at the bottom of the lake. The bigger of the two was eighteen metres (sixty feet) long.

Russian explorer Alexander Remple has been told many stories about dragon-like creatures in the Taiga. Known to the natives as *paymurs*, they are described as having heads like sheat fish, better known as the wels catfish (*Silurus glanis)* and bodies like crocodiles. It should be noted here that Oriental dragons were said to have barbels like those of a catfish on the snout.

One man, Anatoly Komandigu, told of three hunters who made their camp by a snow covered mound in the twi-light, and lit a fire. They sat with their backs to the mound and warmed themselves as the fire heated up. Suddenly, they felt the mound at their backs heave up. The spun round and saw that the "mound" was a huge reptile covered in thick grey and black scales. It had short legs and a long tail. Needless to say the men fled. Three days later they returned for their equipment left behind in the panic. They discovered the remains of an animal, possibly the dragon's prey in the area.

More recently TASS the Russian news agency reported that a snake-like monster seven metres (23 feet) long with a sheep-like head was living in a lake near Sharipovo, South Ural. It had been seen by dozens of witnesses and had been photographed. It left tracks in the grass on the lake's shore. It had supposedly eaten all the fish and frogs in the lake. Tass also reported that some of the older villages recalled a "prehistoric" fish - previously thought extinct - had been caught in the lake fifty years previuosly.

Needless to say the pictures have never reached the west. Nor has any details of this antediluvian fish. Perhaps it is a case of Chinese (or in this case Russian) whispers.

How could large reptiles survive in such cold climates? We know that some dinosaurs coped with cool climates, but nothing so extreme as Siberian winters. The huge leatherback turtle or luth (*Dermochelys coriacea*) is a reptile that can survive in cold waters. It achieves this by being gigantothermic. Its size helps it retain its body heat. The leatherback is not an elongate creature like our Siberian dragons. Elongated animals make much less effective gi-gantotherms than more stubby shaped creatures like turtles. Perhaps our dragons hibernate, and are active during the brief summer months. But this does not explain the sightings of the monsters in ice and snow. Perhaps they are paranormal or interdimensional in nature? Only until dedicated cryptozoologists journey to eastern Siberia in search of these dragons, can we begin to learn the truth.

The Japanese have a history of dragons reaching back many centuries. This is reflected in literature and exquisite works of art. More recently the Japanese dragon or *tatsu* has rampaged across our cinema screens in the guise of Godzilla. The three hundred foot tall radioactive fire breathing mutant *Tyrannosaurus rex* and anti-hero of twenty-two wildly entertaining films from Toho studios. It will come as no surprise then that Japan has modern day drag-ons.

Lake Ikeda near the city of Kagoshuma on the Island of Kyushu has an interesting legend attached to it. It was said that a horse and her white foal used graze the grass on the banks of this extinct volcano. On day a samurai came and took the foal to be his steed. The horse leapt into the lake looking for her offspring. She still surfaces from time to time to the amazement of onlookers. A Japanese horse eel? Well, there is *something* strange in Lake Ikeda. Witnesses describe a hump backed beast with a snaky head and neck.

Several photographs have been taken of the Ikeda dragon. The first was in 1978 by Mr Toksiaki Matsuhara. He was a folklorist investigating the stories attached to the lake. On December 16th he saw a whirlpool form in the centre of the lake and watched it through his telescope. Later he saw a pair of creatures together close to *Metow-Iwa* (married couple) rocks and photographed them. The shots appear to show the two animals together, their humps creating waves. The monster has been christened 'Issie'.

Many respectable people have seen Issie, including the president of a construction firm. Yutaka Kawaji and twenty members of his family' saw a black skinned animal showing six to nine metres (twenty – thirty feet) of its body above the surface. Mr Kawaji pursued the monster in his motor boat. It dove and resurfaced several times.

Iamu Horiouchi says that the thing he saw in the lake was a row of humps twenty metres (sixty-five feet) long. He took eight photos of the phenomena on the 4th of October 1978, but none came out clearly.

A mere four hours later, coffee shop owner Hiromi Nakahama watched for nearly four minutes as two massive humps rose and fell in the waters.

Issie has counterparts in other areas of Japan. Also on Kyushu is Lake Toya, home of a similar entity. On the northern island of Hokkaido lies Lake Kutcharo home to a monster, which has been called 'Kussie'. Local people have formed a protection society for the animal.

Australia has a long tradition of water monsters. The most famous of these is the bunyip. The term itself is probably a corruption of the word *banip* - a term used in the now nearly dead language of the Victorian Aborigines. Bunyip first appears in print in 1812. The bunyips however seem to be distinctly mammalian. They fall into two categories, a short-necked, dog or seal like animal, and a long-necked type with a pointed doggish muzzle. Both kinds are hairy. Many believe that the short-necked bunyip was some king of pinniped, a seal or sea lion that had swam into fresh water. This happens on a regular basis. The grey seal (*Halichoerus grypus*) has been recorded in Loch Ness. In 1850 a seal was shot at Conargo in New South Wales 1,500 km from the sea. It's stuffed remains graced the Conargo Hotel for many years. The long-necked variety may have been some kind of aquatic marsupial. Tragically we shall never know. The long-necked bunyip seems to have died out as there have been no reports of these distinctive beasts for well over a century.

There is a very different kind of fresh water monster in Australia. A reptilian animal that lives far too south to be a crocodile. It haunts the Hawkesbury River north of Sidney. Known to the Aborigines as *Mirreeulla* (giant water serpent) its pedigree runs back many years. Artwork by the Dharuk tribe, depicting *Mirreeulla* have been found in various places. The rock art has been dated to 3000-5000 years old. There have been stories circulating among the white men of some long necked horror lurking in the muddy water since at least the 1930s. Near Dangar Island in that decade, Bill Dunn observed a fifteen metre (fifty foot) long-necked monster pursuing a school of mullet. In 1935 a group of workmen repairing a bridge saw a grey skinned twelve metre (forty foot) long necked animal.

Unlike many of its peers, the Hakwesbury River Monster has an evil reputation. In 1949 a young couple boating in the lower Hawesbury saw a bull on a sand bank. Suddenly a three foot long reptilian head on the end of a six metre (twenty foot) neck lunged out of the murky water, and snatched the bull. A massive body - nine metres (thirty feet) long - heaved up from the river, as the bull was dragged to its doom. The girl started screaming hysterically and the boy rowed away as quickly as possible. The farmer who owned the bull, found the drag marks and bloodstains on the bank but no sign of his bull.

A similar event took place in May 1967, when a farmer near the town of Spencer was overlooking his animals from an embankment as they drank from the river. Suddenly the waters exploded, and a reptilian head atop a long neck, flashed out and seized a cow. The monster effortlessly hauled the unfortunate bovid into the river, leaving a titan wake. The rest of the herd panicked and ran crashing through the reeds.

In 1979 a monster was supposedly trapped in the nearby Nepan river at Yarramundi near the junction with the Hawkesbury for several months. Bushwalkers saw it snatch a cow from the bank.

At this point I reiterate that there are no crocodiles in this part of Australia - it is too cool in winter. Also, crocodiles are not noted for their long necks.

Some think the *Mirreeulla's* tastes run to human flesh as well. In the mid 1970s a woman and a boy who had been on a rowing boat on the river disappeared. The smashed remains of the boat were found near Broken Bay. Further inland, two young couples vanished at Coal and Candle Creek. Their six metre (twenty foot), 200 horsepower boat was found overturned. Another man, a resident of Sydney, went swimming in a lagoon near Ebenezer. The only part of him ever seen again was his hand that washed up on a sandbank.

Some folk even think that the monster has grabbed human victims from boats. In 1960 a policeman was one of a number of guests in a yachting party at Broken Bay. He vanished without trace whilst standing near the stern rail. One of the other guests said:

One moment he was there. We all looked away while someone was talking, and when one of us looked back he was gone. There was a disturbance in the river as if something had come up out of the water and snatched him.

A similar incident occurred in 1977. A fishing party were enjoying the view from their boat, just east of Brooklyn, one afternoon. One person noticed that a friend, who had been standing by the stern of the vessel, had gone. Once again there was a big disturbance in the water. Rumours were rife that he had been taken by the monster.

These people could have easily been the victims of accidents that nothing to do with monsters, but there are an alarming number of reports of the Hawkesbury River Monster attacking boats.

One of the most dramatic attacks happened to George and Jan Cayley who had moored their houseboat in Broken Bay in 1979. Early one morning the couple felt their home rise up and lurch violently to one side. Their bed and furniture was toppled over before the houseboat righted itself again. Scrambling over the chaos they ran to see if another boat had struck them. Instead they saw a gigantic, long-necked, serpent-headed beast with a massive body, swimming away across the bay. Friends who came to help them repair their home claimed to have seen the monster in the past.

The monster attacked another house-boat in Broken Bay in 1979. A number of people on the bank saw a grey skinned, hump-backed creature with a long neck, swimming towards a moored houseboat. The resident family, unaware, were eating lunch on the deck. The observers shouted warnings as the fifteen metre (fifty foot) animal surfaced under the houseboat throwing the family to the floor. Submerging again it swam away.

One man claims to have captured what may be a juvenile specimen of one of the animals. In 1971 whilst fishing at Ettalong in March John Gilbraith and his father caught a weird little critter.

It was 46 centimetres in length and browny-black in colour, with a paddle like tail and fins, a thin neck and a head reminiscent of a snake's. When I attempted to free the creature, it opened its mouth like a snake and hissed, showing teeth about 2.5 cm in length, and needle sharp, which made me jump.

We kept the strange beast for some days, hoping other fishermen could identify it. Like a fool my father later discarded it. Since then I have seen pictures of plesiosaurs and have often wondered if this is what the small creature could have been.

If only Mr Gilbraith had kept his catch. Stories like this make cryptozoologists wince. We shall hear other stories of catches like these, and lost opportunities from elsewhere. If *plesiosaurs* or some other aquatic reptile did have modern day descendents then they would live in warm waters with a plentiful supply of fish. The Hawkesbury River beats Loch Ness hands down in those departments.

Moving across the globe to Africa, we have already considered the reptilian monsters of the deep jungles and rivers. But there are other dragon like brutes lurking in the more southerly regions of the continent.

Howick Falls is a spectacular thirty metre (one hundred foot) waterfall near the town of Howick in Natal, South Africa. The local Zulus and their *Sangomas* (witch doctors) say it is the lair of a serpent monster called *Inkanyamba*. They sacrifice chickens and goats to the water god. *Inkanyamba* is said to relish large fare as well. Bodies lost at the falls are often never recovered and those that are have usually been partially eaten. Around thirty years ago *Inkanyamba* was blamed for the death of a Zulu girl further up river at another waterfall. Whilst playing with friends she was dragged underwater and vanished. Crocodiles? Quite possibly, but odd creatures have been seen in the area.

Local man Bob Teeny claims to have seen the monster one September morning in 1995. Whilst on a viewing platform beside the falls he saw a dark snake-like head and neck of huge proportions rise out of the water. He had no camera but he put up a reward for anyone who could photograph the animal. The two pictures he received were not impressive. One of them was a crude hoax with an illustration of an *Apatasaurus* from a child's book on dinosaurs, superimposed onto the bottom of the falls.

Others have seen the Howick Falls monster though. Johannes Hlongwane was caretaker of a caravan park near the falls between 1969 and 1985. He saw *Inkanyamba* twice. Once in 1974 and again in 1981. He says it had a long snake-like body thicker than his own. It raised its head and neck nine metres (thirty feet) out of the water. It had a crest running along its back.

A Conservation Services Ranger, Mr Buthelezi, saw one of the creatures in 1962 whilst he and a companion were walking along the Umgein River near the Midmar Dam. The horse-headed monster was on a sandbank, and slithered back into the river as they approached.

In April 2000 reports began to come in of a monstrous snake like animal from the community of Ezitapile in South Africa's Eastern Cape. Captain Mpofana Skwatsha of the Aliwal North police, reported that livestock grew agitated when the creature was around. It was described as yellow, with a horse-like head, and a mane down its back. Its body was as thick as a twenty quart barrel. It coiled its tail around a tree.

The legends of *Inkanyamba* are highly interesting when viewed in the context of dragon legends worldwide. The monsters are said to slither from lake to lake. When looking for a mate they fly into the clouds. Angry *Inkanyambas* can create storms and hurricanes like Asian dragons. The storms that effected the Greytown, Ingwavuma, and Pongola areas in 1998 were blamed on the dragons. 52 mph winds, and tennis-ball sized hailstones made around 2,000 people homeless. Some believe *Inkanyamba* mistakes the corrugated iron roofs of shanties as water. Some people even painted their roofs black to discourage the rain-god.

Cave paintings and Bushman rock art depict a horse-headed serpentine beast that archaeologists have dubbed the 'rain animal'. It has a fin running down its back, and horn-like projections on its head. It is often depicted as spewing water. *Inkanyamba's* pedigree seems to be an ancient one.

In South America the lakes and rivers of the jungle lowlands are ruled by the giant anaconda and possibly by even larger serpents. But the deep cold lakes of the Andes hold a different kind of monster.

Lago Nahuel Huapi in Argentina is the best known monster-haunted lake in South America. The first modern sighting occurred in 1910, when Mr George Garret and his son were navigating a government engineer around the lake. They briefly saw a six metre (twenty foot) hump rise six feet from the water. But things didn't really hot up until the 1920s.

In 1922 the director of Buenos Aries Zoo, Dr Clementi Onelli, received a most intriguing letter from an American prospector called Martin Sheffield. Sheffield was a larger than life character who seemed to have stepped out of a western. Heavy drinking and six-gun toting, he always wore a ten-gallon hat. At the time Sheffield was searching for gold in the Andean foothills of the Chebut territory in Patagonia. Beside the lake he had come across the spoor of a large animal that had crushed bushes, and left deep marks in the ground disappearing into the lake. In the lake the prospector claimed to have seen a monster with a swan-like neck and a crocodilian body.

One could have forgiven the good doctor for ignoring the testimony of a such a man as Sheffield, but he had heard other reports from South America himself. Whilst travelling in Patagonia in 1897, he had been told of a monster inhabiting White Lake. A Chilean farmer recounted that he had heard strange noises at night as if some heavy cart were being dragged over the pebble beach. On moonlit nights he had seen a giant beast swimming in the lake raising its reptilian neck high out of the water.

Onelli tried to get funding from a film company but was refused. Undaunted, he raised the 3,000 pesos he needed by public subscription. In May 1922 the expedition set off. It was led by zoo superintendent Jose Cihagi and Emillio Frey, an engineer who had been a member of the Chile-Argentine Boundary Commission for twenty years and who had explored the Chebut territory. Carrying elephant guns and dynamite, the expedition travelled by boat, lorry, and horse into the then wild area.

The enterprise caused outrage in some quarters, with the president of the Society for the Protection of Animals demanding that the Minister for the Interior should not grant the expedition permits to hunt the monster, under the state law 2786, that governed the hunting of rare animals. After confusion about permits that halted the expedition for a while they finally reached the lake on October 18th.

Borrowing a boat from some Welsh colonists, Frey detonated eleven cartridges of dynamite in the lake to absolutely no avail. Finally winter forced the expedition to head home.

Today a city of 100,000 souls, San Carlos de Bariloche has sprung up in the once remote area. The sightings of the monster, now named Nahuelito, continue. Father Maurico Rumboll's mother saw a long reptilian neck break the mirror-like surface of the lake on February 18th 1978. It left a large wake on the surface as it advanced.

In 1989 Cristian Muller had set out at seven am for a days fishing. Travelling by bus he glanced out of the window and saw what he at first took to be a boat. Its dark colour was very odd as all the boats he knew on the lake were light in colour. Suddenly the "boat" submerged, and the bus driver slammed on the brakes. The excited passengers began screaming "Nahuelito, Nahuelito!"

On New Year's Day 1994, Jessica Campbell and several other people saw the monster as a row of humps showing above the surface as it swam.

Paula Jacarbe claimed to have heard the monster breathing. Charlie her brother is the keyboard player in a band, and attempted to replicate the sound with a synthesizer.

A video-tape purporting to show Nahuelito is being held in a bank vault in San Carlos de Bariloche, until its owner decides what to do with it. This scenario sounds worryingly like the Dr Farquhar McRae fiasco at Loch Ness.

In 1996 Jessica Campbell saw the monster twice more. At the beach at Peninsula de San Pedro the beast surfaced in front of a whole group of people including Campbell. The watchers noticed leathery skin and cloak-like fins. Nahuelito submerged but rose again forty-five minutes later, directly in line with Campbell who was sitting on some rocks. As the monster swam towards her she was gripped with terror and fled. Much like Paula Jacabe, she recalls hearing the monster breathing. She says she will never forget those sounds.

Back at White Lake, a British man - Barny Dickenson - who had lived by the lake since the late 1940s, was prompted to write to the *Illustrated London News* in 1959 after a series of articles on the Loch Ness Monster had been printed. He often sat by the lake of an evening watching boats go by. On several occasions he had seen an animal he thought was too large to be any known South American beast in the waters. The local Auracanians called the thing *Curo* - meaning cow hide, on account of its texture. Dickenson said that the local gauchos also reported having seen the monster. It appeared in the evenings as a single huge hump, like an upturned boat with the texture of cowhide.

In 1997 cryptozoologists Paul LeBlond and John Kirk were told of a strange case in Venezuela. Freelance writer Harry Hanbury was working for the *Discovery Channel* re-editing and rescripting a German Documentary called "Islands Above the Rainforests". This documentary followed researchers from the Simon Bolivar University in Caracas to three large mesas known as tepuis that rose out of the jungle. Team leader Armando Michaelangeli claimed to have sighted a family of small "dinosaurs". The team searched for the creatures and interviewed a Latvian man, Alexander Laimay, who had lived in the jungle for twenty years. He claimed to have also seen the small monsters in the past and described them as 33 inches long, with long necks and flippers. They sound like juvenile specimens of the classic lake-monster. Sadly, to my knowledge, no further research has been done in this area.

A creature called *Chan*, who in legend is supposed to hearken back to the days of the Aztecs, supposedly inhabits a net work of seven small lakes in the Valle de Santiago, Mexico. Each September local people bestow gifts upon the creature that they believe to be their protector. Mexican cryptozoologist Leopoldo Bolanos scrutinized the lake and was able to photograph a large creature just beneath its surface. The shot was taken in a lake called La Alberca.

Bolanos was anonymously sent a photograph that purports to be of *Chan*. It was supposedly shot just after an earthquake on September 6th 1958. It shows a brownish barrel-shaped body with a long-neck and long tail. Reservations about the picture have been raised, however, as the background shore-line does not resemble the steep sided cliffs that surround the lake.

Moving across the border into North America we find a continent veritably writhing with serpent dragons. Native American myth is full of such creatures. Perhaps *myth* is the wrong word, for North America's dragons seem hearty and hale to this day.

Lake Okeechobee is a 40 mile square body of water on Florida's tip. It is surrounded by swamps and is connected to the sea via several rivers. For three months in 2001 a dragon-like monster haunted the lake. Startled witnesses described a scaly, long-necked, creature up to 65 feet long. Most saw it a distance of 150 feet or more but one fisherman Mark Tagerton had his boat capsized by the monster.

I will never get over it as long as I live. The water had been rough and choppy all day. It was weird because there wasn't a lot of wind. About 4 o'clock the water started churning and the boat started rocking like crazy. All of a sudden I get chills just talking about it this sea monster thing raised out of the water, not 50 feet from the boat.

I was petrified. It just paused there a moment watching me. Then, all of a sudden, it lunged forward and crashed down against the surface of the water right beside my boat. It sounded like thunder. The impact caused such a massive wake that the boat tipped over lengthways. I thought the thing was going to eat me. But it just disappeared.

Fortunately another fisherman witnessed the whole event and rescued Tagerton. Law Enforcement officials from towns around the lake stated, off the record, that sightings went back years that but there had never been so many so close together.

Australian zoologist, Dr Victor Tandy, who had been in the USA since mid-April collecting photographs and studying documents said:

I don't know if its because the drought has disturbed its habitat or just because of increasing environmental problems on the lake. And though I've never seen it myself I'm convinced something is down there and it's been down there for many years. And I'm also convinced that something is drawing it to the surface more frequently than ever before. It's a mystery I intend to solve.

Arkansas's White River, a tributary of the Mississippi, reputedly had a monster in it as far back as 1915. Sightings were sporadic and little recorded. The exception was a 1924 sighting by Mrs Ethel Smith of Little Rock and her family. They were holidaying in the area and had stopped so that her husband could do some fishing. The children yelled that there was a submarine in the river. The whole family saw the back of a huge animal with a crusty hide for ten whole minutes. The head and tail remained hidden. It let out an awful bellow that badly scared Mrs Smith.

That changed in 1937, when wonderfully named farmer Bramblett Bateman, saw something in the water just below the town of Newport. He did not see the thing's head or tail but a hump some 12 feet long by 5 feet wide rose up from the murk. The hump remained visible for five minutes. The witness observed the same phenomena on several occasions.

Other witnesses came forward, including Bateman's wife and J. M. Gwaf, who had seen the water "boiling" up across the river two feet high. The deputy sheriff of Jackson County went out to look for the monster and saw a mass of bubbles coming to the surface in a circle of nine metres (30 feet). He was convinced that some large animal was alive in the river.

Professional diver Charles E Brown braved the depths of the White River with a harpoon, but found no monster.

The monster, named 'Whitey' by the press did not re-appear until 1971. A person identifying themselves only as "Masterson" wrote to the Newport paper *The Daily Independent* claiming to have witnessed, on Jun 17th, a creature as large as a boxcar, two yards across thrashing in the water. Once again no head was visible and the witness was badly scared.

Hot on the heels of this event came another report. Ernest Denks claimed to have seen the creature a fortnight before. He saw the monster's head and said it was adorned with a horn. He estimated it's weight at 1,000 lbs.

Cloyce Warren and two friends were fishing on the river when they were disturbed by a column of water that erupted some 60 metres (200 feet) from the boat. Suddenly, a large grey form with a spiny back nine metres (30 feet) long rose up. Grabbing his Polaroid Swinger camera, he photographed 'Whitey' before it submerged. The compelling picture shows a long, reptilian, ridged-back and a bulbous front portion.

More pictures were taken by Gary Addington and Lloyd Hamilton near Jacksonport, when a four metre section of spiky back breeched the surface.

Soon after on July 5th tracks were discovered on Townsend Island. The three toed tracks measured 35 cm by 20 cm (14 by 8 inches). They bore claw marks and pads on the toes and heel. A spur extended from the heel. Grass had been flattened and the spoor ran to and from the water. One man claimed to have seen such tracks for the previous two years.

Ollie Richardson and Joey Dupree decided to explore the river around Townsend Island in a small boat. Whilst out on the water, something surfaced beneath the boat, and raised it up out of the water. The pair did not see what it was, but reasoned it must have been huge.

Jim Gates twice saw a car-sized object surrounded by bubbles rise from the water whilst he was fishing near Jacksonport in August 1971, but little detail was visible.

On June 5th 1972, R C McClauglen of Lincoln, Nebraska and his family saw a spiny back creature 18-22 metres (60-75 feet long) and grey in colour. They saw the head and watched the monster thrash the water for 5 minutes.

In 1973 citizens petitioned the Newport City Board of Directors to protect 'Whitey'. They declared the White River adjacent to Jaksenport State to be a White River Monster Refuge.

Cryptozoologist Roy P Mackal has tried to explain the White River monster as an out of place northern elephant seal (*Mirounga angustirostris)*, a gigantic pinniped found of the western coast of North America. Whilst it is true that seals have been known to swim thousands of miles up rivers, the descriptions of Whitey's size and spiny back do not match with this animal.

You could be forgiven for thinking that Loch Murray is in Scotland. Its actual location is South Carolina. This state is home to many American alligators (*Alligator mississipiensis)*, but witnesses are adamant that this animal is not what they have seen swimming in the waters of Loch Murray

The Loch Murray monster was first recorded in 1933, but as with many other lake monsters, early sightings are vague. In 1980 *The Independent News* described it as a "cross between a snake and something prehistoric". Buddy and Shirley Browning and friend Kord Brazell were fishing when the monster allegedly attacked them. Buddy recalled that he had fished the lake for 20 years and had never seen anything like the monster. It was not a sturgeon, eel or alligator. It swam towards the boat and attempted to climb aboard. Buddy battered it off with an oar and the scared trio left hastily.

In late April 2000, Mary S. Shealy saw an odd creature like an upturned boat close to the Loch Murray Dam. It was nine metres (thirty feet) long by three metres (ten feet) high.

The Great Lakes of the eastern USA, and southern Canada; five linked massive bodies of water are not without serpent reports. Samuel Rafinesque, a biologist who catalogued many North American, species wrote of a 35 to 60 foot serpent that had been seen on Lake Erie in July 1817. It was a foot thick, dark-mahogany in colour, and had shining eyes.

In 1933 (that year again!), two fishermen claimed to have captured a strange animal in Lake Erie. This is how the Associated Press reported it.

SANDUSKY. Ohio, July 21st (AP) Inside a tightly boarded box beside the lakeshore tonight was locked what several persons said was a large marine animal having specifications that might qualify it as a serpent, claimed to have been captured by two Cincinnati fishermen in Sandusky Bay.

The fishermen, Clifford Wilson, and Francis Cogentrose, said that the "serpent" measuring about twenty feet long and about twelve inches through at the thickest place, arose late today out of the Lake Erie waters beside their boat.

Although frightened by the beast, they said, they hit it over the head twice with an oar and knocked it senseless, then fastened a line to its head and towed it to shore.

Their catch began to show signs of returning to consciousness when they got it to the beach, Wilson and Cogentrose said, so they obtained a packing box 6 feet long, 3 feet wide, and 2 feet deep and coiled Mr Sea Serpent into it and nailed it tightly shut.

Neither the "owners" or any of the scores of curious who gathered about the box would take a chance on opening it to show the serpent to the scoffers, who were numerous.

Police Captain Leo Schively, E L Ways, managing editor of a local afternoon paper, and C J Irwin and Mel Harmon of a Sunday morning paper said they saw the serpent as it was being boxed up and joined the fishermen in describing it as a huge, snakelike beast, coloured black, dark green, and white and having a hide resembling that of an alligator.

The "owners" were undecided tonight what they were going to do with it. The reported capture came after a number of persons had reported sighting a "sea-serpent" hereabouts.

217

Strange how a fresh water animal is called a sea-serpent. The box was supposedly sent to Cincinnati Zoo, but readers will not be surprised that there is no record of its arrival. Save for the comparatively small size of the monster, it is tempting to write this story off as a hoax. But others have reported monsters from these very waters.

- In 1960, Ken Golic was fishing close to a pier in Sandusky at about 11 pm. He saw a cigar shaped hump protruding 1 to 1.5 feet out of the water.

- In 1969, Jim Schindler came within 6 feet of the monster as it swam a foot below the surface close to South Bass Island. He was unable to guess the monster's length but estimated it's width to be two feet.

- In 1981, Theresa Kovach reported seeing a "snake-like reptile so large it could easily capsize a boat". She observed the thing from her house on the Cedar Point Causeway.

The Lake Erie monster has been named 'South Bay Bessie', continuing the slightly irritating convention of giving monsters "twee" names. Bessie was seen again in 1983 by Mary Landoll off Rye Beach, Huron. Just before dawn, whilst sitting at her porch, she heard a sound akin to rowing. Looking out over the still lake she saw what looked like an upturned boat. It was greenish brown and 12-15 metres (40 to 50 feet) long. A long neck with a head became visible and she noted both a mouth and eyes.

A serpentine beast with five humps and a flat tail was seen in 1985 by Tony Schill whilst out on a boat with his friends. A similar serpentine form was observed off Lorain Coast Guard Station by Dale Munroe. The three humped animal was in view for four minutes, and was twice the size of his 16 foot boat.

Bessie has turned up on sonar. Gail Kasner discovered a cigar-shaped object on a fishfinder image graph in 1985. The object was 35 feet long and 30 feet below the surface.

Jetski enthusiast Bob Soracco thought he was looking at a line of porpoises on September 3rd 1990. He was later informed that there are no such mammals in Lake Erie. The row of grey humps had dived as he drew near them.

The gallant Harold Bricker wanted to get a closer look at Bessie, when the monster rose some 1,000 feet from his family's fishing boat. It revealed a snake-like head and 35 feet of black body. His son, realizing that the monster was bigger than the boat, vetoed his father's idea. The monster submerged; perhaps luckily for the Brickers.

On September 11th 1990, two fire inspectors - Steve Dicks and Jim Johnson - watched the monster from a third story window. It showed three black humps, and remained in sight for three minutes. Several other sightings were reported in the following few days.

Huron Lagoon Marina offered $5,000 to anyone who could prove Bessie's existence. The reward is still unclaimed but 1993 was a bumper year for sightings. Charles Douglas and a companion were eight and a half miles out on the lake when they espied what they thought was a log. It was a particularly lively log, as it swam at about 35 mph and frequently dived. It appeared to be following their boat. Douglas wanted to get a better look but his less courageous chum dissuaded him. Cowardly friends are a bane to cryptozoology!

Another acrobatic log was sighted shortly afterwards by charter fishing operators John and Holly Liles and their party. As they were taking the party out to Kelly's island, at four in the afternoon, they sighted a log floating 180 feet away on the Lake's calm surface. As they drew closer they realised that the 25 foot log was an animal, the like of which they had never seen before. It undulated in a series of vertical humps and reminded the witnesses of a Chinese dragon. It was in sight for around fifteen seconds before the boat engine disturbed it and it dived.

Though Lake Erie boasts the most sightings, it does not have a monopoly on the Great Lakes monsters. 1977 saw a spectacular sighting from Lake Superior. It was Memorial Day, and Randy L Baun was camping at Presque Isle, north of Ironwood, Michigan. Taking a trail that led east from the campsite, he slid down a steep wooded bank to a small beach. Here he began to eat lunch. Looking out across the lake he saw three undulating black humps about 1,000 feet out. The humps swiftly swam towards him, and he became alarmed as he saw a monster he described as looking like "an anaconda with the girth of a Volkswagen". He grabbed his 35mm Yashica camera and took a shot, as a horse like head appeared. It had a large eye and twitching catfish-like whiskers on the snout. We can note again that Oriental dragons are *always* pictured with these appendages.

Baun's photo shows a dark head with a large eye reflecting light. The animal remained in view for 30 seconds, but Baun was frozen with fear. He still has nightmares about being devoured by the Lake Superior dragon, and will not swim in deep water. He says there have been many disappearances in the area, and believes that the monster may have eaten people.

In 1997 a recreational fisherman claimed to have seen a buck bitten clean in two by something in the lake as it waded in the water. It seems that swimming in Lake Superior may well be considered an extreme sport.

Lake Michigan has its resident dragon as well. The *Chicago Tribune* reported that on August the 6th and 7th 1867 the crews of several vessels had seen a serpent 12 to 15 metres (40 to 50 feet) long, and as broad as a barrel. The animal beat the lake's surface into a tempest with its bilobate (fluked) tail.

Joseph Muhlke, a fisherman saw it whilst a mile out on the 6th August. Disturbed by a strange grating vocalization, he turned to see a dark oval object like an upturned-boat some 400 metres away from him. As he watched, the object approached. Then a head, with clearly visible eyes and a tail came into view. It was bluish black, with a paler underside. Along its back were a series of bony plates. Muhlke noticed flippers and a fan like fin on the tail.

Pulling up anchor, Muhlke made for shore. The monster swam off, creating a wake that shunted his boat inshore at a considerable speed. Sightings were recorded for several days afterwards.

In 1976 the owner of a local hostelry and his family saw a dark serpentine beast 18 feet long off Point Nipigon.

Kimberly Poepey Del-Rio was travelling by bus beside Lake Michigan in February 1988. Two stops before her home, she noticed something odd swimming in the water of an cove next to the War Memorial Art Centre. The centre is built on a peninsular reaching out into the lake. Pulling the cord to stop the bus, she ran over and saw a hump - like the top of a car - manoeuvring around large lumps of ice in the cove. It finally swam back out into the lake.

The Centre for Fortean Zoology's Indiana representative Elizabeth Clem, has unearthed several encounters on Lake Michigan. Witnesses e-mailed her with their own stories. One of them claimed to have been fishing with a friend on the lake, when something grabbed his line and yanked so violently that their boat capsized. The two fishermen climbed on top of the upturned boat as the water became more disturbed. Then they saw, about 1,000 feet from them, a horse-like head on a long neck emerge from the lake. The neck sported a mane. They screamed until some of their other friends rescued them in another boat.

Another witness had a strikingly similar experience. He was fishing in a boat with his brother when the vessel was violently rocked. Not being able to swim, and thinking it was his brother fooling around, he told him to stop rocking the boat. His brother insisted it was not him. Just then the boat was shook again, and they saw a large black object swim beneath it. When a large head surfaced only 6 metres (20 feet) from the boat, they started the motor and exited the area quickly.

A third witness and a friend were on the ship *Odyssey 2* when they saw a large animal swimming next to the ship. They could make out little detail other than it was snake-like.

Moving on across this massive country we find dragons elsewhere. The *New York Times* and other papers reported a monster in Nebraska on July 25th 1923. It was seen on the shore of Alkali Lake by A. J. Johnson, and two companions. Whilst out duck hunting one morning, they saw the animal three fourths out of the water.

The animal was probably 40 feet long, including the tail and head, when raised in alarm as when he saw us. In general appearance the animal was not unlike an alligator, except that it's head was stubbier, and there seemed to be a projection like a horn between the eyes and nostrils. The animal was built much more heavily throughout than an alligator. It's colour seemed a dull grey or brown.

There was a very distinctive and somewhat unpleasant odour noticeable for several moments after the beast vanished into the water. We stood for several minutes after the animal, had gone, hardly knowing what to do or say, when we noticed, several hundred feet out from shore a considerable commotion in the water.

Sure enough the animal came to the surface, floated there for a moment and lashed the water with its tail, suddenly dived and we saw no more of him.

Roy P. Mackal has suggested that this may have been an errant elephant seal. However the size is nearly twice that of an elephant seal, and no one can claim that an elephant seal's face looks like that of an alligator.

Montana's Flathead Lake has a monster recorded in the legends of the Kalispell Indians. They spoke of a monster with an arrow proof hide who would snatch up and devour braves. Captain James Kern was the first paleface to see the beast. Whilst piloting his steamboat across the lake in 1885 he saw what he took to be another vessel. Soon it revealed itself to be the humped back of a huge animal. Passengers, with typically human care and concern, opened fire on the creature, which promptly dived.

Another steamboat captain had a run in with the lake's strange inhabitant in 1919. Seeing what he thought was a log, he took evasive action to prevent a collision. The "log" sprang into life like it's kin in other lakes and swam round to the starboard side of the vessel where 50 passengers saw it (though this time no one took pot shots!).

The Flathead Lake monster has been credited with ripping up fishermen's nets for years.

Members of the Zeigler family were alarmed by unusually large waves lapping over the dock by their lakeside home. Upon investigation they discovered a horse-headed monster scratching itself against the pilings. Mr Zeigler, displaying an all-American attitude rushed inside for a rifle. Luckily (more than likely for *him*) the monster had swam out of range by the time he returned.

Another Lakeside resident, Ronald Nixon, saw the monster in 1963. It was 7.5 metres (25 feet) long and threw up a 2 foot head wave. It showed no signs of a dorsal fin and did not seem to be a fish.

A number of locals formed a company called *Big Fish Unlimited* and left huge hooks baited with dead chickens. They captured nothing. A $1,000 reward for the first good photograph has also remained unclaimed.

In the summer of 1969 or 1970, Kay Grice, her sister, her niece, and a friend, were in a boat off Arrowhead island when they noticed a series of "v" shaped wakes in the water. They followed the trail in their boat, watching as it smoothed-out then formed again. Suddenly a large creature rose up 15 metres (50 feet) behind the boat. It had a long neck and reminded them of illustrations of the Loch Ness Monster.

In 1975, a 23 year old girl from Indiana was on the lake in a sailboat belonging to the Olsen family. She returned to the dock pale and shacking and told the Olsens that a long, brown, snake-like thing had swam under the boat.

The Olsen sisters saw the animal for themselves in 1982. Six metres (20 feet) of it's body was showing in two humps. The head was oval shaped and larger than a (American) football.

Major George Cote and his son Neal have seen the Flathead monster twice. The first sighting was in May 1985 as they trolled for trout in Mackinaw bay:

...we saw a large object surfacing and diving off the north point of the bay. At first we thought it must be one or more SCUBA divers. We approached the thing slowly...As we got closer we could see it was chasing large squaw-fish in the shallows. At one point it raised its head out of the water and appeared to be looking at us.

When we got within 60 metres of it, we realized it was nothing we'd ever seen. The thing was big: as long as a tele-phone pole and twice as large in diameter. The skin of the creature was smooth and coal black; it had the perfect head of a serpent. There were 4-6 humps sticking out of the water. It stopped 400 metres out from the bay, looked back, and dove under the waves.

They saw a similar animal in 1987 off Lakeside on the west shore. They estimated its speed at an impressive 100 knots. They had a perfect view of it's head, tail, and body as it swam towards Caroline point.

In July of 1985 George and Elna Darrow observed it from their sail boat 300 feet offshore. It manifested as three dark loops 9 metres (30 feet) long.

Policeman Richard Gaffney of Illinois, his wife, and three children, all saw the monster surface among a shoal of bait fish 150 feet from their boat in July 1993. As it swam, by Gaffney noted that it had shiny skin, a head the size of a bowling ball and humps. It was six metres (20 feet) long. He likened it to "Nessie".

Payette Lake in Idaho is home to a monster with the memorable moniker of 'Slimey Slim'. The now familiar reports of encounters with living logs date back to the 1920s. In 1944 Slim grabbed the public imagination when *Time Magazine* published the story of a mass sighting by 30 people. They had seen a periscope-like head and neck above the waves. Thomas Rodgers, a resident of Boise, Idaho, told of seeing the 11.5 metre (35 foot) monster at a dis-tance of only 15 metres (50 feet). It had a face like a snub-nosed crocodile (recalling the Nebraska beast) and held its head 18 inches out of the water.

In 1977 three people from the town of McCall saw Slim whilst on the patio of a café. It was 300 feet away and 12 to 15 metres (40-50) feet long. It raised a brown coloured back three to four feet out of the water.

'Big Wally' must match 'Slimey Slim' in terms of odd names for monsters. It reputedly makes its lair in Wallowa Lake Oregon. The *Wallowa Chieftain* ran the following report in 1885.

November 5, 1885. A prospector, who refuses to give his name to the public, was coming down from the south end of the lake on last Friday evening in a skiff shortly after dusk, when about midway across the lake he saw an ani-mal about 50 yards to the right of the boat, rear its neck up out of the water 10 or 12 feet, but on seeing him it im-mediately dived.

The prospector ceased rowing and gazed around in astonishment for the strange apparition which he had just seen, when it raised about the same distance to the left, this time giving a low bellow something like that of a cow. It also brought it's body to the surface, which the prospector avers was 100 feet in length.

The monster glided along in sight for several hundred yards. It was too dark to see the animal distinctly, but it seemed to have a large, flat head, something like that of a hippopotamus, and its neck, which was about 10 feet in length, was as large around as a man's body.

This story may have been coined in the imagination of the narrator, but he was very earnest in his recital. However it is a known fact that there is a tradition among the Indians that the lake has a big sea cow in it, which on one oc-casion, many years ago, came up one evening and swallowed a young warrior and his dusky bride as they were gliding over the surface of the lake in a canoe. And to this day Indian tribes who formerly frequented its shores cannot be induced to go upon its waters.

The lake has been sounded to a depth of 270 feet, and it is a bare probability that some monster does inhabit its unexplored depths.

Calling the monster a sea-cow is odd. 'sea-cows' or *Sirenians* are harmless aquatic herbivores distantly related to elephants. The name may have been mistranslated from 'water bull', a term used in Scotland for some lake monsters.

In 1978, a Mr and Mrs Bryant saw Wally twice. Whilst driving towards the head of the lake they saw what looked like the tops of 3 loops on the surface. They covered 7.5 metres (25 feet) long and were two feet wide. The loops began to undulate then submerged. A few minutes later they re-emerged in the same spot. Later in the year they watched a six metre (twenty foot) serpentine form swim around the lake from a vantage point on the shore.

In the early 1980s Bert Repplinger and Joe Babic saw a serpentine monster that held its neck three feet out of the water. The sighting was backed up by several old ladies who had watched the monster from the road above at the same time as the men.

In 1982, Marjorie Cramner and Kirk Marks spotted a disturbance whilst driving on the east side of the lake. Marjorie saw it from her car first and flagged down Kirk who was on a motorbike. They watched the fifteen metre (fifty foot) creature for over ten minutes.

Crater Lake, also in Oregon boasts a dragon. In 2002 Hood River Valley resident Mrs. Hatcher went boating and got a nasty surprise. What she and her fellow passengers saw while looking overboard made their blood run cold.

That thing must have been a block long. I have never been so scared in my life. What I saw was a monster. To me, it looked like a dragon. I know why the Indians call that place Lost Lake. They say monsters live in it. I believe them. I know, because I saw one there.

We ignore native people's testimony at our peril.

The state of Wisconsin has a number of lake-monsters. The ancient Indian beliefs in these were very interesting in the light of what I have written elsewhere in this book. The Winnebago Indians believed in two kinds of lake monster; the *Wak Tcexi,* and the *Winnebozho. Wak Tcexi* was a spirit and was evil. *Winnebozho,* though it resembled *Wak Tcexi* was a flesh and blood animal and was harmless. This is interesting when we recall the extreme fear experienced by some witnesses. Could it be that the "spirit" dragons have their genesis deep in mankind's gestalt brain as a ancient terror?

Rock Lake in Jefferson County is close to what was once a big Indian settlement called Aztalan. The Aztalan Indians are a puzzle. Among their artefacts are shells from the far Pacific and Atlantic. It is thought that they may have traded and travelled widely. One legend says they left a monster in Rock Lake as a guardian.

- In 1867, a man called Harback claimed to have seen a "saurian" in the lake on several occasions, and even once on land were the creature had hissed at him. On another occasion it seized his trolling - hook and dragged his boat along.

- A Mr R Hassam saw the monster lying among the rushes at the lake's edge. At first he took it to be a tree branch. When he saw it was the monster, he threw a spear at it, to no effect.

- Fred Seaver saw it twice. On one occasion it grabbed his trolling-hook as it had done with Harback. It pulled his boat at speed for half a mile until he cut the line.

- In 1882, the same thing happened to John Lund. His hand was cut before he severed his line. The same year Ed McKenzie and D W Seybert were racing across the lake in rowing boats. A large animal rose three feet out of the water beside McKenzies craft. In a panic they shouted to men on shore, one of whom was John Lund who recognized the monster. A man named Wilson ran to fetch a gun, but the monster had vanished by the time he got back. McKenzie recalled a foul odour around the beast.

- In 1943, 15 year old Joseph Davis was out fishing when he saw a brown, 7 foot hump emerge from the lake. He sat watching for several minutes, before the animal dove, but did not see the creature's head.

In the same county lies Red Cedar Lake. Here, in 1890, a farmer claimed to have seen a twelve metre (40 foot) serpent carrying off his hogs. In 1891 a fisherman said that a huge, undulating, snake-like animal had tried to over-turn his boat. Another farmer, William Ward, said it devoured five of his sheep. Others who saw the monster said it was up to fifteen metres (50 feet) long and had protuberances on its head.

Lake Mendota lies close to Wisconsin's capital, Madison. Sightings of a monster began in the 1860s. W J Park and his wife were boating on the lake when they came across a log. Mr Park prodded it with his oar. I don't really need to tell you what happened next, but the log dived, churning up the water and the Parks made for shore like Oxford's finest.

Lake Mendota is linked to Lake Monona by the Yahara River. In July 1892 Darwin Boehmer and a friend saw a monster whilst boating. It moved quickly in the direction of Ott's Spring, near Easter Beach, with an undulating motion. It was over four metres (fourteen feet) long at the surface.

On October 7th the same year, an anonymous witness said that a six metre (20 foot) animal had passed under his boat as he was fishing. He had hired the craft from John Schott's boat livery. It tried to turn over the boat, and the man made for shore. He said that he would not go out on the lake again for all the money in Capital City. Nor would he return to Madison without a Winchester rifle and two revolvers.

Ten days later, back on Lake Mendota, twelve men saw a 11.5 metre (35 foot) serpent. At around the same time, a young man said that a "living log" had attacked his boat on the Yaharar River.

On June 11th 1897 the monster was back in Monona. It was seen by Eugene Heath, who said it looked like a large upturned boat. He shot at it twice but the bullets had no effect, and the monster came for him. He fled. It was said that a few days before the monster had eaten a dog swimming in the lake.

John Schott - who had previously rented a boat to a monster witness - had his own sighting. He and his two sons saw its dark hump, twice the length of the boats he rented, by moonlight. The Schotts were convinced the animal was dangerous, and refused to row two ladies across the lake after seeing the thing for themselves.

The action switched back to Lake Mendota again in 1899. A tourist from Illinois was anchored in the lake when he saw the water swell some 30 metres (100 feet) from his boat. A massive beast, 18 to 21 metres (60 to 70 feet) long rose to the surface. It had a serpent-like head and seemed to be sunning itself.

In the summer of 1917, a monster with blazing eyes, large jaws, and a snake-like head, was seen by a fisherman off Picnic Point Lake Mendota. He ran off leaving his rod and basket behind him.

The same year a young couple were sunning themselves on a pier on Lake Mendota. As they lay on their backs, they hung their feet over the edge. The girl felt a tickle on the sole of her foot and thought it was her boyfriend. But on turning over she saw what she called "a huge snake or dragon" in the water. The panicked couple ran to a nearby fraternity house. That year many boats were overturned and piers damaged. The monster was blamed.

Shortly before this wave of sightings a large, thick scale washed up on Picnic Point. It was sent to the University of Wisconsin were it baffled experts. The State Historical Society records that one anonymous professor believed it was from a sea serpent.

Part of the lake was dredged in the 1890s, near Olbrich Park. Some massive vertebra were uncovered, belonging to some unidentified creature.

The scale may have been from a sturgeon, and the bones may have been fossils. But one would think that university professors would have recognized these. No one seems to know what became of the relics.

One US lake monster stands pre-eminent among its kin. A long-neck above the others in terms of the number of sightings and its worldwide fame. The monster is, of course, 'Champ' of Lake Champlain. This 109 mile long lake lies between upstate New York and Vermont. It just crosses the boarder into Canada at its north-eastern tip. It was formed around 10,200 years ago as the Champlain Sea, an arm of the Atlantic, receded and glacial meltwaters formed a freshwater lake.

The Iroquois Indians, who lived on the lake's western shore believed in a great horned serpent that lived in the body of water they called "*Petoubouque*" (the waters that lie between).

Since 1819 there have been hundreds of reported sightings of 'Champ'. Let us look at a few of the more dramatic.

In 1960 Walter and Dorothea Hard moved to a cottage in Burlington. Mr Hard, editor of *Vermont Life* recounted what he saw shortly after their arrival.

Neither my wife or I were familiar with the legend of the sea monster. One day I was looking over the lake just after a thunderstorm. I saw something about a hundred yards offshore. At first I figured it was a swimmer. I saw it had a globular, dirty white head. I realized it was much too large to be a swimmer. Beneath the water was something that appeared reddish in colour and about 20 feet in length.

He called his wife and asked her to bring his binoculars.

As I tried to focus the glasses it started to swim across the lake. The head never submerged. We saw something out there that was definitely larger than any fish. It didn't fit the description of anything I'd seen or heard of before. As far as I'm concerned there is some kind of marine monster in Lake Champlain.

Tommy Heinrich, a 15 year old high school student from Burlington, had a breathtaking encounter whilst flyfishing from a boat on the lake in the 1970s. A snake-like wriggling form, 7.5 to 13.5 metres (25 to 45 feet) long, humped up from the depths water cascading of its rust coloured skin. A horned, equine, head swung round to look at him before the leviathan dived back from whence it came. Fishing forgotten, he made shore in record time.

Fred Shanafelt and Morris Lucia were two experienced Scuba-divers from New York. No amount of experience could prepare them for their run in with 'Champ' however. It occurred whilst they were on holiday near Moquam Bay in May 1972.

After breakfast, the men were scuba diving from a small boat. Upon surfacing Shanafelt saw Morris frantically signalling to him.

From his actions I knew we were in some kind of danger. After he saw I understood the situation was dangerous, we both started back to shore. I surfaced about 10 feet out, looking back to see what had given Morry such a fright. That's when I saw this thing that couldn't have been anything other than a sea serpent. Christ! That sounds crazy but there's no other way to describe it.

Lucia described Champ thus…

It was hard to judge how long the body was. I estimated around 40 feet, and Fred believes it was more like 45 to 50. We agreed the head looked about like a horse. It was slightly rounded in appearance, a sort of mushroom grey colour. The head sat on a long round neck that was dark brown or black. The neck rose up about 8 feet out of the water at the highest point.

The men swam to the beach and clambered up. The beast swam closer, apparently appearing more curious than threatening. It cocked its head whilst regarding them. The monster and the men stared at each other for two minutes before Champ swam away and dived.

1972 was a busy year for Champ. In June, Barry James Jarrett twice saw it. It was over 18 metres (60 feet) long and showed five coils at the surface. It's horsy head was held seven feet high and had deep eyes. It was reddish brown.

The summer of 1977 saw the taking of the best still photograph of a lake-monster. Sandra Mansi and her husband Tony had taken their children for a day out beside the lake. The happy atmosphere was shattered as something incredible happened. About 50 metres (162 feet) from shore, something began to emerge. Sandra thought it was a large fish until she saw an elongate neck atop a large body rise. The Masnsi's thought it looked like a "dinosaur". The monster swivelled its head and neck to look around it. Tony ran to get the camera from the car as the monster moved in closer. They estimated the visible length to be 6 metres (20 feet). Thinking it might be aggressive the Mansi's moved their children away from the water. Tony handed his wife the camera, as he bustled the kids back towards the car. Sandra shot one picture of the monster, before she too fled, and the family sped away in the car.

The picture appears to show a snake-necked animal looking backwards over a substantial body. It is of startling clarity in comparison to most other lake-monster pictures. The family were badly frightened by the encounter, and forgot at exactly what point in Champlain's vast waterline they had been at.

The Mansi's never sought any publicity about the picture, and it was not until several years later that they went public, and *that* was by chance. When her bosses at General Dynamics selected her to take part in a project in Scotland she did not want to go. A co-worker who went in her place, said that he wanted to visit Loch Ness as he had an interest in the monster. Sandra told him that he did not have to travel that far to see a monster.

The man did not believe her until she showed him the photograph. Soon news got around, and Sandra went to Washington D.C to formally have the photo copyrighted. The snap was brought to the attention of Dr Phillip Rines of the State University of New York. Dr Rines passed on the information to long-time Champ Researcher Joseph Zarzynski who sent a print on to Dr George Zug at the Department of Vertebrate Zoology at the Smithsonian Institute. Dr Zug felt that the photograph was probably genuine, and sighted the recently discovered fact that sea turtles can travel much further north and withstand much colder climates than was ever thought possible.

The picture was examined by Dr B Roy Frieden of the Optical Sciences Centre at the University of Arizona. He was confident that it was not a superimposition or montage of any kind, on account of a set of waves being made by the objects itself and separate from the naturally occurring waves on the lake.

Paul H LeBlond of the Department of Oceanography at the University of British Columbia has also studied the picture.

Empirical results relating to the appearance of the sea surface to wind speed, and thence to the length of wind waves are used to provide an estimate of the dimensions of "Champ" as seen in the Mansi's photograph. Over the possible ranges of wind speed and fetch, for the lower and upper water-line dimension of "Champ" range from 4.8m to 17.2 m.

The Mansi's estimate of the monster's size falls close to the lower end of LeBlond's size range findings.

In the 1990's an expert from Kodak who was highly experienced with the make of camera Sandra used (Kodak Instamatic), examined the picture for the cryptozoological documentary series *"Supernatural"*. His conclusions closely matched LeBlond's and Freiden's. They photo is not a montage or superimposition. The size of the object in the picture is between 6 metres and 21 metres (20 to 70 feet).

Champ has also been caught on sonar. On the 3rd of June 1979, Joseph Zarzynski and Jim Kennard picked up a reading with a side scan sonar at Whallton bay. The object was moving at a depth of 175 feet.

In the early 1970's, Dennis Hall claimed to have caught a foot long reptile with an elongate neck, and forked tongue. It was quite unlike anything he had ever seen before. He thought it might be a baby Champ. Hall's father suggested that he send it to the University of Vermont. The experts at the University could not match it to any known reptile and surprise, surprise, subsequently lost the specimen. Perhaps somewhere there is a private museum full of these cryptozoological relics that seem to vanish on such a regular basis.

Several years later Hall found a creature identical to the one he had captured in everything but size. The picture was in a book of prehistoric animals, and was of a semi-aquatic reptile called *Tanystrophus longobardicus*, that had its heyday in the Late Triassic Period around 220 million years ago.

As recently as 1984 a mass sighting occurred when Bette Morris, Michael She, and sixty others watched Champ for ten minutes from a boat off Appletree Point, Burlington. It was nine metres (30 feet) long and showed three to five humps.

Monsters do not recognize the false boundaries that humans erect between countries. As we cross over into Canada, we discover a country seething with serpent dragons; perhaps more than in any other country. Literally dozens of bodies of water in Canada are the reputed homes of such creatures. It would be a gargantuan task to look at each of them so I have selected the ones with the best or most numerous sightings, leaving the greatest of the all until last.

Lake Manitoba in Manitoba is home to a monster known as 'Manipogo'. It was named after the better known 'Ogopogo' of Lake Okanagan (more of whom later). Manitoba is shallow in comparison to most monster haunted lakes (9 metres/30 feet) but it may be that Manipogo is not a full time resident of the lake.

In August 1955 Al Gott and Joe Parker were fishing with their sons off Graves Point when they saw something odd around 1,200 feet away. It was a living animal exposing 1.5 metres (four feet) of body. They reckoned the width to be about 2.5 feet.

In the summer of 1957 a group of journalists set out to find Manipogo. They came across a cave that had the remains of many small animals in it. They said traces of a heavy snake-like body were visible. None of the journalists laid eyes on the creature, but their Indian guide Solemn Fleury claimed to have seen a nine metre (30 foot) animal in the lake, that roared at him before diving. The shock caused him to faint. A not so brave, 'brave' I guess.

Twenty picnicking people were stunned by the appearance of Manipogo in July 1960. One man, A R Adams, ran along the shoreline keeping pace with the monster. It showed three black humps. He saw the top of its flattish head. This mass sighting caused Dr James McLeod, head of the Zoology Department of the University of Manitoba and Siggi Oliver of the Provincial Fish and Game Department to investigate the sighting seriously. They ended up more baffled than when they started, as it was quickly apparent that the creatures in the lake were unlike anything known to science.

Meanwhile, the monsters were not idle. One surfaced just yards from a man and two women rowing off Graves Point, causing them to panic and head for shore. Then in August 1960, three of the creatures appeared to seventeen people at Manitoba Beach. They resembled huge brown snakes. Two swam side by side, while the third trailed behind. One witness, Thomas Locke, tried to film them, but discovered he had ran out of film.

Richard Vincent and John Konefall were more lucky two years later. Whilst returning to their camp after a day's fishing they saw a serpentine form in the water 900 feet from their boat. It drew closer, some 225 feet away, and they took a photo. Twelve feet of the black, snaky animal showed above the water throwing its body into a vertical arch. To date it remains the only photograph of Manipogo.

The most recent sighting was in the summer of 1987, when Allen McLean and his family were boating in Portage Bay. A large, black object swam towards them.

Many years can pass without one of these animals being reported in a given body of water, (though some larger lakes have reports every year). This has led sceptics to denounce the monsters as imaginary. But as I have noted elsewhere they have been seen in rivers connecting different bodies of water.

One such sighting occurred in Clearwater River. Robert Forbes saw a six metre (twenty foot) grey coloured serpent snatch a calf off the river bank. He hurled stones at the monster, but it ignored them, and swam away with the calf in its mouth.

The monster of Muskrat Lake in Ontario has the truly bizarre name of 'Hapyxelor'. In 1968 Don Humphries saw it on land and described it as looking like across between a fish and an alligator. He observed it as he was canoeing. It was silvery grey in colour and he saw a large tooth hanging down from the jaw.

Frank and Betty Stark saw Hapyxelor in a two-humped aspect, common in lake monster reports. They watched the animal for several minutes before it swam from view.

Author Michael Bradly observed a greyish hump from 750 feet away in 1988. It stayed on the surface for 10 seconds.

Also in Ontario, Lake Huron boasts the record for the most monsters seen at one time. In 1975 no less than 10 unidentified creatures were seen swimming against the waves on the lake. In 1989 a witness saw two log-like creatures on the lake that lifted their heads clear of the water.

Lake Ontario itself has produced reports. In 1829 two children near Grantham, claimed to have seen a hideous nine metre (thirty foot) serpent. In 1882 a 15 metre (50 foot) serpent was observed, dozing on the surface off Toronto. Upon being disturbed it lifted up an eel-like head on a maned neck, and slowly swam away. In 1888 near Kingston the crew of the aptly named yacht *No Joke* were scared as the creature swam very close to them. One crew member kept a rifle with him from then on, in case the thing returned.

The Ontario monster seems curious about boats. In 1892 a Mr Parks struck out at the head of a huge eel-like creature that ventured towards his skiff. A brace of doctors were on collision course with a serpent on the lake in 1931, and had to swiftly manoeuvre their boats out of the way. The creatures have been observed by some very worthy witnesses. In the 1970s an officer from the Ontario Ministry of Natural Resources twice saw creatures slither off land and into the lake.

Another in the trinity of "pogo", namely 'Igopogo', is said to be seen from time to time in Ontario's Lake Simcoe. In 1963 a Presbyterian minister and funeral director Rev L B Willams and Neil Lathangue, together with their families, were boating on the lake. They saw a huge animal coming towards them. It was the colour of charcoal, and nine to twenty-one metres (30 to 70 feet) long. It had a dog-like face, and a neck as thick as a stovepipe. It also sported dorsal fins along the back.

A sonar reading of a large animal, was taken in Simcoe in 1983 by William W Skrypets, from the Government Dock and Marina.

Quebec too has its own monsters. 'Poink' of the jaw-breaking Lake Pohenegamook is one of them. The monster's most famous attribute is a long saw-toothed crest running along its back. Its head is said to resemble that of a horse or cow.

In 1958 the Quebec Department of Game and Fisheries sent Vadim D Vladykov to investigate reports. He collected accounts of a creature up to 11.5 metres (35 feet) long with a saw-toothed ridge along the spine. He did not see the creature himself and the report he submitted to the ministry vanished when he left for the University of Ottawa in 1960.

Vital Nadou and his family were walking along the beach near the Hotel Pohenegamook in the summer of 1977

227

when they saw a three humped, black creature nine metres (30 feet long) some 300 feet out in the lake.

The same summer Donald McPhee, Robert Murray, and Josef Vykydal obtained a sonar trace of a 7.5 metre (25 foot) object only 7.5 metres below their boat. As the started the motor to pursue it, the object vanished. On August 3rd 1988, Louis Therrien-St-Pierre saw a 6 to 7.5 metre (20 to 25 foot) beast with a ridged fin, 200 feet away in the water off St Eleuthere beach.

Another Quebec lake with a monster is the equally tongue twisting Lake Memphremagog. 'Memphre' (as the monster is known) follows the classic serpentine, horse headed pattern. Pioneer Ralph Merry first spoke of the monster, citing several witnesses to a "great serpent".

- In 1845, Henry Wadleigh saw a large log-like animal holding its head 2 feet clear of the water.

- A seal-like, long-necked creature was reported in Fitchbay in 1977.

- Memphre was photographed in 1983 by Barbara Malloy. She saw and snapped a black hump whilst boating.

- Even the one time sceptical Mayor Denis Lacasse, saw the monster himself on June 19th 1996 at Cummins Bay.

- Patricia de Broin Fournier shot a video of Memphre in 1997 at Les Trois Soeurs Island. It shows a 5 metre, elongated creature creating a wave.

- A 22.5 metre (75 foot) horse-headed serpent was seen on June 4th 2000 by Bruno Johanne and Serge Nadueau from their boat in Sergent's bay.

The residents of the tiny hamlet of Robert's Arm, Newfoundland have named their monster 'Cressie'. It lurkes in Crescent Lake and has been spoken of long before the white man trod these lands. The Indians called it *hahoot tuwedyee* or swimming daemon. The first resident of Robert's Arm to see it was an elderly woman called Grandmother Anthony. She reported a giant serpent at the beginning of the 20th century.

Sightings took off in the 1950s. Two woodsmen saw what looked like an upturned boat off shore. Fearing an accident had occurred, they launched their own boat to try and rescue any survivors. As they drew closer, the upturned boat began to move away into the wind. They were astonished to see that it was the back of some titan beast that slipped away into the lake.

In 1960, four loggers saw the same phenomenon, an upturned boat measuring about four metres (14 feet). As they watched it sprang into life and moved across the lake. One of the loggers Bruce Anthony recalled that it easily ploughed through a sand-bar as it swam away.

In the early 1980s, a large hole was found in the ice that formed on the lake in winter. It was feared that a snowmobile had crashed into the lake. The Royal Canadian Mounted Police were called in to investigate. The Mounties found no trace of a crash. Some residents speculated that the monster had smashed a hole in the ice.

In the 1990s another witness reported a serpentine, black animal that rose five feet out of the water, and a year later retired teacher, newspaper correspondent and former "Citizen of The Year", Fred Parsons saw a dark serpent over 6 metres (20 foot) long. It undulated across the lake.

Pirce Rideout - a local man - noticed a disturbance on the lake on September 5th 1991. Looking out of the window of his pickup truck, he observed a fifteen foot black object rolling and plunging in the water. It did not seem to possess fins like a whale.

New Brunswick's Lake Utopia has a monster called 'Old Ned'. Ned was first seen in 1867. In 1871 a witness described him as serpent or eel-like. Ned was said to leave huge furrows were he rested, and measured 20 metres (67 feet) long. In 1982, four people watched a three metre (ten foot) hump, black in colour, rise and dive like a submarine. More recently, a couple canoeing on Utopia, saw the monster between Woodbury Cove and Cannonball Island. John Willcox said:

We jokingly said, there's the Loch Ness Monster. Then as the thing started coming out of the water even further, it became obvious it was something strange. I would take it, all in all, the object was between 40 and 50 feet long. As we watched it for about 20 seconds, its movement was undulating and it was upwards, not sideways as you would normally see in eels and snakes. It was definitely moving up and down in a vertical motion.

As it submerged Wilcox reckoned its width was around five feet.

Norma Stewart, who has been researching the Utopia monster, believes that it migrates to and from the sea via the Magagudavic River that leads into the Bay of Fundy. Past reports tell of a trail of slime attributed to 'Old Ned' and of specimens that have been seen on land.

Without a doubt, the most famous monster in Canada is 'Ogopogo', the monster of Lake Okanagan. In sheer numbers of sightings Ogopogo is second only to the Loch Ness Monster. The lake itself is shaped like a writhing serpent, mouth agape. It lies in British Columbia. It extends some 80 miles from Vernon in the north to Princeton in the south. Its maximum depth is 1000 feet. It is impressive, but far from the largest of the North American monster lakes. But size is not everything, for no other lake on the continent can hold a candle to Okanagan.

Legend holds that in the time of the Indians, an old wise-man lived by the lake. His name was *Old Kan-He-Kan*. The sage could communicate with animals and was a councillor for his people. One day an evil man called *Kel-Oin-Won* murdered the wise-man. The distraught people named the lake Okanagan in his memory and the gods transformed his murderer into a gigantic serpent dragon, a creature so horrific that only rattlesnakes could tolerate his company. The beast was known as *N'ha-a-itk.*

The Indians had a great fear of the dragon, and believed that it could only be placated by sacrifice. If crossing the lake they would carry a chicken or some other small animal. These they tossed into the water for the monster to eat. One story tells of a visiting Chief called Timbasket was said to have ignored the advice of the local tribes. Both he and his canoe were never seen again.

The first non-native to clearly see Ogopogo was Susan Alison in 1872. She was looking across the lake for her husband, who was due to return from a trip. She saw a strange animal swimming against the waves. She had studied native folklore and realised that this must be the dreaded *N'ha-a-itk.* She was filled with foreboding that the creature had destroyed her husband's vessel and eaten him. Upon her husband's return, she told him of her sighting, but was not believed. She wrote an atmospheric little poem about her sighting that runs thus.

Miles to westward lies an island,
An island all men dread,
A rocky barren island,
Where a monster makes his bed.

So busy are the fishers,
That they hardly spare a glance,
To the black line of white crested waves,
That so rapidly advance.

From the westward-from the island,
The island all men dread,
From the rocky barren island,

Where the monster makes his bed.

The island in question is Rattlesnake Island off Squally Point. Mrs Alison's husband may have laughed but soon others had seen the serpent. John McDouall, for example, would certainly not have laughed. He was a trader who would always cross the lake by canoe with his horses in tow. On one occasion in 1860, he was horrified to see his horses dragged one by one beneath the surface. He had to cut the tow rope to prevent his canoe being pulled under.

Early settlers took the treat of *N'ha-a-itk* very seriously and carried guns whenever they were close to the lake. In 1926 a ferry operating on the lake, was armed in case of attack by the monster.

It was also in 1926 that the monster got its modern name Ogopogo. The name comes from an English music hall ballad of 1924, written by Cumberland Clark, and sung by Mark Strong. It concerns the hunt for a banjo playing monster called *Ogopogo* in the hills of Hindustan and runs…

I'm looking for the Ogopogo
The funny little Ogopogo
His mother was an earwig
His father was a whale
I'm going to put a little bit of salt on his tail
I want to find the Ogopogo
While he's playing on his old Banjo
The Lord Mayor of London
Wants to put him in the Lord Mayor's show.

Quite why the name was applied to the Okanagan monster is anyone's guess, but it stuck and the lake monster has become far better known around the world than the almost forgotten music-hall song.

Ogopogo follows the typical North American lake monster template, with its horse-like head and elongated body, with a crest or mane running along it. Sometimes horns are reported on the head. Here is a fairly typical sighting, made by Patricia Ireland in 1931.

In the early 30's my girlfriend and I were at a school picnic near the Westside Ferry Landing at the old Rotary Beach. She and I hiked off up the cliffs on our own. About halfway between the ferry dock and what is now the bridge approach, we saw a creature in the lake below.

I remember comparing it in length to the ferry, for it was at least that long. It had three coils out of the water and a large head that was slightly higher out of the water than the coils.. The head was surmounted by what appeared to be antlers. Hanging down from these was something that gave the appearance of seaweed, dangling in such a way that it concealed the shape of the head.

It was dark in colour and travelled quite fast, heading north. We found it hard to keep in view as it disappeared around the curve of the cliffs. I may say that I was around 17 at the sighting, and I had never had a drink. My friend's address is available.

Another early 20th century sighting was by Edythe March.

I had been told of Ogopogo by my father, Henry J Blurton, who worked as a game warden when I was a child. The Indians advised him never to go canoeing on the lake without fist tying up a grouse or piece of venison behind the canoe as a precaution against Ogopogo upsetting it, for they believed that should an upset occur the elusive monster would go after the bait rather than the man.

Our teacher's father, who often went fishing at the northern end of the lake, failed to return one day. They found his boat on the lake right side up with all the fishing gear intact, but no Mr Homuth. I truly believed Ogopogo had gotten him.

The first time I saw Ogopogo he was amusing himself by swimming at a fantastic rate, stopping suddenly, then re-peating this performance by going in the opposite direction. This happened in the late Autumn of 1933. This time there were two of us travelling from Princeton to Vernon. I spotted a wake behind an object that was moving at a tremendous speed, so we stopped to look. It was certainly not a boat, as it resembled something like a huge snake's head. We knew it was Ogopogo.

Edythe March had two subsequent sightings in 1951 and 1977.

Ogopogo's name has been raised in connection with other disappearances as well. In 1932 Henry Murdoch was practicing for a marathon swim in the Okanagan Regatta. He was swimming from the Maud Roxby Bird-Sanctuary Point to the Eldorado Hotel. He was accompanied by his friend John Ackland in a rowing boat. Murdoch was swimming about six metres (20 feet) behind the boat.

When Ackland reached the shore at a point called Boyces Field, Murdoch was nowhere in sight. He was a strong swimmer and was a lifeguard. There were no undercurrents in the area. A two day search failed to find his body.

A similar event happened in 1988 when Allan Skarbo and his friends were swimming from his houseboat. A breeze blew off a hat belonging to Dan Kerr, and another friend dived in to save it. Despite being a strong swimmer he was never seen again. The ensuing search included underwater cameras but no body was ever found. The events frightened Skarbo so much that he sold his houseboat and never went out on the lake again.

In the summer of 1936, Geffory Tozer and Andy Aikman were fishing on Lake Okanagan. Their attention was grabbed by a seagull squawking loudly about 150 feet away. The bird rose into the air, but a huge grey animal lunged up, grabbed it and dived back into the lake, as the friends looked on in shock. The bird had been 12 to 15 feet in the air when the monster had struck. Its girth was about 18 inches, and it was silvery grey in colour.

On July 18th 1949, three youths working at an orchard, saw Ogopogo showing dark-green, sinuous coils. They shot at it with a .22-calibre rifle but it had no effect. The monster was spotted three times in a half hour period.

One good thing *did* come out of this encounter. The attorney general of British Columbia said that the monster should be protected under Section 26 of the Fisheries Act that prevents aquatic animals being hunted with guns or explosives.

Further evidence that Ogopogo includes birds in its diet was observed by Mrs Alice de Fyffer at 9.30 on October 1st 1951. Her garden overlooked the lake, and she was not a believer in the monster – never having never seen it. This changed one day when she was removing a bouquet from her living room window. 225 feet away were three dark humps visible above the waters of the lake. They picked-up speed as they approached some coots (colloquially known to the Canadians as mud-hens), which panicked and flew squawking away. The humps slowed down and sank after the birds made their escape.

Mrs E. A. Campbell was sitting with two friends on the lawn of her home on the afternoon of July 6th 1952, when they saw Ogopogo a few hundred feet out on the lake. Mrs Campbell said:

I am a stranger here. I did not even know such things existed. But I saw it so plainly. A head like a cow or a horse that reared right up out of the water. It was a wonderful sight. The coils glistened like two huge wheels going around and around. The edges were all ragged like that of a saw. It was so beautiful with the sun shining on it. It was all so very clear, so extraordinary, as it came up three times, submerged and disappeared.

Birds were on the menu again in 1969 when Roy P MacLean, publisher of the *Kelowna Daily Courier,* saw Ogopogo (in water only a metre deep), some fifteen metres from his house. He had seen a flock of ducks he daily fed fly up in a panic. He then observed, something as thick as a car tyre, showing three humps, undulating through the shallows. It appeared to be feeding before heading back out to deeper water.

Graham Merrick must be one of the few people in the world who has been lucky enough to spot a lake monster from a plane. On March 21st 1990 he was flying out of Penticton on an Air B.C flight at 9.30 a.m. Looking out of the right side of the plane, he saw three large animals slither over a sandbar at the south end of the lake. The creatures ranged from 9 to 21 metres (30 to 70 feet) long. They were *light* brown in colour and stood out against the clear water.

Due to mechanical failure the plane had to return to Penticton. Graham saw one of the smaller specimens again as they flew back. Its body looked like an upturned canoe.

There have been many multiple witness sightings of Ogopogo. One of the best occurred on July 13th 1994, when Darlene Viala, two other adults, and five children came too close for comfort to the monster whilst boating on the lake. A snake-like monster showing between eight and ten coils of its fifteen to eighteen metre body surfaced next to their craft. The monster came within six metres of the boat, causing the witnesses to become hysterical with fear. It had greenish skin, and was about a metre thick.

These have been just a few examples of Ogopogo sightings; the tip of the iceberg. There have been literally hundreds and there are new reports every year. The monster has also been tracked on sonar, photographed, and filmed on no less than twelve occasions. It is beyond the scope of this book to list all the evidence from Lake Okanagan. I would point readers interested in further research to the three excellent books by Ogopogo's chief researcher Arlene Gaal.

It seems highly likely that Lake Okanagan supports a population of large animals unknown to science. Sadly the lake's ecosystem is under threat. The kokanee salmon have been dying off in their thousands thanks to the unwise introduction of the shrimp *Mysis relicta*. The shrimp were introduced to Okanagan as food for the salmon. However the fast breeding shrimp compete with young kokanee for food and have upset the balance. Boats with special shrimp nets are now trying to control the crustacean's numbers. In fact one of these boats reported that its nets had been torn by a twelve metre animal.

Another alien introduction is milfoil weed - a fast growing aquatic plant that can quickly clog up waterways. This species is usually found in fast flowing bodies of water. When introduced to sluggish or still waters they can grow out of control.

Dudley Fuller put the situation best in the closing lines of a poem he wrote in 1977.

If we poison Ogopogo can we face our children's scorn,
Knowing he is lost forever to generations yet unborn.
Shall we cynically keep saying 'Ogopogo is a fake'
Till we see his bloated body belly upwards in the lake!

But now we must leave behind the beautiful waters of Lake Okanagan and head out into the sea. If lakes can hold large undiscovered creatures, then how many more surprises lie in wait for us in the world's seas and oceans?

CHAPTER EIGHT

Dragons of the Oceans

"The dragon green, the luminous, the dark, the serpent haunted sea".

Gates of Damascus' James Elroy Flecker (1884-1815)

rofessor Bernard Heuvelmans, the 'Father of Cryptozoology', made a mammoth study of sea serpent reports from 1639 to 1964. He published his work in a book, *Le Grand Serpent-de-Mer* in 1965. This was later translated into English, under the evocative title *In The Wake of the Sea Serpents*.

Heuvelmans classified nine different types of sea monster.

1. **THE LONG NECKED**: A long-necked beast with a small head, a large body and four flippers. It undulates vertically - that is up and down - as opposed to side to side. Heuvelmans believed this to be a pinniped - a member of the seal and sea lion family - with a vastly elongated neck.

2. **THE MERHORSE**: An animal with very large eyes, a horse-like face, whiskers, and long hair. The merhorse is also a vertical undulator. This too, he thought of as pinniped of some kind.

3. **THE MANY HUMPED**: An animal with a fairly short neck, a long body and either a row of humps on the back or a flexible spine that loops up in coils out of the water. It undulates vertically. Heuvelmans thought that the many humped was a relative of an archaic group of whales called *Basilosaurs*.

4. **THE MANY FINNED**: A weird beast with a scalloped tail, plated skin, and spines protruding from its sides. It undulates in the vertical plane. This too, he contended was a primitive whale with armour plating.

5. **THE SUPER-OTTER**: A huge creature of northern latitudes that bore a passing resemblance to an outsized otter. It undulates vertically. This, the Professor said, was likely to be an even more primitive form of whale. One that still had legs.

6. **THE SUPER-EEL**: A fish - a titanic eel larger than any known to science - that undulates horizontally.

7. **THE MARINE SAURIAN**: A reptilian monster resembling a giant crocodile, but far larger than any known species. It undulates horizontally.

8. **THE FATHER OF ALL THE TURTLES**: A turtle that dwarfs all known species either extant or from the fossil record.

9. **THE YELLOW BELLY**: A huge tadpole-shaped animal. Undulating horizontally, and showing a tail, he thought that it was possibly some form of giant ray.

Heuvelmans was a genius and a man ahead of his time. If it were not for him, cryptozoology as a science would not exist, and I would not be writing this book. I owe the man my career and he is one of my heroes. He has, however, been criticized for there classifications. He seemed biased to the marine mammal explanation of many sea serpents, and was known to shoehorn sightings into categories that did not really fit, to support his ideas. We shall see examples of this later.

Heuvelmans also based some of his marine mammal ideas on knowledge that we now know to be mistaken. For example it was once thought that the basilosaurs had highly flexible backbones that could be arched up to form coils. This gave rise to the theory that the 'many humped' sea-serpent was a *basilosaur*. We now know that these ancient whales had ridged spines, no more flexible than those of modern whales, and a cucumber-shaped body.

It was also once thought *basilosaurs* had armour-plated skin. This was due to scutes found in association with *basilosaur* fossils. These bony plates are now known to have come from fossil turtles. Ergo, the theory that the 'many finned' sea-serpent was also a *basilosaur,* has been shot-down in flames.

The pinniped idea does not stand up well. All seals, sea lions, and walruses need to haul up on land to give birth to their young. Colonies of such massive creatures doing so would surely have been discovered by now. Sea serpents it would seem give birth to live young in the sea. The merhorse may well be a mammal of some description, but it doesn't seem to be a pinniped.

Not all sea monsters are sufficiently dragon-like for this book to deal with. The following ones are the categories I shall be looking at.

- The marine saurian is an obvious choice. Elsewhere in this book we have looked at giant crocodiles in both fresh and salt water. Some sightings of marine saurians occur in cold northern waters where crocodiles could not survive. We shall look at such cases.

- The super otter, the many humped, and the many finned may well be one and the same species viewed under differing conditions. Alternatively they may be closely related species occurring in differing areas. For simplicity's sake I will call them *all* many humped.

- The long-necked, one of the commonest reported sea-serpent types. It bears a superficial resemblance to a *plesiosaur* but this may be due to parallel evolution. It may well be reptilian in nature as many reports speak of a long tail, (a feature not possessed by pinnipeds), and a feature that Heuvelmans chose to ignore.

But first we will begin with a marine monster that Heuvelmans did not include in his book. An obscure monster known as "three toes".

One of Heuvelmans' closest friends was the Scottish zoologist Ivan T Sanderson, a man who could equally be credited with the creation of cryptozoology. Before his untimely death in 1973, he explored many remote corners of our monster haunted-planet. In his 1969 book *More Things,* he tackles the subject of the three toed sea monster.

In 1937 a Mr Aleko Lilius applied to the Department of Zoology at the University of Witwaterstrand, Johannesburg, for help in identifying some strange animal spoor. This consisted of large three toed tracks and piles of droppings containing fish bones. They were discovered on a beach in Natal close to the border with Mozambique. His letter was completely ignored. When Mr Lilius contacted the University again, the "scientist" whom his letter had been passed on, to refused to comment, other that that he had seen Mr Lilius's photographs of the tracks.

The Zulus, Tongas, and Shangaans who lived in the area, told Mr Lilius of a monster they called *silwane manzi,* that came up out of the sea. The animals were covered in scales (like-crocodiles) but they were much bigger than any crocodile. They stood up on two legs, and had heads like turtles. No one had ever managed to kill, one or discover a skeleton, but they often saw the three-toed tracks. Their dung was considered to be powerful *muti* or medicine used in magickal rites. One witchdoctor was caught making false *Silwane manzi* droppings, and was killed for his chicanery.

Lilius visited the area, and set up camp close to where the Umfolozi and Mkuzi rivers reach the Indian Ocean. The place was made up of scrub, white beaches, and shallow, brackish lagoons. A game warden there told him that the year previously, a retired banker called G. F. Timbrell, had set up camp in the same area. The man had seen two dragon-like creatures walking on their hind legs, coming up out from the sea, and walking along the beach. Mr Timbrell bravely stalked the brace of weird beasts, hoping to get close enough to take a picture. The creatures saw him however, and ran back into the sea.

The local natives told him of some fresh tracks a little way along the coast, but they had been destroyed by rain by the time he got there. But soon he was to see some much fresher tracks.

One night his dog started barking madly, and rushing in and out of the tent. As he rose, Lilius heard some massive animal crashing through the scrub. Grabbing his flashlight he investigated. The torch illuminated two small eyes held high above the ground. Their owner was making an odd snorting sound. The intruder made for the sea, and entered it with an almighty splash. It left behind a set of three-toed tracks. He had no flash in his camera, so he could not take photos until the morning. Sadly the wind got up in the night, and destroyed the prints.

Four days later the same thing occurred. The odd snorting alerted Lilius to the strange visitor and he took off in pursuit across the dunes. The thick bush and soft dunes slowed him down, and the monster escaped into the sea. Again it left tracks that were obliterated by wind before he could photograph them.

The following day the wind dropped, and he went to the beach to fish. He noticed several vultures squabbling over something. Upon investigation he saw masses of the three-toed tracks. This time he took photographs.

The spoor consisted not only of the three-toed prints but other marks as well. It looked as if the thing hopped around on two legs like a giant reptilian kangaroo. From time to time it fell down onto all fours, and the marks of its smaller front claws appeared in the sand between the larger hind legs. Long slash-marks were also made by what looked like a big tail. Following the trail down the beach he came upon a large pile of dung containing fish-bones.

The tracks were 16 inches long by 13 inches wide, and bore claws. The stride was 49 inches, and the toes curled to grip as their owner walked up inclines.

From here on in the story gets confusing. Mr Lilius sent Ivan Sanderson an article he had had published in a magazine in 1944 about the monster. A witchdoctor had been found faking three toed tracks with some wooden stilt-like instruments. He seemed to be using the monster story as cover for murder. Human body parts and stashes of entrails where found in several places along the beach. The body parts may have been used in ritual *muti*, a practice still rampant in parts of Africa today. The reader may recall the grisly story of the dismembered torso of an African boy found in the Thames at the turn of the 21st Century. He seemed to have been murdered to provide human body parts for *muti*. The witchdoctor was executed for murder. That all wraps up the story nicely in a 'Scooby-Doo type' ending, but all good Forteans are suspicious of such neat conclusions.

The witchdoctor insisted at his trial that he was imitating the tracks of a *real* monster as a cover. He fully admitted to the murders, but was adamant that there was an actual monster. He had been caught when Mr Lilius's servants had tracked him and found human tracks next to the 'monster' tracks. However, the servants also insisted that there were *real* monster tracks, ones that had no human tracks near to them, and went places that they could not follow.

Mr Lilius himself was seated in a tree, when he actually saw the monster in the distance in the Umfolozi Lagoon.

He said that it looked like a huge weasel with horns. This bizarre description bears little resemblance to the monster reported by local tribes, but it was in the distance and it is possible he only saw in silhouette. Climbing down to try and get a shot, he and his helpers came upon a human torso tossed up in the water, when the monster surfaced.

No one has ever followed up this case. One wonders if the tradition of the *silwane manzi* still exists in the area, or if anyone has seen it in recent years. This is an obscure and frustrating case with no analogue elsewhere. For now it must remain locked in the deep leaden safe of forteana.

The most obviously reptilian of the sea monsters is the type Heuvelmans calls the marine saurian. These animals generally resemble scaled-up crocodiles. In areas of the tropics where the Indopacific crocodile is found, I tend to think these sightings are of very large specimens of this species. However, the marine saurian is reported in places where finding a crocodile would be akin to finding a polar bear in the Sahara.

In February 1849, Edward Newman published the following account in the magazine *Zoologist*. The sighting took place in the late 1830s or early 1840s.

Captain the Hon George Hope states that, when in H.M.S Fly, in the gulf of California, the sea being perfectly calm and transparent, he saw at the bottom, a large marine animal, with the head and general figure of the alligator, except the neck was much longer, and instead of legs the creature had four large flappers, somewhat like those of turtles, the anterior pair being longer than the posterior: the creature was distinctly visible, and all its movements could be observed with ease: it appeared to be pursuing its prey at the bottom of the sea: its movements were somewhat serpentine, and an appearance of annulations or ring like divisions of the body was distinctly perceptible.

Captain Hope made this relation in company, and as a matter of conversation: when I heard it from the gentleman to whom it was narrated, I inquired whether Captain Hope was acquainted with those remarkable fossil animals, Ichthyosauri and Plesiosauri, the supposed forms of which so nearly correspond with what he describes has having seen alive, and I cannot find that he had heard of them: the alligator being the only animal he mentioned as bearing a partial similarity to the one in question.

I have been favoured with a communication, announcing existence of huge marine animals closely related to the Enaliosauri of by-gone ages, that appears to me in all respects the most interesting Natural-History fact of the present century, completely overturning as it does some of the most favoured and fashionable hypothesis of geological science.

Mr. Newman may have been a tad overenthusiastic in his report. but it is certainly interesting. The neck is too long for a crocodilian, and the flippers also argue against any extant species. Also, it has to be pointed out that the Gulf of California is way out of the range of any known crocodilian species. It is a pity that colour and size were not commented upon.

One would not expect to encounter a crocodile in the middle of the Atlantic ocean. And certainly not a crocodile 18 metres (60 feet long). The creature in the following report, is clearly unknown to science. The *Sacramento* was travelling from New York to Melbourne in July 1877, when John Hart, the helmsmen, called the captain up on deck to observe the awesome sight. The helmsman later wrote the encounter up for the *Australian Sketcher*, together with a drawing of the monster.

This is a correct sketch of the sea-serpent seen by me while on board the ship Sacramento, on her passage from New York to Melbourne, I being at the wheel at the time. It had the body of a very large snake; its length appeared to me to be about fifty to sixty feet. Its head was an alligator's, with a pair of flippers about ten feet from its head. The colour was reddish brown. At the time seen it was lying perfectly still, with its head raised about three feet above the surface of the sea, and as it got thirty or forty feet astern, it dropped its head.

The First World War saw a dramatic encounter with a marine saurian off the coast of Ireland. The commander of the German Submarine *U 28*, George Gunther Freiherr, reported:

On 30 July 1915 our U 28 torpedoed the British steamer Iberian (5,223 tons) carrying a rich cargo in the North Atlantic. The steamer, which was about 600 feet long, sank quickly, the bow sticking almost vertically into the air, towards the bottom a thousand fathoms or more below. When the steamer had been gone for about 25 seconds, there was a violent explosion at a depth which was clearly impossible for us to know, but which we can reckon, without risk of being far out, at 500 fathoms. A little later pieces of wreckage, and among them a gigantic sea animal, writhing and struggling wildly, were shot out of the water to a height of 60 to 100 feet.

At that moment I had with me in the conning tower my officers of the watch, the chief engineer, the navigator, and the helmsman. Simultaneously we all drew one another's attention to this wonder of the seas. As it was not in Brockhaus or in Brehm we were, alas unable to identify it. We did not have time to take a photograph, for the animal sank out of sight after 10 or 15 seconds…It was about 60 feet long, was like a crocodile in shape and had four limbs with powerful webbed feet and a long tail tapering to a point.

That the animal should have been driven up from a great depth seemed to me very understandable. After the explosion, however, it was caused, the "undersea crocodile" as we called it, was shot upwards by the terrific pressure until it leapt out of the water gasping and terrified.

The marine saurian has reared its head even further north in colder waters, far colder than any crocodile could endure. In July 1976 off Cape Sable Island , Nova Scotia Keith Ross and his 24 year old son Rodney saw such a beast. Whilst anchored in foggy waters off Pollock's Ledge, several miles offshore, they saw a 15 metre animal emerge and approach their boat. Says Rodney:

I never seen crocodiles other than on television, but its head was sort of like that coming out of the water. Peaked at the top, with a big wide mouth, its neck was full of things that looked like gigantic barnacles. Its eyes were in sockets, but popped out of the side of the head, and it has two tusks maybe two or three feet long and four inches or so round… I didn't think it was a whale. Not with a head like that and those tusks.

The second type of sea-monster with a draconic nature, is the kind Heuvelmans classed as 'Many Humped'. This is an elongate animal of massive size. It shows many arches in a row above the surface. Heuvelmans believed these to be true humps on the creature's back. I would like to contend that they are actually coils in a very flexible, serpentine spine. Often witnesses speak of being able to see the sea through the coils, making them loops rather than true humps. The animal moves in vertical undulations but also seems quite capable of undulating horizontally. The 'many humped' sea-serpent has a head variously described as like a snake, crocodile, horse, cow, camel, or seal. The neck is comparatively short, but it may raise itself up, giving the illusion of a longer neck. It often sports a crest or ridge along the back and sometimes scales are reported. The scaled reports are more common in warmer water. It could be that there are two kinds of 'many humped'; a scaled warm-water variety, and a type with rubbery skin seen in cooler northern seas. Let us examine the former kind first.

On August 18th 1901, First Officer F Wolfe in charge of the Chinese customs launch *Lung-tsing* was off Tai Yue Shan Island, Hong Kong. He spotted a dragon-like animal coiled on the sea's surface. It held its head about three feet above the water. It bore a crest on its head, and two fins high on its neck. He ordered his second officer V Kuster into a gig with a number of sailors, and (stupidly) commanded them to attempt to kill it with a boathook. This seems to the author akin to attempting to knock over Nelson's Column with a fly-whisk. In any event, the serpent bit at one of the oars and reared up fifteen feet out of the water before diving and vanishing. The men estimated its length at twelve to fifteen metres.

You will recall that *lung* is Chinese for dragon. The launch was thus appropriately named. Another series of sightings occurred in Along Bay, on the coast of Vietnam four years previously. *Long* is another spelling of *lung*. The French gunboat *Avalanche* several times encountered dragon-like creatures in this island dotted bay on the coast of Tongking. The first was on July 1897. Lieutenant Lagresill takes up the story.

In the month of July last (1897) the Avalanche saw for the first time, off Along Bay two animals of weird shape and large dimensions; their length was reckoned at about 65 feet, and their diameter 6 to 10 feet. The feature of these animals was that their body was not rigid like that of known cetaceans, but made undulatory movements similar to a snake's, but in a vertical direction. A revolving gun was loaded and fired at 600 yards, at slightly too short range. They immediately dived, breathing loudly and leaving a wash on the surface like breakers. They did not reappear, but we thought we saw their heads, which we judged to be of small dimensions.

On February 12th of this year (1898), when crossing the Bay of Fai-tsi-long, I saw similar animals again. At once I gave chase and had the revolving guns loaded. Several shots were fired at one of them, at ranges of between 300 and 400 yards, and the last two shots reached them without seeming to do them the least harm, the shells bursting on the surface. I also tried to reach them with the bow of the ship, but their speed was greater than that of the Avalanche. Each time, however, that this animal came into shallow water, it turned back, which enabled me to gain upon it and confirm its great size. It frequently emerged, and always one noticed its undulatory movements. Each emergence was preceded by a jet of water, or rather of water vapour made by a loud breath, unlike ordinary blowers which inhale water, and blow it out to a certain height.

The colour of the animal was grey with several black fins. Its trail was easily followed by the release of its breath, which formed circles 4 to 5 yards in diameter on the surface of the sea, which was then perfectly calm. At one moment thought I had reached it. The chase went on for an hour and a half and had to be abandoned as night was falling.

Lagresille is quite wrong in asserting that blowers (whales) take in water and blow it out. A whale's spout is actually air (and a little water) that collects in the concave blowhole which is 'spouted out' as the whale surfaces to exhale. He was invited, a week after his latter adventure, to a reception organized by Admiral de la Bedolliere, given in the honour of Paul Doumer, Governor General of Indo-China and later president of France. On hearing his story, many of his fellow officers scoffed, but Lagresille was vindicated the following day.

He invited several of the nay-sayers to visit the Fai-tsi-long archipelago on the *Avalanche*. Whilst at lunch it was reported that the two sea-dragons had returned. They all rushed on deck, and there before the sceptic's eyes, the monsters swam some 600 feet away. Lagresille said:

We gave chase to one of them for thirty-five minutes, and at one particular moment we saw it clearly 200 yards off the beam, floating horizontally. It had three undulations without a break, which ended with the appearance of its head, which much resembled a seal's, but almost double the size. We could not see if it had a neck, joining it to the body, of relatively much greater dimensions: this was the only time we saw the undulations appear without a break. Until then we might have thought that what we took them for were humps appearing in succession: but from the testimony of all the witnesses doubt is no longer permissible, for, before they appeared, we saw the animal emerging by the same amount along its length. Two of the officers present possessed a camera: they ought to have been able to use it then, but they were so surprised by what they saw, that when they thought of aiming their cameras the animal dived, only to appear much further away in much less clear conditions unfavourable to taking a photograph.

To sum up, the animals seen by the 'Avalanche' are not known. Their length is about 65 feet (minimum), their colour is grey and black, their head resembles that of a seal, and their body is subject to undulations that are sometimes very marked: finally, their back is covered with a sort of saw-teeth which removes any resemblance to known cetaceans; like the latter they reveal their presence by blowing noisily, but they do not spout a jet of inhaled water like whales; it is rather their violent respiration which causes a sort of vaporization of water that is ejected in drops and not a jet. Undoubtedly these animals, known and feared by the Annamites, must have provided the idea of the Dragon, which modified and amplified by legend, has been, if I may so term it, heraldized into the national emblem.

The sinuous, crested body, aquatic habit, and the spouting of a cloud of vapour. One could hardly ask for a better description of an eastern dragon. The other officers who had joined him were from a ship called the *Bayard*, and included the commander. He wrote off to Admiral de la Bedolliere telling him what he had seen. The Admiral wrote at once to Lagresille and apologized for doubting his word. He wanted a concerted effort to capture a specimen of the species with the gunboats. He planned to chase one into shallow water where it would be stranded and could be caught. A diplomatic crisis in China saw to it that the plan was never carried out.

On the 11th of July 1898 Jean Baptiste A… was a Marine on guard at the port gangway of the *Vauban* when he saw one of the Along Bay dragons.

I was looking at the sea at the bottom of the ladder, when my attention was attracted by a strange beast which passed about ten feet from the bottom of the gang ladder making undulations like those of a snake and in the fore-and- aft direction of the boat.

This animal measured 35 to 40 feet long, and seemed to be 16 to 20 inches in diameter in the middle of its body. It bore scales of the size of a turtle's; the neck was much thinner than the body, and the proportion of the head to the body was as in a snake; the tail ended in a point. The eyes seemed to be a little higher on the head than in an ordinary snake; two very conspicuous holes were seen a little way back on the nose. The colour of the animal seemed to be greenish grey, but no doubt this was due to the colour of the sea and the reflection of the sky. It was about five to six feet below the surface.

The *Charles-Hardouin* was on passage from Nantes to Hong Kong in November and December of 1903 in Tourane Bay. The helmsman alerted the mate to a dark mass very close to the ship:

15 to 20 yards from the ship a double mass appeared, the length of each part must have been about 25 feet and the distance between them 18. The bulk of each of these coils could be compared to that of a big half hogshead barrel: a spiky crest gave the coils a quite singular appearance.

It all undulated like a snake in motion, and its speed was markedly greater than that of the ship, which was then doing 9 knots as I recall. The colour was dirty black. A few seconds later the animal dived, churning the waters violently.

What I heard during a long period on the south China coast leads me to believe that they are amphibious (i.e. air-breathing), and that their appearances were once fairly frequent on the coasts of the China sea, and I think that the Taiwan embroidered beast on Imperial and Annamite flags is just a stylised version of this animal.

On February 12th 1904 Lieutenant Peron saw the serpent of Along Bay whist taking soundings from the steam launch *Chateau-Renault*. An elderly native was pointing out submerged rocks for him as they progressed. A sailor shouted out a warning and Peron looked round.

I stood up and stopped the engines, then I saw, not very far ahead, a grey mass shaped like a turtle's back, which we reckoned to be more than 12 feet across; almost at once it disappeared. I supposed it was a sperm whale. The launch still having way, we came near to where it had surfaced, and I saw that there was a big patch of oil on the surface.

I still remained stopped, and I'm glad I did; soon afterwards we heard water churning to the west, and we saw, almost touching the nearby shore a little south of Chandelier Rock, two huge coils which I supposed must belong to a monstrous eel at least 3 feet in diameter. I saw to my great surprise that the skin of the beast and the rocks on the shore were the same colour; dark grey with patches of dirty yellow. From the distance where I was, the skin seemed smooth and even. It appeared briefly, the two coils disappeared with a repetition of the noise we had already heard.

Once again we looked all around us; there was not a breath of wind, the surface of the water was very smooth; in the end we saw ripples rather far away in the direction of Crapaud. We could not see clearly, for we were too low down. All the same I got the impression that the animal was just awash and moving by vertical undulations.

Peron gave chase, but the creature outpaced his ship. He saw jets of water spurt up from the head from time to time and found patches of oil on the water. He reckoned the animal to be over 18 metres (60 feet) long. As we know, eels and for that matter all other fish swim by horizontal undulations. Ergo, this animal was no eel.

Lieutenant L'Eost made an official report to Rear Admiral de Jonquieres of a monster he saw from the gunboat *La Decidee* a fortnight after Peron's encounter.

Sir, On the afternoon of 25th of February last, when steaming out of Along Bay, La Decidee *met near the Noix Rock a strange animal apparently of the same species as seen in the same locality in 1897 and 1898 by Lieutenant La-gresille on board the* Avalanche, *which observations were published in the* Bulletin de la Societe Zoologique de France *(1902), which I had no knowledge until after I made my own.*

I first saw the back of the animal at about 300 yards, on the port bow, in the shape of a rounded blackish mass, which I first took to be a rock, then seeing it move, for a huge turtle 12 to 16 feet in diameter.

Shortly afterwards I saw this mass lengthen, and there emerged in succession, in a series of vertical undulations, all the parts of the body of an animal having the appearance of a flattened snake, which I reckoned to be about a hundred feet long and the greatest diameter 12 to 16 feet.

The animal dived. I did not observe it again, my attention being distracted by handling the ship.

The observations which follow were gathered from various members of the staff and crew.

The animal appeared a second time about 150 yards away and dived beneath the ship just aft of the gangway. Its back on this second appearance, was all that was visible at first. It was semi-circular in section, not at all like that of the cetaceans (Dr Lowitz). Its skin was black showing patches of mottled yellow (Able Seaman Sourimant); according to Seaman Leguen, it was dark yellow and quite smooth.

The back then disappeared, leaving big ripples, and the head alone appeared near the gangway. Here are the observations of Leading Engineer Ponaurd, who was in this position. All other seamen present have confirmed every detail.

When he heard voices on the bridge, he looked out and saw waves like the sea breaking or a rock awash, or like those made by a submarine diving. He turned to call his mates, and they all came and watched.

The head and neck came out of the water only 40 yards away. The head was the colour of the rocks in the bay (greyish, white mixed with yellow). It was like a turtle's; the skin seemed rough, and this roughness seemed due to scales rather than hair.

The witnesses estimate the diameter of the head varied between 15 and 30 inches; it was slightly greater than that of the neck.

The head blew two jets of water vapour. The rest of the body appeared fleur d' eau. *It undulated in a horizontal direction. The animal moved at a speed estimated at 8 knots.*

When it was almost alongside, the head dived, and a series of vertical undulations were seen running along the body, just out of the water.

The animal once reappeared near the ship's starboard quarter. Marine Lecoublet and Seaman Le Gall were there.

The body moved forward in vertical undulations. In its whole length there were 5 or 6 marked undulations. This length is estimated by these two witnesses at more that 30 feet. They describe a head wider at the back than the front and longer than a seal's.

The body seemed to them to be of almost the same dimensions all along its length. They compare it to a Blower's. This estimate, together with what seems to me much too small a figure for the length, makes me think these witnesses saw only part of the body.

The skin was smooth. Nobody saw fins. The animal did not blow at this time. It dived again and appeared some way astern. One could now only make out a long, blackish body, with moving curves and jets of water vapour.

From what the witnesses at the gangway saw, the animal breathes through its nostrils rather than through the top of its head.

Nobody observed the head in detail.

This is an interesting case as it has many witnesses, all experienced seamen, who observed the monster from a number of differing vantage points. It also shows that the many humped is capable of undulating in both the vertical and the horizontal plane.

In December 1903, several crew members of the cruiser *Gueydon,* saw the monster in Along bay. When the same ship returned in May 1904, a hundred people saw the dragon.

In 1934 the following report of a scaled many humped was published in *The Victorian Naturalist* by Mr. A. H. E. Mattingly. The sighting was made by Oscar Swanson of Townsville, Queensland, his son Harold, and William Quinn. On August 18th the three went to fish. Soon after leaving Townville breakwater in their motor launch they saw four dark objects in the water and moved closer to investigate. They got within about 450 feet of the animal when it submerged.

Then we thought it would come at us, and we turned to make for the Beacon, which has a ladder to the top on which the lamp is lit.

We were wishing we were in a speed boat. We stowed the little fellow up forward under what bit of decking we had, and hoped for the best. I might mention that the sea at this time was as smooth as glass. After about five minutes the monster arose again in the same place (coming up just like a submarine).We were about three quarters of a mile past the Beacon; on reaching it we caught hold of the ladder and watched to see what movements the monster would make. After waiting half an hour and seeing no movements, excepting the head swaying side to side as if watching us, we decided to make back to town, get rid of the boy, and get a camera, as it looked as though the monster would stop there all day. On reaching the jetty wharf, I rang Mr Jim Gibbard, sub-editor of the Townsville Bulletin, who picked up press photographer Mr Ellis, and armed with two cameras, we once more set out (without the boy).

Sadly, the monster seemed to have been disturbed by a ship and had moved further out. The watchers saw two large humps, but it was out of camera range. Mr Swanson described the animal and made a drawing of it.

You will see by the rough sketch submitted, what the monster was like. The head rose 8 feet out of the water and resembled a huge turtle's head; the mouth remaining closed. The head was about 8 feet from the back of the head to the front of the mouth, and the neck was arched. The colour was greyish-green. The eye (we could only see one, being side on) was small in comparison to the rest of the monster. The other part in view was three curved humps about 20 feet apart, and each one rose from 6 feet at the front to a little less at the rear. They were covered with huge scales about the size of saucers, and also covered in barnacles. We could not get a glimpse of the tail, as it was under water.

A week later, the *North Queensland Register* reported that the monster had been seen near Bowen. The witnesses were H Hurst and three others. They said that it looked like a huge armoured hose and was 9 metres long. It raised its head 8 feet out of the water. Three other parties of fishermen reported it further westward on the same day.

Another week later it was reported as seen off Mackay, by the *Trentbank,* which that was carrying a cargo of sugar to Canada. A motorboat saw it several weeks later coming north from Brisbane to the Palm Islands. The man who was on deck said he saw two big greyish green humps 7.5 metres apart and covered with scales as big as saucers.

In October 1939 Cecil W Walters was on anti-submarine watch on the naval oil tanker HMAFA *Karumba.* The ship was two days out of Darwin and northwest of King Sound, Western Australia. At 1 pm he and Jack Mack, another seaman, were manning telescopes either side of the stern-gun. They saw a huge animal about four miles distant of the ship and travelling at about fifteen knots. It threw up a huge bow-wave and reared its head and neck around three metres out of the water. The body was thrown into two loops through which water was visible. The telescopes had been calibrated for distance, and Mr. Walters thought the visible parts of the monster must have been over 27 metres. The monster was a brownish-yellow in colour, with blotches of pale blue, green and yellow. The animal's jaw seemed to be moving, and a tongue flickered in and out. Mr. Walters took a photograph through the telescope and - after the war - sent it to his brother in law …who lost it!

The warm waters off the southern Pacific coast of the USA have been visited by the scaled Many Humped as well. Such a dragon first reared its head in 1976 near San Francisco. The *Great Western Pacific Report* ran a story about Tom D'Onofrio, a Minister from Bolinas, California. Tom's account runs thus:

On September 30, 1976, at 12 noon I experienced the most overwhelming event in my life. I was working on a carved dragon to use as a base for a table, and couldn't complete the head. I felt compelled to go down to Agate Beach were I met a friend, Dick Borgstrom.

Suddenly, 150 feet from shore, gambolling in an incoming wave, was this huge dragon, possibly 60 feet long and 15 feet wide.

The serpent seemed to be playing in the waves, threshing it's tail. We were so overpowered by the sight we were rooted to the spot for about 10 minutes. I literally felt as if I were in the presence of God. My life has changed since.

A colourful account, and one that would have probably attracted little attention if the monster had not returned. Upon its second visit, the dragon was seen by an entire road construction crew from the Californian Department of Transportation. On November 1st 1983, they were on a cliff top road, part of Highway 1, just south of Stinson Beach. It was 2.30 in the afternoon. Safety engineer Marlene Martin takes up the story:

The flagman at the north end of the job-site hollered, "What's that in the water?"

We all looked out to sea, but could see nothing, so the flagman, Matt Ratto, got his binoculars. Finally I saw the wake and I said, "Oh my God, it's coming right at us, real fast."

There was a large wake on the surface and the creature was submerged about a foot under the water. At the base of the cliff it lay motionless for about five seconds and we could look directly down and see it stretched out. I decided it must have been 100 feet long, and like a big black hose about five feet in diameter. I didn't see the end of the tail.

It then made a u-turn and raced back, like a torpedo, out to sea. All of a sudden, it thrust it's head out of the water, it's mouth went towards the sky, and it thrashed about.

Then it stopped, coiled itself up into three humps of the body and started to whip about like an uncontrolled hose-pipe. It did not swim sideways like a snake, but up and down.

I had binoculars and kept them focused on the head. It had the appearance of a snake like dinosaur, making coils and throwing its head about, splashing and opening its mouth. The teeth were peg like and even there were no fangs. The head resembled the way people drew dragons except it wasn't so long. It looked gigantic and ferocious.

244

I did not see any fins or flippers and it had bothered me that it could move so fast in that way. It was scientifically impossible for anything to go that fast without them. It was not like a snake going sideways; it went up and down.

It stunned me, never in my life, could I ever have imagined a thing so huge could go so fast. I thought, when I saw it, this is a myth.

There were six of us at this time, all looking over the rail in disbelief. I was so glad everybody saw the same thing.

I've never really told anybody this before, and I cannot swear to it but the eye I saw looked like it was red, a deep burgundy-ruby colour. When I think about the thing I still see that colour and what's amazing about it is that I've never seen that particular red on anything before.

Another member of the crew, truck driver Steve Bjora, estimated that the monster was moving at 50 mph. The crew at first said nothing of their sighting, but they were overheard talking about it at a pizza parlour and the news got out. As a result, other witnessess came forward. Marlene visited Tom D'Onofrio, and saw his carved dragon. She said it was similar to the animal she had seen.

The most detailed account of the monster was given by Bill and Bob Clark who saw it on February 5th 1985.

From the start this particular morning was different. The day before had been beautiful with no wind and temperatures of 70 degrees. The fifth was just gorgeous, with a clear sky, calm water, and high tide. We had never seen the San Francisco Bay so calm. It was like looking in a mirror. Anything sticking above the surface of the water was easily seen. As a result, at around 7.45 AM, we noticed a group of sealion about 150 yards in front of us. While watching them, we thought we saw another sea lion come around Stone Tower point and approach the group. When it got within a few yards a long, black, tubular object telescoped about ten feet straight out of the water and lunged forward almost falling on top of the sealions. They immediately began swimming away, leaping in and out of the water as the fled toward shore.

The creature churned the water as it swam behind them moving so fast it was a blur, but we could see three or four vertical undulations moving down the length of the animal. Suddenly, it went underwater. Meanwhile the sealions were coming closer and closer to where we were parked along the Marina Green only yards from the bay. They came so close that Bob was able to make eye contact with one and see the fear of death in its eyes as it leaped out of the water. The creature followed close behind, stirring up the water as it made a final attempt to procure a meal.

Now only 25 yards away, an arch of the animal was exposed, which looked like half a truck tyre. It appeared black and slimy, yet at the same time glistened in the early sunlight. The creature was swimming slightly below the surface almost parallel to the shore. The water was very clear allowing the outline of the serpent's head to be observable. A short flat snout, eyebrow ridges, and lots of neck could be see. It must have been 30 feet of neck because we both thought a big snake had just swam by. We were expecting to see the end of the snake but instead of getting smaller it began to get much larger. What we watched wasn't a big snake, but something even more unbelievable.

There was a loud crash and with a spray of water the creature seemed to stop dead in its tracks (later at low tide the next day we realized that a ledge with large rocks on it extended 20 yards into the bay at the location where the creature crashed). Instantaneously, a long black neck popped up, twisting backwards away from the shore, then splashed as it hit the surface of the water and disappeared. The serpent twisted clockwise like a corkscrew, and exposed its midsection above the water, giving us an excellent view of the underbelly, which was creamy white with a tint of yellow. It resembled an alligator's belly with a soft leathery look, but was divided into many sections several feet wide. The midsection was about 20 feet long, black on top, and slowly changed from a mossy green to a grassy green and ultimately to a yellow-green as it approached the underbelly. It had hexagonal scales next to each other rather than overlapping. The largest scales appeared at the widest part of the midsection where the underbelly and the side of the creature met, gradually reducing in size as they approached the top, front and end of the midsection. The largest scales were bigger than a silver dollar and the smallest were the size of a dime. There was a distinct line where the texture of the skin changed from scales to the smooth, leathery underbelly.

While it continued twisting, another section six to nine feet long arched upwards three feet above the water. The arch twisted away from us, exposing a fan-like appendage that was attached to its side at the waterline. It looked like a flag flapping in the wind. It was triangular in shape with a serrated outer edge. Mossy green ribbing ran from a single point attached to the side of the animal like the spokes of a wheel. A paper thin green membrane stretched between each rib which extended farther than the membrane, creating a serrated edge. The appendage was equilateral with each side almost two feet in length reminding us of a "dragon's wing". Bob concentrated on counting the ribs but stopped when he got to six as there were too many. Bill looked at the rest of the animal and saw two appendages, one at the beginning and one at the end of the midsection. They looked like stabilizer fins as opposed to flippers for propulsion. Slowly the body sank beneath the water onto the rocks below. Under the surface of the water we could see the upper section of the neck. Four tightly folded coils were formed directly behind the head.

The creature moved its neck with a whipping motion, and the four coils travelled backwards in a packet, dissipating upon reaching the midsection. Instantly it created another packet of four coils behind the head, and again these were whipped backwards toward the midsection. This was repeated several times, until the creature began to pull itself into deeper water. It was like watching a freight train pull out of a station; each section had to wait for the section in front to move.

The outline of the head could be seen as it sat underwater but no details were observable except a snake like head with large jowls. When it began to swim north toward the middle of the bay we thought we saw a ridge line along the top of the rear section. However, we never saw the tail. As it swam away at a leisurely pace, several arches could be seen undulating above the water. A few seconds later it slopped beneath the water. Since we never saw the rear end of the animal, it is hard to estimate the total length but it had to be at least sixty feet and probably closer to a hundred feet.

This is perhaps the most detailed account of a sea serpent on record. It is highly interesting for a couple of reasons. Firstly it is one of the few accounts of a sea serpent observed hunting prey. It seems that this species can deal with large marine mammals as food sources just as a killer whale or white shark would. The observations of how the creature moves are also fascinating. This mode of locomotion is unknown in any other animal, but seems highly efficient, moving the animal at high speeds.

The Clark twins had several more sightings of the dragon. They saw it again on February 28th in the same area, but a little further out. Its head was sticking three feet out of the water and looking towards Alcatraz island. A single arch was observed running down a twenty foot section of the neck just below the water. Another arch followed, then the head turned left and dove. This makes you wonder about the fate of the prisoners who escaped Alcatraz, but were never heard of again!

On March 1st, whilst parked at the St. Francis Yacht Club, they saw the neck rise five feet out of the water. An hour later they observed the monster creating a V-shaped wake as it swam, just below the surface, 300 feet offshore. It submerged when a boat approached.

On their next encounter, on December 22nd, the brothers were ready with a camera.

It was 8 am on a foggy, misty morning when we had our next sighting. The water was calm. Bob was looking at a buoy 50 yards from the shore, and 75 yards west of where we were parked. On its right side he saw what appeared to be two floating telephone poles bobbing in the water. He half jokingly told Bill the serpent was back and pointed to the buoy. When we looked, the two logs had disappeared. In front of the buoy, about a foot above the water, we saw the head looking directly at us. It started to swim very slowly in our direction and without warning the head and neck raised five feet out of the water like a periscope. The head had a flat snout with two black, oval nostrils as large as a man's fist. As it continued to swim towards us Bob grabbed the camera out of the glove compartment and handed it to Bill. When he looked back it was gone. It then reappeared 50 yards in front of us.

Bill attempted to take a picture, while Bob looked through the 7x35 binoculars. He saw the shape of a Long Necked archaic marine reptile swim by with the slender neck arching gracefully like a swan's. Bill jumped out and ran down the beach road trying to get a pictures of it. As Bill ran the creature surfaced 150 yards away and lifted its neck several feet above the water. Before the creature submerged he took a picture. It resurfaced 100 yards away and once again he took a pictures of it before it submerged. Bill continued to run and after 25 yards the creature reappeared only 50 yards away. He stopped and snapped a third picture as the creature swam slowly with its head slightly above the surface of the water and a single arch undulating westward. Bill continued along the beach to its end, then down some rocks to the water's edge to where the creature was 25 yards away with its head still above the water. The creature submerged after another picture was taken.

We decided to have prints made immediately but half the film was unexposed so we walked round the area taking pictures of anything. We went to a one hour film developer and asked him to develop every photo regardless of how bad they were. After an hour we returned to get the pictures. When Bill opened the envelope all four photographs of the creature were missing. We ran back to the store and asked the developer about it. He said he didn't develop them because there was nothing on them. Holding back our anger, we told him to make the prints anyway. When we finally got the prints, although overexposed, the creature could be seen in all of them. Because of the rain, fog and time of day, we felt lucky to get anything on film.

- *Picture 1: The animal is offshore with rocks in the foreground. It was hard to see but it looked like at least ten feet of the neck was above the water.# 12 on the negative*

- *Picture 2: Four black spots are above the water. It looked like several arches, and part of the upper neck sticking out of the water. # 13 on the negative.*

- *Picture 3: The head and an arch slightly above the water. # 14 on the negative.*

- *Picture 4: Two black spots, it looked like the head and a portion of the neck behind it. # 15 on the negative.*

Bob saw the creature (or another of the same species) again on December 23rd 1986. The head and neck of the dragon rose up beside a buoy off Alcatraz, but dived before he could get a picture.

A month later Bill was looking toward the Golden Gate Bridge at 8 am when he saw a specimen approaching a buoy. The head and several loops were visible. Bob watched the animal swim around near the buoy, as Bill attempted to take photographs. Two sealions appeared where one of the monster's coils had been. One seemed to have been wounded, possibly by a bite from the dragon. They dived and did not reappear. Sadly, water on the lens had ruined the film. This is a shame as this account seems to reinforce the idea that the dragon was in the area to hunt and eat sealions. They had better luck on their next encounter on February 25th 1987.

Our next sighting occurred in the same area as January 24th 1987. Once again it was hanging out near the same buoy. It was only a short time and not very far out of the water. At first we weren't sure if it was the creature, but Bill took two photos anyway. About half an hour later Bill saw something pop up in front of us about 35 yards away. Bob got out the binoculars and saw two objects intertwined. One looked like a black hose. It was twisted round the second object which was an arch of the creature. Bob saw the first object create an undulation in it's body and pull itself across the arch. Then everything went underwater. Fifteen minutes later, only 20 yards away, a small black head stuck a foot or two out of the water and stared at us After angling its head slightly, the mouth opened and it began to "growl". Actually, it was more like a growl and hiss at the same time. We got the distinct impression it was warning us not to mess with it. Bill took a picture through the car window, then got out and leaned on the roof and took two more pictures before it sank straight down like a rock. The intertwined creatures must have been an adult and a juvenile creature we happened to observe.

This time two photos seemed to show the phenomenon. One caught a head sticking up from the water. Another, part of the long body.

The adult and juvenile creature theory is interesting. We tend to think of reptiles abandoning their young or eggs but some, like crocodilians, make excellent parents. The smaller object may well have been a youngster of the same species, but it may also have been a parasite of some kind like the remora or sucker fish (*Remora remora*).

The brother's final sighting was on March 1st 1987 when Bob spotted two coils moving in unison.

The reaction of the scientific community, even those who should have known better, was not what it could have been. Professor Bernard Heuvelmans, the zoologist who created the discipline of cryptozoology had this to say about the sightings in an August 1985 letter.

...your report, and your brother's report, are not only the best I have seen in many years about sea serpents as far as detail and precision are concerned, but also the most intriguing. Your sea serpent does not fit at all within any of the categories I have been able to distinguish. However, it looks very much like some of the fabulous sea-monsters from ancient reports which I have always thought to be the product of hoaxes or delirious imagination. All the same I am perfectly convinced that you and your brother are quite honest and sincere, and you reported with a wealth of unambiguous details what you saw, or lets us say with more scientific vigour, what you think you saw.

In fact the creature fits nicely into Heuvelmans's category of the many humped sea serpent. He was obviously distressed by the clearly reptilian nature of the animal. Heuvelmans believed that most sea serpents, including the many humped, were marine mammals. Here, when he is presented evidence which suggests otherwise, he is at a loss and tries to sweep the sighting under the carpet with phrases such as "what you think you saw". This is highly un-objective and shameful behaviour from a great man of whom we should rightly have expected more.

Forrest Wood, a marine biologist (not a tree surgeon) had the following to say.

...the creature they describe cannot be assigned to any known class of animal: it is a chimera. Taking the descriptions on face value, we can identify it as a vertebrate, but beyond that its features become contradictory. No known fish or aquatic reptile swims with vertical flexations of the body...Cetaceans, sirenians, and true seals do flex their bodies in the vertical plane, but these flexations are modest and they are quite incapable of forming the humps or "coils", such as those described.

The scales, slimy appearance, and pairs of rayed fins could only belong to a bony ray-finned fish (except I am not aware of any fish in which the fins are attached to the body along one edge). With the exception of seahorses and some of their relatives, no fish has what could be called a neck. In all cases, cervical vertebrae are lacking: neck movement is impossible.

In any case, the described creature cannot be assigned to any class of vertebrate. On the basis of zoology, including palaeontology and phylogenetic principles, it is an impossibility.

As a zoologist myself I find the above comments both pathetic and indicative of an armchair zoologist. Wood is comparing the description with *known* animals, whereas the sea serpent is clearly an *unknown* animal. His statement that marine reptiles do not flex vertically is only accurate when applied to modern marine reptiles. Some fossil species seemed to have been quite capable of vertical flexation. Fish are not the only animals with fins and scales; reptiles possess them as well. The flexible neck rules out a fish. The animal can only be one thing; an unknown marine reptile. Mainstream scientists have minds like trains - they run on rails. They cannot think outside of the box.

In 1996 the brothers gave the photographs to John Morgan III of Michigan. Morgan claimed he could computer enhance them for free. After months of messing about and abusing Bill and Bob's trust, he vanished taking the photos with him. Thus ended one of the most promising cases in cryptozoological investigation.

In the cooler waters of more northerly latitudes, the many humped is still reported, but eyewitnesses do not mention scales as often as those in warmer seas. This could mean that there are two sub-species, or perhaps two closely related species; one scaled and one without scales. It could however be just a vagary of human perception.

The many humped is no stranger to our shores. Many have been seen around the British Isles, often off the east coast of England. Mr George Ashton, a 49 year old shot-blaster from Sheffield, and his wife May saw such a beast 300 feet from shore at Chapel St Leonard's in October 1966.

It had a head like a serpent, and six or seven pointed humps trailing behind. When I have been out at sea, I have seen seal and sea snakes swimming about and what I saw was neither of these. At first I thought it was a log but it was travelling at about 8mph and going parallel with the shore. We watched it for some time, coming from the direction of Chapel Point, until it disappeared out of sight towards Ingoldmells. I just didn't believe in these things and tried to convince myself it was a flight of birds just above the water. I even thought of a miniature submarine, but after watching it for sometime, I knew it couldn't be.

If the word of a shot blaster isn't good enough for you, then how about the daughter of one of our country's greatest novelists? On July 20th 1912 Miss Lilias Haggard, daughter of Sir Henry Rider Haggard, was privy to a sighting that could have slithered from the pages of one of her father's novels. She wrote to him from her home, Kessingland Grange, East Anglia, to tell him of the encounter:

We had great excitement here this evening. And we are convinced we saw a sea serpent! I happened to look up when I was sitting on the lawn, and saw what looked like a thin, dark line with a blob at one end, shooting through the water at such a terrific speed it hardly seemed likely that anything alive could go at such a pace. It was some way out over the sandbank, and travelling parallel with the shore. I tore into the morning room and got the glasses, and though it had, at that moment nearly vanished in the distance, we could make out it had a sort of head at one end and then a series of about 30 pointed blobs, which dwindled in size as they neared the tail. As it went along it seemed to get more and more submerged, and then vanished. You can't imagine the pace it was going. I suppose it was about 60 feet long.

Her father sent the letter to the *Eastern Daily Press* along with a letter from himself asking if anyone else had seen the creature. A number of people responded. Mr. C. G. Harding said that he has seen saw a long, dark creature moving through the water like a torpedo the day after Miss Haggard's sighting. Mrs Adelaide J Orams and her son had seen a dark object swimming out to sea at Mundesley. An anonymous woman claimed to have seen it three weeks previously, moving with "lightning rapidity" opposite the harbour mouth at Gorleston. Mr W. H. Sparow and his wife had seen it the day before the Haggard sighting from the promenade at Cromer. It was moving at 40 mph, and undulating. He estimated it to be nine metres long.

As recently as 2003 the many humped has been seen in British waters. The staff at the Shipwright pub, Milford Haven (where the author did the residential week of his zoology degree), saw a sea serpent swimming across the bay past the gun tower. Comparing it to the car ferry that crosses the bay, they said that the dark, humped, snake like creature was about five times the length of a car. This would make it around eighteen metres long.

In Europe it is the cold waters of Scandinavia that had the most sea serpent sightings recorded in them. The tradition of the many humped sea serpent goes back centuries in these seas. In 1555 Olaus Magnus, the exiled Archbishop of Upplasa, then residing in Rome, published his book *Historia de gentibus serpentrionabilus*. This dealt with sea monsters in Scandinavian waters. The most infamous was of monstrous size.

They who in Works of Navigation, on the coasts of Norway, employ themselves in fishing or merchandise, do all agree this strange story. That there is a serpent there, which is of vast magnitude, namely 200 foot long and moreover 20 foot thick: and is wont to live in rocks and caves towards the sea coast about Bergen, which will go alone from his holes in a clear night, in summer, and devour calves, lambs, and hog, or else he goes into the sea to feed on polyps, locusts, and all sorts of sea crabs. He hath commonly hair hanging from his neck a cubit long, and sharp scales, and is black, and he hath flaming shining eyes. This snake disquiets the shippers, and he puts his head on high like a pillar, and casteth away men, and he devours them: and this happeneth not, but it signifies some wonderful change of the Kingdom near at hand: namely the princes shall die, or be banished: or some tumultuous wars shall presently follow.

Nearly 200 years later another cleric took up Magnus's reigns and continued his work. Eric Pontoppidan, Bishop of Bergen, studied and collected stories of encounters with these creatures, mainly by fishermen and sailors. The Bishop devoted a whole chapter of his book *Natural History of Norway* to these monsters, and asked the question, are they maneaters?

I return again to the most interesting inquiry concerning them, which is whether they do mankind any injury? And in what manner they may hurt the human species. Arndt Bernsen, in his Account of the fertility of Denmark and Norway, p308, affirms that they do; and says that the Sea-snake, as well as the Trold-whale, often sinks both men and boats. I have not heard any accounts of such an accident hereabouts, that might be depended on; but the North traders inform me of what has frequently happened to them, namely that a Sea-snake has raised itself up, and thrown itself across a boat, and sometimes even across a vessel of some hundred tons burden, and by its weight has sunk it down to the bottom. One of the aforesaid North traders, who says he has been near enough to some of these Sea-snakes (alive) to feel their smooth skin, informs me that sometimes they will raise up their frightful heads, and snap a man out of a boat without hurting the rest...

It is said that they will sometimes fling themselves in a wide circle around a boat, so that the men are surrounded on all sides. This Snake, I observed before, generally appears on the water in folds or coils: and the fishermen, in a known custom in that case, never row towards the openings, or those places were the body is not seen, but is concealed under the water, if they did that the snake would raise itself up and upset the boat. On the contrary, they row full against the highest part that is visible, which makes the snake immediately dive; and they are released from their fears.

Such was the fear instilled by these creatures, that ships made special provision for an encounter.

Of late, our fishermen have found the way, in the warm Summer months, of providing themselves with castor, which they always carry with them when they go far out to sea: they shut it up in a hole in the stern, and if at any time they are particularly apprehensive of meeting with the Sea-snake they throw a little of it overboard: for by frequent experience they know of a certainty, that it always avoids the drug.

The trold-whale seems to be a local name for the giant squid (*Architeuthis dux*). At one time this beast was every bit as legendary as the sea serpent - that is until it turned up alive and kicking off the coast of Newfoundland in the 1870s.

A dramatic encounter with a sea serpent is recounted here from Pontoppidan's tome.

Sir, in the latter end of August, in the year 1746, as I was on a voyage, on my return from Trondhjem, a very calm and hot day, having a mind to put in at Molde, it happened that when we arrived with my vessel within a mile of the aforesaid Molde, being a place called Jule-Naess, as I was reading a book, I heard a kind of murmuring voice from amongst the men at the oars, who were eight in number, and observed that the man at the helm kept off from shore. Upon this I inquired what was the matter, and was informed that there was a sea serpent ahead of us. I then ordered the helmsman to keep to land again and to come up with this creature of which I had heard so many stories. Though the fellows were under some apprehensions, they were obliged to obey my orders.

In the meantime the sea-snake passed us by, and we were obliged to turn the vessel to get nearer to it. As the snake swam faster than we could row, I took my gun, which was loaded with small shot, and fired at it; on this it immediately plunged under water. We rowed to the place it sank down (which was calm and might easily be observed) and lay upon our oars, thinking it would come up again to the surface; however it did not. Where the snake plunged down, the water appeared thick and red; perhaps the small shot might have wounded it, the distance being very little.

The head of this sea-serpent, which is held more than two feet above the surface of the water, resembled that of a horse. It was a greyish colour and, the mouth was quite black, and very large. It had large black eyes, and a long white mane, which hung down over the surface of the water. Besides the head and neck we saw seven or eight folds, or coils, of this snake, which were very thick, and as far as we could guess there was a fathom's distance between each fold.

I related this affair in a certain company , and there was a person of distinction present, who desired that I would communicate to him the authentic detail of all that had happened, and for this reason two of my sailors who were present at the time and place where I saw this monster, namely NIELS PETERSON KOPPER and NEILS NEILSEN ANGLWIGEN, will appear in court to declare on oath the truth of every particular herein set forth and I desire the favour of an attested copy of the said description.

I remain, Sir, your obliged servant
L. von Ferry

Bergen. 21ˢᵗ February 1751

It is unlikely that small shot did much damage to such a creature. Mr Ferry and co. were lucky it did not turn on their boat. Such an occurrence happened in 1815 in Ronsdal Fjord. A small sail boat with five men aboard encountered a sea serpent. One man, J. C. Lund, shot at the monster's head from close range. The beast seemed unhurt, but angry, and pursued the boat until it reached shallow water.

In 1894, during an exceptionally hot July, two sea serpents blockaded the isolated fishing village of Ervinken in Norway, close to the border with Finland. The newspaper *Finmarkeposten* reported that the town's residents came down to watch the sea serpents swimming back and forth in front of the harbour's entrance. Several fishermen admitted that they had never seen anything so big in their voyages. The newspaper went on:

The sea serpent was dark yellow in colour, had a round body, and a length of at least 180 feet. It moved very fast through the water with serpentine coils. The head was about the size of a barrel, but rather more pointed in front, and immediately behind it the creature had a large ring situated between the head and the body, which seemed to be smooth and without fins...

A whaling vessel from Hammerfest had met up with three crews from fishing ships that had come into port babbling in terror about giant snakes. The whaler had set out to engage the monsters, but they had vanished by the time it arrived.

At the opposite end of Norway, at the mouth of the Oslofjord, eleven people aboard the yacht *Tommy* encountered a sea serpent. The Reverend Hans Davidsen describes what they saw on the 4ᵗʰ of August 1902.

We soon saw that it was an unknown sea animal moving at-so far as we could judge— about 4 mil (probably 4 sjomil, ie 16 miles) an hour. It was one or two cables away from us.

From time to time three big humps showed on the surface, and three of us also saw the creature's head, oblong in shape, and as far as we reckoned, about three feet long. The humps formed a continuous series and were dark in colour, with a shining surface. They seemed to be at least two feet in diameter. Seen from the side the animal's motion seemed to be undulating. It is impossible to give an exact estimation of the creature's length. From what we saw the head and the three visible humps were certainly 20 feet long altogether. From the distance between the head and the humps, and the length and thickness of the latter, the total length must have been 60 feet. We all saw that the humps were joined, and could not belong to a series of creatures swimming in line.

Because of its great speed, the animal left a broad wake behind it. We did not see foam, but we noticed that the front part of the body raised a considerable wave. The head was held near the surface in a slightly oblique position. One of the passengers thought he saw a fin on the creature's back. We watched for five to ten minutes, with the naked eye, and through powerful binoculars.

W. E. Parkin worked in the office of an iron-ore mine at Bogen in the Norwegian district of Norland from 1910 to 1914. In June or July of 1914, a lady burst into the office, telling him to come and see an extraordinary thing that had just swam into the bay. He ran outside.

What met my gaze was an object sticking out of the water at an angle of approximately 45 degrees. It appeared, from where I was, to be five or six feet out of the water. Behind it was a gap, then several regular humps. The largest number I counted at one time was seven, the smallest five.

The animal swam slowly round the bay before the astonished eyes of several ladies fishing on the pier, several employees of the mining company, the peirmaster, the postmaster, and some old men and children. Several people launched rowing boats to try and see the animal from closer, but this seemed only to frighten it off, and it gradually made it off to sea.

On June 1st 1999 Arnt Helge Molvaer was walking along the coast near Alesund, north west Norway. Around 200 metres offshore he noticed a huge animal. It was brown in colour, 30 metres long and 1.5 metres thick. He observed the creature through his 7x 35 binoculars and saw it had a squarish fin 40 cm high behind its head. The head was like that of a huge anaconda. After watching it for ten minutes he ran home for his video camera.

He returned 40-50 minutes later accompanied by his teenage son Per Tore Molvaer. The serpent was now engaged in feeding off the carcass of a humpbacked whale (*Megaptera novaengliae*). It was observed to move with both vertical *and* horizontal undulations. It appeared to be biting flesh from the carcass and dragged it further out into the fjord. Per said *"It resembled an anaconda, only it was much bigger"*. The footage is downloadable from the internet but is very blurry. There is a rounded shape that may be the whale floating belly-up and an elongate shape is visible close to it.

This feeding behaviour is highly interesting in the light of other accounts of snake-like sea dragons attacking whales. Perhaps cetaceans form part of the diet of these huge predators.

Let us look at a couple of cases.

In his book *The Whale and his Captors* the Reverend Henry T Cheeves writes of a whale/sea dragon battle.

From a statement made by a Kinebeck shipmaster in 1818, and sworn to before a justice of the peace in Kinebeck County, Maine, it would seem that the notable sea serpent and whale are sometimes found in conflict. At six o'clock on the afternoon of June 21st in the packet Delia, plying between Boston and Hallowell, when Cape Ann bore west-south-west about two miles, steering north-north-east, Captain Shuback West and fifteen others on board with him saw an object directly ahead, which he had no doubt was the sea-serpent, or the creature so often described under that name, engaged in a fight with a large whale...

The serpent threw up its tail from twenty five to thirty feet in a perpendicular direction, striking the whale by it with tremendous blows, rapidly repeated, which were distinctly heard, and very loud, for two or three minutes; then they both disappeared, moving in a south-west direction; but after a few minutes reappeared in-shore of the packet, and about under the sun, the reflection of which was so strong as to prevent them seeing it so distinctly as at first, when the serpent's fearful blows with his tail were repeated and clearly heard as before. They again went down for a short time, and then came up to the surface under the packet's larboard quarter, the whale appearing first, and the serpent in pursuit, who was again seen to shoot up his tail as before, which he held out of the water for some time, waving it in the air before striking, and at the same time held his head fifteen or twenty feet, as if taking a view of the surface of the sea. After being in this position for a few minutes, the serpent and the whale disappeared, and neither was seen after by any on board. It was Captain West's opinion that the whale was trying to escape, as he spouted but once at a time on coming to the surface, and the last time he appeared he went down before the serpent came up.

On January 8th 1875 the Barque *Pauline* was twenty miles off Cape Rogue, on the north eastern corner of Brazil when, at 11 am, an odd commotion was noticed:

The weather fine and clear, the wind and sea moderate. Observed some black spots on the water and a whitish pillar, about thirty five feet high, above them. At fist glance I took it to be breakers, as the sea was splashing up fountain like about them, and the pillar, a pinnacle of rock bleached with the sun; but the pillar fell with a splash, and a similar one rose. They rose and fell alternately in quick succession, and good glasses showed me it was a monster serpent coiled twice round a large sperm whale. The head and tail parts, each about thirty feet long, were acting as levers, twisting itself and victim round with great velocity. They sank out of sight about every two minutes, coming to the surface still revolving, and the struggles of the whale, and the two other whales that were near, frantic with excitement, made the sea in the vicinity like a boiling cauldron; and a loud and confused noise was distinctly heard. This strange occurrence lasted some fifteen minutes, and finished with the tail portion of the whale being elevated straight into the air, then waving backwards and forwards, and lashing the water furiously in the last death struggle, when the whole body disappeared from our view, going down head-foremost towards the bottom, were, no doubt, it was gorged at the serpent's leisure; and that monster of monsters may have been many months in a state of coma, digesting the huge mouthful. Then two of the largest sperm whales moved slowly thence towards the vessel, their bodies more than usually elevated out of the water, and not spouting or making the least noise, but seeming quite paralysed with fear; indeed a cold shiver went through my own frame on beholding the last agonizing struggle of the poor whale that had seemed as helpless in the coils of the vicious monster as a small bird in the talons of a hawk. Allowing for the two coils around the whale, I think the serpent was one hundred and sixty or one hundred and seventy feet long and seven or eight in girth. It was in colour much like a conger eel, and the head, from the mouth always being open , appeared the largest part of the body...I think Cape San Roque is ok for whales leaving the south for the North Atlantic...I wrote thus far, little thinking I would ever see the serpent again; but at 7AM, July 12th, in the same latitude, and some eighty miles east of San Roque, I was astonished to see the same or a similar monster. It was throwing its head and forty feet of its body in a horizontal position out of the water as it passed onward by the stern of our vessel. I began musing why we were so much favoured by such a strange visitor, and concluded that the band of white paint, two feet wide above the copper, might have looked like a fellow serpent to it, and, no doubt, attracted its attention...While thus thinking, I was startled by the cry of "there it is again", and a short distance to leeward, elevated some sixty feet in the air, was the great leviathan, grimly looking towards the vessel. As I was not sure it was only our free board it was viewing, we had all our axes ready, and were fully determined, should the brute embrace the Pauline, *to chop away for its backbone with all our might, and the wretch might have found for once in its life it had caught a Tartar. This statement is strictly true, and the occurrence was witnessed by my officers, half the crew, and myself; and we are ready, at any time, to testify on oath that it is so, and that we are not in the least mistaken...A vessel, about three years ago, was dragged over by some sea monster in the Indian –Ocean.*

George Drevar
Master of the Pauline.

The vessel referred to by Captain Drevar as being dragged over in the Indian Ocean was the *Pearl,* a 150 ton schooner. It was attacked and sunk in the Bay of Bengal in 1874, apparently by a giant squid rather than a sea dragon.

Another of these titanic maritime struggles was reported in the *San Francisco Californian Mail-Bag* in 1879. It was observed in the Sea of Japan from the deck of the steam ship *Kiushiu-maru,* one of the fleet of the Mitsubishi company. Captain Davidson's statement runs thus.

Saturday, April 5th, at 11.15 am, Cape Satano distant about nine miles, the chief officer and myself observed a whale jump clear out of the sea, about a quarter of a mile away.

Shortly after it leaped out again, when I saw there was something attached to it. Got glasses, and on the next leap distinctly saw something holding on to the belly of the whale. The latter gave one more spring clear of the water, and myself and the chief officer then observed what appeared to be a creature of the snake species rear itself about thirty feet out of the water, the upper end going first. It appeared to be about the thickness of a junk's mast, and after standing about ten seconds in an erect position, it descended into the water, the upper end going first. With my glasses I made out the colour of the beast to resemble that of a pilot fish.

It is interesting to speculate as to whether the global crash in whale populations has had an adverse effect on sea serpents. The old whaling grounds of New England were once a hotbed of sea serpent reports. Such a creature was observed by the America Commodore Edward Preble on 1779 during the War of Independence. Preble was aboard the ship *USS Protector*.

A huge serpent was spotted and examined through glasses. The Captain ordered Preble to man and arm a boat and attack the creature. A twelve oar boat with a swivel mounted gun in the bow, and an armed crew approached the animal. It raised its head about three metres out of the water ,and began to swim away. The gun was discharged, but did not seem to harm the animal, which soon outpaced the boat. Preble estimated it to be 39 metres long, with a head the size of a barrel. Small wonder the firearms did it no damage!

The Reverend Abraham Cummings was a missionary based in Maine. In 1802 he was travelling from island to island in the course of his duties. On several occasions he saw sea serpents.

It was one time in July 1802 that we saw this extraordinary sea monster, on our passage to Belfast, between Cape Rosoi and Long Island. His first appearance was near Long Island. I then supposed it to be a large shoal of fish with a seal at one end of it, but wondered that the seal should rise out of the water so much higher than usual; but as he drew near to our boat, we soon discovered that this whole appearance was but one animal in the form of a serpent. I immediately perceived that his mode of swimming was exactly as had been described to me by some of the people of Fox Islands, who had seen an animal of this kind before, which must confirm the veracity of their report. For this creature had not the horizontal, but an ascending and descending serpentine motion. This renders it highly probable that he never moves on land to any considerable distance and that water is his proper element. His head is rather larger than that of a horse, but is formed like that of a serpent. His body was judged to be more than sixty feet in length. His head and as much of his body as we could discover was a blue colour except a black circle round his eye. His motion was at first but moderate, but when he left us and proceeded towards, he moved with the greatest rapidity.

In the summer of 1817, off Cape Ann near Gloucester, Massachusetts, a whole wave of sightings occurred. On August 6th two women saw the creature enter the harbour of Cape Ann. Most people ignored their story but it was seen again by a number of fishermen. Amos Story, a seaman, saw it near Ten Pound Island. on August 10. Two days later Solomon Allen, a shipmaster, saw it from a boat. On the 14th thirty people including the Hon. Lonson Nash, Justice of the Peace for Gloucester saw it. Mathew Gaffney, a ship's carpenter, fired a musket ball at its head from point blank range. The monster was not in the slightest bit affected.

The Linnaean Society of New England set up a investigation committee in Boston consisting of three carefully chosen members. Jacob Biglow - a doctor, Francis C. Grey - a naturalist, and the Hon. John Davis - a judge were chosen. They asked Lonson Nash, a Justice of the Peace, to collect sworn evidence from all the witnesses.

The monster was not idle whilst the learned trio planned their investigation. On the 15th a merchant called James Mansfield saw it close to shore. The next day Colonel T. H. Perkins and the entire crew of a ship, including its captain were treated to a view. On the 17th, three men in a boat said it had come so close to them that it had touched their oars. On the same day another witness watched it from the shore. William Pearson and a friend saw it from their sailing-boat the following day. On the 22nd a woman watched it through a telescope, as it lay half out of the water on the beach at Ten Pound Island. A Mr and Mrs Mansfield saw it sunning itself on the same occasion. Amos Story saw it again on the 23rd, apparently dozing on the surface. On the 28th two miles off the eastern point of Cape Ann, Captain Sewell Toppan of the schooner *Laura* and two of his crew saw it whilst they were bound for Boston.

Lonson Nash questioned the witnesses separately and asked them not to discuss their sightings with each other. As not to influence their statements, he always asked them to describe their encounters in their own words, before he asked any questions. He then asked a carefully drawn up series of questions from the Linnaean Society. Of the many affidavits he collected, Matthew Gaffney's was the most dramatic.

I MATTHEW GAFFNEY, of Gloucester, in the County of Essex, Ship carpenter, depose and say: That on the fourteenth day of August, A.D. 1817, between the hours of four and five o'clock in the afternoon, I saw a strange marine animal resembling a serpent, in the harbour, in said Gloucester. I was in a boat and was within thirty feet of him. His head appeared full as large as a four gallon keg, his body as large as a barrel, and his length that I saw, I should judge to be forty feet at the least. The top of his head was of a dark colour, and the under part of his head appeared nearly white, as did also several feet of his belly, that I saw. I supposed and do believe that the whole of his belly was nearly white. I fired at him, when he was nearest to me. I had a good gun and took good aim. I aimed at his head , and I think I must have hit him. He turned towards us immediately after I had fired, and I thought he was coming at us; but he sank down and went directly under our boat, and made his appearance about one hundred yards from where he had sunk. He did not turn down like a fish, but appeared to settle directly down like a rock. My gun carries a ball of eighteen to the pound; and I suppose there is no person in town, more accustomed to shooting, than I am. I have seen the animal at several other times, but never had so good a view of him, as on this day. His motion was vertical, like a caterpillar.

It is heartening to hear of a scientific organization taking an active interest in unknown animals. But sadly the Linnaean Society was about to make a big blunder. They reasoned that the animal must come onto land to lay eggs. In fact there is no evidence that sea dragons breed on land, and it is probable that they give birth to live young in the water. However a frantic search for the apocryphal eggs began, but that was not the blunder. Two boys playing in a field near Lollboly Cove found a small black snake. Their father saw it had humps running along its back and promptly killed the poor animal, believing it to be a baby sea serpent. The body was sent to the Society who accepted the claim without batting an eyelid. The specimen was dissected and detailed plates were drawn up of its anatomy. They even gave it a Latin name: *Scoliophis atlanticus*.

Unfortunately, the zoologist Alexander Lesure identified the specimen as a black racer (*Coluber constrictor*) with spinal deformities. Thus the promising investigation collapsed under a sea of red faces and mocking laughter. It did not seem to matter that Lesure himself seemed open minded about the existence of the sea serpent, claiming to want to visit the area himself, the Linnaean Society had had quite enough, and stopped the investigation. This is a shame, as the following summer the serpent was back.

On the 29th of July a boat full of armed men set out to hunt it after several appearances earlier in the month. A specimen received seven or eight rounds without being hurt. The following day Captain Webber and several whalers approached it, but found their harpoons did no more damage than bullets. The serpent caused such a wash as it swam away, that the boat was almost capsized.

On August 12th it had moved to Salem and was seen off the harbour there. By the 16th it was back in Gloucester and seen off Squam Lighthouse. Some whalers pursued it to no avail. Their luck was a little better on the 19th when their quarry surfaced by Squam jetty. Captain Richard Rich hunted it from a large whaleboat and managed to attach a harpoon into its hide. It swam off faster than a whale, taking 20 fathoms of line with it. But the harpoon fell out .

In 1819, it was back again off Massachusetts. Captain Hawkins Wheeler, of the sloop *Concord,* and his first mate, swore an oath that they had seen it at no more than 300 feet away.

His head was as long as a horse's and was a proper snake's head, there was a degree of flatness, with a slight hollow at the top of the head, his eyes were prominent, and stood out considerably from the surface, resembling the eyes of a toad, and were nearer to the mouth of the animal than to the back of the head.

The visage is clearly that of a reptile not a mammal. They reckoned it to be 18 metres long.

Soon after it was seen by some soldiers at Fort Independence. Then on August 13th it cavorted before 200 people off the beach at Nahant. Judge Amos Lawrence and James Price, Marshal of the District were among the crowd. They sent a description to Judge Davis:

His head appeared about three feet out of the water; I counted thirteen bunches on his back: my family thought there were fifteen...and...judged he was fifty feet in length, and, at the extend, not more than sixty; whether, however, the wake might not add to his appearance of length; or whether the undulations of the water, or his peculiar manner of propelling himself, might not cause the appearance of protuberances, I leave for your better judgement.

On the 26th of August the marvellously monickered Reverend Cheever Flech, chaplain of the US gun ship *Independence*, wrote to the *Boston Sentinel* with a sighting that occurred on the morning of the same day. Gloucester harbour was being surveyed by the schooner *Science* and the Reverend was going down the harbour in the Schooner's boat. The Schooner's commander William T Malbone alerted the others to a creature that had surfaced.

The animal was then between thirty and forty yards distant from us. Mr Malbone, Midshipman Blake, myself, and four other boatmen, had a distinct view of him. He soon sunk; but not so deep as we could not trace his course. He rose again within twenty yards distance of us, and lay some time on the water. He then turned and steered off for Ten Pound Island; we pulled after him, but finding that he was not pleased with the sound of our oars, they were laid in, and the boat sculled. We again approached him very near. He continued some length of time playing between Ten Pound Island and Stage Point.

As he often came near the Point, we thought we could get a better view of him there, than from the boat, of which he seemed suspicious. Mr Malbone and myself landed; and the boat was sent to order the schooner down, for the purpose of trying what effect a twelve pound carronade would have upon him.

He did not remain long after we had landed, so that I was unable to effect my intention, of ascertaining, accurately, his length, with my instruments. From my knowledge, and habits of intimacy with marine appearances, I could not be deceived. We had a very good view of him, except the very short period he was under water, for half an hour.

His colour was a dark brown, with white under the throat. His size we could not accurately ascertain, but his head was about three feet in circumference, flat, and much smaller than his body. We did not see his tail; but from the end of the head to the furthest protuberance, was not far from one hundred feet. I speak with a degree of certainty, from being much accustomed to measure and estimate distances and length. I counted fourteen bunches on his back, the first one say ten or twelve feet from his head, and the others about seven feet apart. They decreased in size towards the tail. These bunches were sometimes counted with, and sometimes without a glass. Mr Malbone counted thirteen, Mr Blake thirteen and fourteen, and the boatsman about the same number.

His motion was sometimes very rapid, and at other times he lay nearly still. He turned slowly and took up considerable room doing it. He sometimes darted under water, with the greatest velocity, as if seizing prey. The protuberances were not from his motion. They were the same whether in slow or rapid movement. His motion was partly vertical and partly horizontal, like that of freshwater snakes. I have been much acquainted with snakes in our interior waters. His motion was just the same.

I have given you in round numbers, one hundred feet, for his length, that is what we saw, but I should say he must be one hundred and thirty feet in length, allowing for his tail.

The Reverend's account differs from most in not noticing motion in the creature's coils. But here, he may be mistaken. He most certainly *is* mistaken in asserting that true snakes can flex in the vertical plane. All snakes flex horizontally.

For more than a decade afterwards, the monsters were a fixture along the eastern coast of America during the summer months. In 1820 Colonel H. T. Perkins saw it again. Then by four men at Swampscott, three of whom pursued it in a boat, counting twenty humps along its 18 metre body.

In 1821, Massachusetts was the scene again, as it was observed by a Captain Bennet. The Colonel and his family saw it again at Nahant. It then turned up off Nantucket and was seen by Frances Joy a local merchant. A specimen turned up at the harbour of Portsmouth, New Hampshire and was watched by customs inspector Samuel Duncan and his son.

In 1822 it was seen almost every day in summer off Nahant, and the following year was observed off Plymouth Bay. In 1825 there were no reports from New England, but there were some from Nova Scotia four hundred miles further north. It was back to its old stamping ground the following summer. A whole ship's crew saw a serpent off Cape Cod.

In 1827 one was seen near Nantucket, and Captain David Thurlow of the schooner *Lydia* claimed to have harpooned one of two 24 metre serpents he saw six leagues off Mount Desert Rock, off the coast of Maine. The monster tore free and escaped.

In 1830 the action moved further south. Captain Deland of the Schooner *Eagle* had a close encounter with a sea dragon in Simon's Bat, South Carolina. The monster had a scaly, grey, humped, snake, like body and a head like that of an outsized alligator. It had surfaced some 900 feet from his ship. He manoeuvred his vessel to within 75 feet of the monster, then shot at it with musket. The monster dove and lashed the ships underside three times with its tail, causing the *Eagle* to rock violently. It was then joined by another, smaller serpent, and the pair swam away. Captain Deland thought that he had got off lightly, as he was convinced the monster could have wrecked his ship. This begs the question of why he shot at it in the first place. It might also answer the question of what has happened to some of the vessels that vanish without a trace. Perhaps they angered a less laid-back sea dragon!

And so the sightings continued. Even the British consul in Massachusetts saw it on two occasions from his hotel window! But we have examined quite enough here. Suffice to say that from Nova Scotia right down the east coast of the United States, the Many Humped sea serpent was seen almost every year until a sharp drop-off in the 1840s. Why was this?

In 1845 Dr Albert Koch's sea dragon hoax involving a skeleton made from fossil whale bones was exposed. After such a public dressing-down, perhaps witnesses to the real deal were less forthcoming. Alternatively, increased shipping and pressure on the whale population may have had an adverse effect on the many humpeds off the Atlantic coast of the United States. They are still occasionally reported from these waters, but with nothing like the regularity of the sightings in the first half of the 19th century.

In more modern times sea serpents have occasionally graced Chesapeake Bay, a tongue of the Atlantic that is bordered by Maryland and Virginia. Witnesses have included a naval officer, a coastguard, two airline pilots, an FBI agent (very *X-Files*) and an ex CIA official. In 1980 no fewer than four charter boats with a total of twenty five people on board observed the animal - nicknamed 'Chessie' by the press - off Smith Point. Bill Jenkins, skipper of the *Miss Cathy II* told the *Times Dispatch* of Richmond, Virginia, what they had seen.

It was a serpent like thing. It was swimming with its head out and then it started towards my boat. I've been a charter boat captain for 35 years and I've seen a lot of porpoises and turtles. This was different.

Another boat called my attention to it. We started kidding one another that it was about to eat Don Kuykendall's boat, then it began heading for my boat and we made out we were going to gaff it, but you couldn't have done that. It was too big.

They witnesses said it had a turtle-like head and spines along its back.

On the 24th of May 1981 Kathryn Pennington took a colour photo of a serpentine animal a third of a mile from shore on the upper Choptank river. She offered the photo to the Maryland Department of Natural Resources, but with the pig-headed arrogance common to mainstream "scientists" they ignored her. But they could not ignore what happened on 31st May the following year.

Businessman Robert Frew was at home with his wife Karen and some friends, whom the had over for lunch. At 7.30 PM Charlotte Rosier, one of the Frew's guests, spotted something out in the bay around 30 metres away. Robert initially thought that it was an otter, but as it reappeared it showed over 6 metres of body. It dived, then surfaced for a third time. The Frews and their friends all watched, and by comparing it to the Frews' eleven metre swimming pool, they estimated it to be a similar length. There were humps about every two feet along its back, and it swam against the current at about five knots.

Robert watched it through binoculars, then he recalled that he had a video camera and rushed too get it. He filmed the beast - that was now 60 metres from his house - and was horrified to see it approaching a group of children who were swimming. He shouted a warning but they did not seem to hear. As it was, the animal passed close by them without them even noticing it. His wife Karen described what they saw on the tape when they replayed it.

It shows two or three head shots-the head and the first seven or eight feet. At one point it came up and the whole thing surfaced and that's when we saw all-thirty five feet of it. One of the most notable things is the absence of any clear cut markings. It was just very dark in colour, from very dark brown to black.

The tape was analysed by Western Electric who thought that it was not a fake. It also caught the eye of the Smithsonian Institute. A panel of experts led by Dr George Zug of the Department of Vertebrate Zoology, examined the film. Craig Phillips of the Division of Hatcheries and Fishery Management Services of the US Fish and Wildlife Service concluded…

To my eye this did not appear to be an artefact (floating branch etc), but some kind of living creature; elongate or serpentine in shape, without visible appendages, or possibly two or more swimming closely together in tandem. If I recall correctly its estimated length was 40 feet; I cannot think of any known creature that would exhibit this combination of size and shape.

Dr Zug was sure that the object in the film was animate and not just floating garbage, but he could not identify what it was.

On the 12th of July that year Clyde Taylor and his daughter Carol were walking on the beach at the mouth of the Chester River when they both saw Chessie.

My daughter noticed something come up onto the surface of the water. The surface at the time was like a mirror, there wasn't a ripple, it looked like a piece of glass. There were no waves, no boats in sight. Its head appeared and Carol said to me, Dad what is that?

We followed it along the short stretch of beach and the monster showed, as I remember five humps, and his head showed above the glassy surface of the water. As he came to our right he was running into a cul-de-sac, where a rock jetty protruded out from the sandy beach and he couldn't go any further unless he came on shore.

Meanwhile my daughter was off to his other side, by a bulkhead on the rock jetty, and I'm on the opposite side. I'm looking at his right, and she's looking at his left.

He raised his head slightly, as I remember, and he noticed the motion of Carol, who was walking towards him. At that, he turned his head slowly, like you turn round the head on a ventriloquist's dummy it almost went round 360 degrees, it seemed to me and he put his head into an arc. He didn't just sink into the water, to me he put his head down into the water and disappeared, just slid out of view from alongside the rock jetty.

Now in colour he was black, brown, or amber and I say he was thirty feet long. I don't think he was as thick as a telegraph pole, but he was very thick, at least 12 inches. His head had the appearance of a football, except the nose was blunt. I couldn't see any scales or appendages, and I saw the highlight of his eye as he turned to look at my daughter. The eye looked like a serpent's eye, like a large snake eye; it had a light yellowish green tinge to it. It looked quite big, a couple of inches across.

It moved in (vertical) undulations instead of snake-like; a snake would slither side-by side and progress in a loop across the ground., but this was like a roller coaster, up-and-down loop, and all the loops were the same size as it swam. When it came to a stop, its head remained in a stop position even though its body just drifted behind it and sank to the shallows were it came to rest. It moved at about 10 mph.

It saw me first but I didn't move I thought it was coming ashore…it is my belief that it comes ashore at night to eat, while the water is dead calm and there are no boats in sight.

I could see no markings on the body - it was just a long tube like an anaconda or a python. It didn't look like a fish but like a giant serpent.

That sums up my sighting of Chessie; I still didn't believe it, I stood there thunderstruck.

Mr Taylor's report is intriguing. One wonders how far onto land Chessie would have crawled. Back in 1978 fisherman James Dutton found a huge track, like that which would have been made by a giant snake. It crossed a field and entered Nanjemoy Creek, a tributary of the Potomac River. Two fishermen reported seeing the monster there, and were so scared that they abandoned their boat. It seems that these creatures can tolerate both salt and fresh water. Indeed they may be closely akin to certain types of lake monster. The observant reader could hardly have missed the similarities in the reports.

We now shift our attention from the east coast of North America to the west coast. Unlike the eastern population the west coast many humped sea serpents seem to be doing well, especially around the coasts of western Canada. The Indians have long known of sea dragons in the area and recorded them in rock art and carvings. The Chinook of British Columbia called it *hiachuckaluck*. The Hurons of Saint Lawrence Velley knew it as *angoub*. To the Manhousat of Flores Island and the Sydney Inlet it was *hiyitl'iik*.

The first good sighting by a non-Indian took place off the Queen Charlotte Islands in 1897. The description is by a prospector called Osmond Furgusson and was found in the British Columbia Provincial Archives by archivist David Mattison. It occurred on the morning of the 26th of June.

About 4.30 this morning we left Caedoo. I was steering the boat and pushing the oar at the same time. There was no wind. The boat was 100 yards from shore, going south with a fair tide. I saw ahead of us what I thought was a piece of drift wood. On getting closer, I noticed it was moving towards us. When within 50 yards, I said to Walker (my partner), what is that? It seems to be moving this way. What we could see was an object sticking out of the water about two feet. When within a few feet of it the end uncoiled and raised a long neck about five feet out of the water with a head like a snake's on it. The arched portion making a broad flat chest like I have seen on the cobra I think.

When the serpent or whatever it was saw us it turned slightly towards land to avoid the boat. The head and neck were almost immediately put underwater again. As it passed the boat, at a distance, that with an effort, I could have thrown an oar on it we could see a body about 25 feet long tapering with a fish like tail and I think a continuous fin running the length of the body.

A slow undulating motion went along the body, while the tail part had a steady sweep from side to side of about six feet. A curious thing was the broad neck or chest part that formed the arch. The only part out of the water when the head was down was not exposed broad-ways in the direction the fish was going, but had a decided twist to the left allowing the water to flow through it.

Though the animal is unlikely to be a fish, Fergusson's report amply illustrates the many humped sea serpent's ability to flex both horizontally and vertically.

In 1917, R. M. Elliot saw a serpent whilst working on a telegraph line between Jordan River and Port Renfrew. It showed eight feet of head and neck plus seven humps. He shot at it from 600 feet away (what is this obsession people have with trying to kill anything that moves?) The animal reacted by thrashing violently, but calmed down and swam on towards Victoria.

The animal was fired upon again in 1925 by Jack Nord. We was returning from Cape Mudge to Menzies Bay with his friend Peter Anderson. When abreast of Race Point, they noticed a huge animal resting on the surface of the water. Nord estimated it was 30 to 33 metres long and about two and a half feet in diameter. It had a saw-toothed fin on its camel-like head, and its mouth bore eight inch fangs. Nord fired twice at it and missed. It did not seem bothered by the attack.

In 1932, Hubert Evens, Dick Reeves, and Bob Stevens saw the monster off Robert's Creek. They watched a series of humps break the surface, then an eight foot neck with a horse-like head. The trio had a camera, but amazingly, no film!

FW Kemp, an officer of the Provisional Archives gave the most detailed account. He made his report to the *Victoria Daily Times* in 1933.

On Aug 10, 1932, I was with my wife on Chatham Island in the Strait of Jaun de Fuca. My wife called my attention to a mysterious something coming through the channel between Strong Tide Island and Chatham Island. Imagine my astonishment on observing a huge creature with head out of the water travelling about four miles per hour against the tide. Even at that speed a considerable wash was thrown against the rocks, that gave the impression that it was more reptile (ie lizard or saurian) than serpent to make so much displacement.

The channel at this point is about 500 yards wide. Swimming to the steep rocks of the island opposite, the creature shot its head out of the water on to the rock, and moving its head from side to side, appeared to be taking its bearings. Then fold after fold if its body came to the surface. Towards the tail it appeared serrated with something moving flail-like at the extreme end. The movements were like those of a crocodile. Around the head appeared a sort of mane, which drifted round the body like kelp.

The thing's presence seemed to change the whole landscape, Which makes it difficult to describe my experiences. It did not seem to belong to the present scheme of things, but rather to the Long Ago when the world was young. The position it held on the rocks was momentary. My wife and sixteen year old son ran to a point of land to get a better view. I think the sound they made disturbed the animal. The sea being very calm, it seemed to slip back into deep water; there was a great commotion under the surface and it disappeared like a flash.

In my opinion its speed must be terrific, and its senses of smell, sight, and hearing developed to a very high degree. It would be terribly hard to photograph, as its movements are different from anything I have ever seen or heard of. I say its length to be not less than 80 ft. There were some logs on Strong Tide Island which gave me a good idea of the size of the monster as it passed them. I took a measurement of one the next day which was over 60ft, and the creature overlapped it to a large extent at each end. I put a newspaper on the spot it rested and took an observation from our previous point of vantage. The animal's head was very much larger than the double sheet of newspaper. The body must have been at least five feet thick, and was of a bluish-green colour which shone in the sun like aluminium. I could not determine the shape of the head, but it was much thicker than the body.

Mr. Kemp had kept the sighting to himself, but came forward after another sighting was made by Major H. W. Langley in the same area. The Major and his wife saw a 30 metre serpent as wide as a car, and with a serrated back, from their yacht.

The Major's sighting was the first to stir up much media interest. Inevitably the creature was given a name *'Cadborosaurus'* (after Cadboro Bay) by Archie Wills, editor of the *Victoria Daily Times*. It was soon shortened to 'Caddy' and stuck.

On the morning of that most dragon haunted of 20th century years, 1933, two young friends went out duck hunting off Gowlland Head. Cyril Andrews and Norman Georgeson got an amazing view of Caddy feeding.

I succeeded in shooting a golden eye duck, but as I had only broken its wing, it began swimming to a kelp bed about fifty yards from shore. Seeing I could not get the wounded bird I sent Norman home for a small punt, five feet long. Returning, he was paddling across the bay towards me as I walked over a little rise to see if he was coming. As I looked across the water I heard a disturbance some distance out. From were I was standing I could plainly see the whole body of a sea monster just moving a foot underneath the surface.

Thinking I might alarm Norman I did not draw his attention to what I saw, so he came along and picked me up at the point from which we had shot the bird. From there we paddled to the wounded bird in the kelp bed. I was sitting in front of the punt ready to pick the bird up, when about ten feet away from it, out of the sea rose two coils.. They reached a height of at least six feet above me, gradually sinking under the water again, when a head appeared. The head was that of a horse, without ears or nostrils, but its eyes were in front of its head, which was flat just like a horse.

I attracted Georgeson's attention to it and he saw one coil and the head well clear of the water. Then the whole thing, except the head, which remained just out of the water, sank. I was still only ten feet away from it, with the duck right beside the thing. when to my horror it gulped the bird down its throat. It then looked at me, its mouth wide open, and I could plainly see its teeth and tongue, which were those of a fish. I would swear to the head being three feet long and two feet wide. When it closed its mouth, all the loose skin folded in neatly at the corners while its breathing came in short, sharp pants, like a dog after a run. At that point a number of sea gulls swooped down at the creature, which snapped at them when they came too close. Shortly after this it sank beneath the surface.

The friends called Justice of the Peace G.F. Parkyn, who took down an affidavit of what they had seen. Then the monster surfaced again 18 metres from shore. Eleven other people - including Mr Parkyn - saw it. Cyril, and two friends – Kathleen Georgeson and Arthur Pender - saw the animal twice again. On one occasion they saw it snap at sea gulls once more.

This duck eating and water bird stalking has been observed in the behaviour of Ogopogo at Lake Okanagan. Could the animals be related? Sea serpents have been seen swimming up rivers on many occasions. They may well be the same as some types of lake monster.

In 1940 Isaac Krook and E. H. Luoma were in Discovery Passage aboard a 14 foot boat. At half past two in the afternoon a massive serpent rose some 60 metres from their boat. The beast dived violently with a great crash, and threw up huge coils. As it dove it left a trail of bubbles and surfaced again 180 metres from the boat. It looked at the astounded men and dove again.

Mr Luoma reckoned it to be 15 to 22.9 metres long and as thick about as an oil-drum. It threw up its coils to a height of eight feet. It had eyes on the side of its head and a centrally positioned mouth like a snake.

In 1968 near De Courcy Islands, Captain W. Hagelund caught what may have been a juvenile Caddy. He was yachting through the islands with his family and had anchored off Pirate's Cove. Spotting a small disturbance he dropped a dinghy and investigated with his son Gerry. They came upon an eel-like creature swimming with its head clear of the surface and with portions of the back breaking the surface. All in all an very un eel-like way of swimming, and furthermore one that suggests vertical undulations. It had large dark eyes and a slightly hooked snout.

Despite the failing light they managed to capture the tiny beast with a dip-net and took it aboard the yacht for examination. It was 16 inches long and an inch thick. Sharp little teeth were in both upper and lower jaws. The back was protected by scales and the underside was covered in a kind of yellow fuzz. It possessed two flippers in the shoulder area and the tip of the tail bore horizontal flukes. The mini-monster was placed in a plastic container full of water. Hagelund intended to take it to the Pacific Biological Station in Nanaimo for identification. But during the night the animal's frantic splashing and scratching caused Hagelund to worry that the tiny beast might die during the night. He released the creature back into the sea, and it swam away.

Once again it is frustrating to see a cryptozoological specimen slip away. All the same I cannot blame Captain Hagelund for his compassion. I only wish more humans were as merciful and kind as he.

Was a baby Caddy captured that night? It's hard to say. The animal does not tally with any known species. It bears some resemblance to the pipefishes (elongated relatives of the sea horses, some of whom are referred to as sea dragons), but the sharp teeth, yellow fuzz, and swimming mode all argue against that. Who knows. Perhaps if the Captain had taken his prize back to shore, we would have had an adult Many Humped sea serpent in captivity today!

Sightings of Caddy continue along the Pacific Coast of Canada, and in particular off British Columbia. But now we must leave Caddy and his many humped cohorts, to look at another kind of sea dragon, the long necked.

The long necked sea serpent - as its name suggests - has a snaky, elongate neck. Its body is shorter than the many humped but considerably wider. The animal has two sets of flippers attached to the barrel-shaped body, as well as a tail at the rear. Overall it superficially resembles the extinct marine reptiles known as *plesiosaurs.* Some confusion may arise between the many humped and the long necked. The body of the long necked can show up to five humps, but never as many as the many humped. The humps of the long necked seem to be flexations in the back or possibly fat storage as in camels. The humps of the many humped would appear to be the loops of its elongate body showing as it propels itself. When rearing up with the front portion of the body, the many humped can seem to have a long neck. The long necked however really *does* have a long neck, quite separate from the bulbous body. Sometimes a dorsal fin is reported on the back of the long necked, but these reports are in the minority.

The long necked is reported from all the world's seas. In fact, apart from out of place big cats, and the North American Sasquatch, it may well be the most commonly reported of all monsters. A catalogue of all the long necked reports would be a thick as a phone book. Obviously I will not attempt to recount them here!

What follows is a smattering of reports to give the reader a feel for the animal:

Scientists have in the main poured scorn on sea serpents, but in 1905 two well respected zoologists had a sighting of their own. E. B. G. Meade-Waldo and M. J. Nicoll were fellows of the Zoological Society, and well known in ornithological circles. The friends were on a zoological research cruise on board Lord Crawford's yacht *Valhalla.* They were fifteen miles out from the mouth of the Parahiba in Brazil. Meade-Waldo writes…

On Dec 7th, 1905, at 10.15 am, I was on the poop of the "Valhalla" with Mr Nicoll, when he drew my attention to an object in the sea 100 yards from the yacht; he said; "Is that the fin of a great fish?"

I looked and immediately saw a large fin or frill sticking out of the water, dark seaweed-brown in colour, somewhat crinkled at the edge. It was apparently about six feet in length, and projected from 18 inches to two feet out of the water.

I got my field glasses on it (a powerful pair of Goerz Trieder), and almost as soon as I had them on the frill, a great head and neck rose out of the water in front of the frill; the neck did not touch the frill in the water, but came out of the water in front of it, at a distance of certainly not less than 18 inches, probably more. The neck appeared to be the thickness of a slight man's body, from 7 to 8 feet of it was out of the water; head and neck were all about the same thickness.

The head had a very turtle like appearance, as had also the eye. I could see the line of the mouth, but as we were sailing pretty fast , and quickly drew away from the object, which was going very slowly. It moved its head and neck from side to side in a peculiar manner: the colour of the head and neck was dark brown above and whitish below-almost white I think...

Another finned long necked sea serpent was seen in Australian waters, showing just how far these animals range. The steamer *Saint-Francois-Xanier* was on the Tongking-New Caledonia-Australia run when she encountered a sea dragon. Her captain, Raoul Jaillard, recorded the sighting.

Haipong, 18 March 1925

Sir, I am sending you a little sketch drawn at sea several minutes after the appearance of the famous sea serpent. The second captain, the second lieutenant, the radio officer, and the third engineer are unanimous in confirming the following lines:

On 2nd February 1925 while on passage from Noumea to Newcastle, the ship was making 10 knots, at 18.30 hours abeam of Port Stephens on the east coast of Australia, two masses like turtle's shells were seen floating 30 feet from the ship on the starboard bow.

Abeam of the engines there rose a big head like a camel's head, on a long flexible neck having a great similarity to a swan's neck. The height of the neck was about eight feet. The body, thick as the big Bordeaux barrels, formed a chain of five loops; on the fourth loop, an aileron as on sharks of large dimensions, measuring five feet in height and in width at the base. The aileron seemed to be black in colour; the colour of the animal was dirty yellow, the skin smooth without appearance of scales.

As it passed astern of the ship and was abeam of the starboard screw, the animal's head began to move backwards and forwards, which led us to think it had been touched by a blade of the screw; it's movement seemed hindered and it was not at all like that of the very little snakes seen near the coast.

The animal was visible for fifteen minutes, no optical illusion is possible. For besides the testimony of the Europeans, the Blacks from New Caledonia serving as seamen on board, the Annamite boys and the Chinese stokers all gave one cry: "There is the Dragon!". The Chinese even made an offering to it.

As night falls very quickly at that time of year we could not give other details, being one and all fairly taken aback by this fantastic apparition...

Raoul Jaillard.

It is interesting to see that the Chinese recognised the creature for what it was.

The next encounter I am recounting is one unparalleled in sea serpent history. Despite their large size and massive strength, they do not seem to look on humans as a food source. But if one Edward Brian McCleary is to be believed then the long necked sea serpent sometimes counts the 'long pig' as his prey.

The story begins on a sunny Saturday morning; 24th March 1962. Cleary - together with four friends, Eric Rule, Warren Sulley, Brad Rice, and Larry Bill - intended to go skin diving. They planned to dive on the wreck of the *Massachusetts,* several miles off the coast of their Florida home in Pensacola. The youths were all aged between 14 and 16. They had a seven foot Air Force life-raft to transport them to and from the wreck. A seemingly flimsy craft for five teenagers, but the weather forecast had been good.

As they rowed out to the ship they found that the tides were stronger than they had anticipated. Also storm-clouds were beginning to gather on the horizon. Three of the boys started to swim behind the raft, passing it onwards. They saw a boat and signalled for help but it did not seem to see them. The group saw a buoy about a mile distant, and decided to head for that. As they paddled towards it, the waves grew higher and started to swamp the raft.

They managed to get to the large buoy and clambered onto its metal scaffolding. Their raft was dragged under, as the buoy began to sway violently in the wind. The skies became black, and icy rain lashed down on the stricken divers

After a while the rain slowed and became a fine mist. The mountainous seas calmed to a mill-pool stillness, then a thick fog rolled in. Through the fog the boys heard a splashing sound. A foul odour like dead fish permeated the area. Then - silhouetted in the fog - the boys saw something like a telegraph pole rise up from the water, and dive back in. A strange whining cry filled the air. That was the last straw, the boys panicked and dove into the water. In the cold dark water they heard the sea dragon hissing and splashing.

Warren called out: *"Hey! Help me! It's got Brad It got Brad! I've got to get outta here…"*

His scream was abruptly cut short in the dark. The three remaining boys tried to cluster together. Brian, Larry, and Eric found each other. They tried to swim away through the fog but the seas were once more getting rough. Suddenly Larry vanished without a trace. Brian wrapped the exhausted Eric's arm around his neck for support but a wave pulled them apart. Then next to the stricken Eric the monster's head and neck emerged. It had a face like a turtle's but more elongate, with green eyes. The ten-foot neck was a greeny brown in colour.

It opened its jaws bent over Eric and dragged him under.

Brian, unsurprisingly recalled little after this. He swam, expecting death at any moment, through the cold dark sea. He sank and felt the tranquillity of death over take him.

He awoke on a beach some miles from Pensacola on Sunday morning with no memory of how he got there. He was found by a group of children. He was taken to Pensacola Naval Base Hospital suffering from shock, exhaustion, and exposure. When the Director of the Search And Rescue units, E. E. McGovern, came to see him McCleary told the whole story.

The bodies of Eric, Warren, and Larry were never found. The body of Brad was washed ashore a week later. I have no idea what the outcome of his post-mortem was. Brian understandably suffered a breakdown, and in later life became an alcoholic and now refuses to talk of the events.

What did happen to those boys on that night? Did Brian hallucinate the whole event through fear or guilt at his survival? Or did his friends fall victim to an unknown carnivorous sea beast? It seems unlikely that he would have made up such a story about the death of his four best friends. We shall never know. The last word on the case is best left to E. E. McGovern, who when visiting Brian in hospital said…

The sea has a lot of secrets. There are a lot of things we don't know about. People don't believe these things because they are afraid to. Yes, I believe you. But there's not much else I can do.

The long necked sea serpent is no stranger to the British coast. The largest concentration of sightings have been around Cornwall where the monster is known as *'Morgawr'*, (which allegedly means sea giant in archaic Cornish). Harold T. Wilkins and a friend saw two specimens whilst at the shark fishing port of Looe in 1949.

Two remarkable saurians 19-20 feet long, with bottle green heads, one behind the other, their middle parts under the water of the tidal creek of Looe, east Cornwall, apparently chasing a shoal of fish up the creek. What was amazing were their dorsal parts: rigid, serrated and like the old Chinese pictures of dragons. Gulls swooped down towards the rear of one. These monster - two of which were seen resembled the plesiosaurus of Mesozoic times.

Forty-nine years later, the *Falmouth Packet* newspaper reported the first in a whole series of modern sightings. Two witnesses, Mrs Scott and Mr Riley, had seen the thing off Pendennis Point. They described a long neck and a small head furnished with stubby horns. The neck had what looked like a mane of bristles running along it. The monster dived, and surfaced holding a large conger eel in its mouth. Mrs Scott commented that she would never forget the face on the thing as long as she lived.

On the 28th of December 1975 Mr Gerald Bennett wrote to the same paper about his own sighting.

I myself, during the last Christmas holidays, witnessed the sighting of a similar creature (to that seen by Mrs Scott and Mr Riley), although until now I have remained reticent about it. It was off the shore at Durgan, Helford, about 4pm, near dusk. When I first spotted it, I thought it was a dead whale, but as I drew nearer it started to move away, smoothly, and I could see it was not a whale, nor like any creature seen round here. I judged that the part of it I could see above water was about 12 feet in length with an elongated neck.

In January 1976 Duncan Viner, a dental technician, saw a 12 metre (40 foot) monster off Rosemullion Head. He too thought it was a whale until a long neck emerged from the water.

Later the same month, Amelia Johnson saw it in the same area, and described it as *"A sort of prehistoric, dinosaur thing, with a long neck, which was the length of a lamppost."*

Soon after the *Falmouth Packet* received two photographs from a woman calling herself "Mary F". The appeared to show a large animal with a long neck on the surface of the water. Unfortunately there was little in the shots to give scale. In the accompanying letter "Mary F" said she had seen the monster off Trefusis Point in early February. She claimed to have been badly frightened by the animal. She had sold the negatives, or so she said, to "an American gentleman".

It has since been suggested that the "Mary F" pictures were fakes made using modelling clay on sheets of glass. It has also been suggested that the Culprit was the late John Gordon, a friend of 'Doc' Sheils. The faked photographs of 'Shiela' - the so-called Loch Shiel monster which appear in *'The Shiels Effect'* a book about (and probably by) Shiels, are credited to a J. B. Gordon. The fact that the negatives or their American buyer have never surfaced, seems to reinforce the idea that they are fakes, even though the perpetrator cannot conclusively be named.

Sightings continued. Two London bankers, Tony Rodgers and John Chambers, were fishing on the rocks of Parson's Beach at the mouth of the Helford River, when they saw *Morgawr*. It was greeny grey in colour and bore humps. Rodgers thought he saw a second smaller creature accompanying the first.

In the summer of 1976 George Vinnicombe and John Cock were fishing the war time wrecks 25 miles out from lizard point! Once again, a dead whale was thought to be the object they saw floating on the calm surface. The idea was quashed as a serpentine head and neck rose up before the monster dived.

Brother and Sister Allan and Sally Whyte came upon the monster on land. The brown coloured six metre (20 foot) animal was resting on Grebe beach and slithered into the sea at their approach.

The editor of *Cornish Life*, David Clarke joined Doc Sheils on one of his monster invocations on the rocks below Mawnan as Doc attempted to raise *Morgawr* from the Helford river on 17th November 1976. Clarke took shots of Doc's incantations beside the river, then to his amazement a rounded back and small head surfaced. Clarke noticed small horns on the greenish creature's head as it swam up and down the river in a zigzag pattern. Clarke took shots with a telephoto lens. Sadly the pictures were damaged by a triple exposure. However an odd-looking object can be seen lying low in the water.

More photos were taken in 1980 by Geoffory Watson in the Mawnan area. He saw a pair of black humps rise up and move along the river from 900 feet away. He took a series of shots of the object as it swam away. Upon development the humps were too distant and indistinct to glean any useful information.

In July of 1985 two girls, Jenny Halstead and Alice Lee, from the lovely Yorkshire town of Hebden Bridge spotted the beast whilst on a cycling holiday.

At some time between 6.30 and 7 pm, from a position at Rosemullion overlooking the sea, we witnessed a genuine living monster of the deep, which we believe must be your legendary monster Morgawr. The creature's back broke the surface and looked rather like a massive overgrown black slug. We both watched the animal for about ten seconds as it wallowed in the water. Then the creature sank beneath the waves and did not surface again. Even though we had a camera to hand, we were too astounded by the sight by the sight of the monster to think of taking a photo-

graph until it was too late.

Josh Tomkins, a fisherman, and his son were out in a boat a mile off Falmouth on 24th August 1999 at 4.30pm when they saw something rise from the water.

Initially I thought it was a dead body rising to the surface. As we watched the mound it dropped back under the water, causing a terrific swell. Moments later it resurfaced, about fifty yards from our boat. I could see that it was no dead body, but a large creature. My son thought it was the back of a whale as this was the most logical explanation we could find. Our opinions altered when, about ten yards in front of the mound, a small head appeared above the surface. The head lifted out of the water only very slightly but sufficient for both of us to see part of what seemed a long slender neck.. It then dropped back down in a colossal disturbance.

We were both shocked by the immense size of the creature; it was like no fish I have ever seen, in fact it wasn't like anything I had seen before. I am pretty sure it must have been "Morgawr" the sea monster. I didn't believe in this before and I am still not certain now, but that thing sure did look like a dinosaur-like creature.. I would think it was dark brown or black, but the colouration was not evenly distributed, it seemed to be patchy in parts, slightly lighter in areas. We both saw it's eyes, no ears and no mouth. It made no noise, just created a huge wash as it submerged. After seeing it, I would not be too happy about going out into open water after dark in a small boat; it's very large and could inflict some serious damage to a small vessel.

Perhaps someone aught to tell him the story of Brian McCleary! Mrs Elsie Morgan saw it at around about the same time in the waters off Falmouth.

I saw, about one hundred yards seaward a black object appear in the water. It appeared before my eyes and seemed to be stationary. I would estimate that it was about ten feet long and, at its highest point out of the water, about two feet. As I watched, something rose out of the water close to the "hump-like" mound. It appeared to rise to an angle of 45 degrees, and looked a bit like the curved end of a question mark, but more angular. I then realized that this was either the tail or the head and neck of some large marine animal. This dipped in and out of the water several times, it's highest point appeared to be moving from side to side, like the head of a snake looking around. It remained in sight for a minuet of two before sinking from view. I could see white foam on the sea surface where it disappeared. It wasn't like any sort of animal or fish I had ever seen, nor could I imagine what it looked like as a whole, but it was very large and looked quite cumbersome.

The most recent sighting to date occurred off Falmouth again on 16th May 2000. Derek and Irene Brown had parked there caravan overlooking the sea.

The sea was quite calm, not choppy or heavily disturbed, and the weather was reasonably good, by that I mean that no mist or rain was falling and visibility was clear for a considerable distance out to sea. As we sat next to our caravan overlooking the sea, I saw something appear in the water perhaps 200 yards away, certainly no more. I took no notice of the object as the sea does throw up debris and bits of driftwood and I had no reason to concentrate on the object. I looked away and heard Irene ask me "What is that out there?" I looked again as she pointed to the object I had glimpsed a few moments earlier. The object now took the form of defined humps, two of them very close together. I would think that overall they measured about 15 feet. I estimated that from my height, I am just over 6 feet tall. The humps were still, and as I sat searching for an explanation to give Irene, a periscope-like object came out of the water very close to these humps. It was moving in a flexible manner, not at all rigid. I would think it looked close to the stance a cobra or python makes, raising it's head and neck before it strikes. Irene shouted "It's an octopus", but it clearly wasn't. I took the humps to be the back of a large body, the periscope-like object being the head and neck. I told Irene that I thought it was a monster and to get the camera from the car as we should take a picture of it.

As she got up to leave me, the creature seemed to roll forward, dipping head first into the water. There was a huge commotion as it disappeared. Irene came back with the camera but it had gone. We stayed to look for the creature for another hour, but it never resurfaced.

I cannot begin to explain how we felt about what we saw. We decided to keep it to ourselves, as no one would believe us and we would look stupid. I think the creature you are looking for is not one known to zoological science, but more to archaeologists who search for fossilized remains of creatures that existed many millions of years ago. This may sound stupid and far fetched, but somehow I believe that some of them lived on and exist in our waters. It wasn't a fish, more like a water based dinosaur, like something you see in those 1960 films about prehistoric times.

I am not a storyteller, not do I wish to capitalized upon what my wife and I saw, but I felt I should report this to someone, as it genuinely happened.

Almost every county in Britain with a coastline has had reports of Long Necked sea serpents. In August 1963 Mr P. Sharman was on holiday in Wales when he saw one from his vantage point on the cliffs. He was near New Quay, Cardigan Bay. He wrote to the late Tim Dinsdale with the details.

I noticed an animal greatly disturbing a colony of seals. The creature drawn was slowly moving it's four paddles two and fro as if in readiness to make a sudden move. At one end of it there appeared to be a long neck and small head poised above the water as if to strike out suddenly. The seals around it were making off as though the fear of death was upon them. This led me to suspect that the creature was making ready to kill a seal. After I had watched the thing for a few minutes I realised there was a remote possibility that I was looking down upon a floundering basking shark. This seemed more and more probable, so I left the scene.

Later, during that week I was exploring another cove about half a mile from the spot were I saw the strange animal. Here I saw the carcass of a seal with a huge chunk bitten off from its neck and shoulders. This practically cut the body in two and I could not help wondering what creature could have made such a horrible wound. Of course it could be that I saw a basking shark half in and half out of the water and mistook the tail for the head and neck of a Plesiosaur type creature. But I saw no dorsal fin; and are basking sharks aggressive to seals? The creature, comparing it with the seals must have been 30-40 feet long, and was a brownish black in colour. I was looking down at it from about 100 feet at an angle of 50 degrees. It must have been 8 feet wide.

Mr Sharman provided a drawing with his statement. It shows a large long necked animal with a bulbous body, two pairs of flippers and a stout tail. All around, seals are scattering from it.

Filey Brig is a long, low spur of rocks jutting a mile out to sea from the coast of the Yorkshire seaside town of Filey. In local legend they are said to be the bones of a dragon. Fittingly it was here that one of the spookiest encounters with a long necked sea serpent occurred. In February 1936 Wilkinson Herbert, a coastguard, was walking along the Brig on a dark moonless night…

Suddenly I heard a growling like a dozen dogs ahead, walking nearer I switched on my torch, and was confronted by a huge neck, six yards ahead of me, rearing up eight feet high!

The head was a startling sight, huge; tortoise eyes, like saucers, glaring at me, the creature's mouth was a foot wide and its neck would be a yard round.

The monster appeared as startled as I was. Shining my torch along the ground, I saw a body about 30 feet long. I though "this is no place for me" and from a distance I threw stones at the creature. It moved away growling fiercely, and I saw the huge black body had two humps on it and four short legs with huge flappers on them. I could not see any tail. It moved quickly, rolling from side to side, and went into the sea. From the cliff top I looked down and saw two eyes like torch lights shining out to sea 300 yards away. It was a most gruesome and thrilling experience. I have seen big animals abroad but nothing like this.

Further up the coast lies the county of Tyne and Wear. Nestled below South Shields is Marsden Bay; one of the strangest and most myth-ridden places in Britain. The small cove has an unearthly air about it, and it seems almost totally cut off from the rest of the world. One can easily forget the houses and shops a few hundred yards from the cliff tops. It is a tranquil, eerie place. Several hundred years ago an elderly man known as 'Blaster Jack' used blasting powder to blow himself a cave in the living rock. He and his wife used this as a home and later opened it up as a tavern. The tavern, known as Marsden Grotto, is still there today. From the time of Blaster Jack it was handed down from landlord to landlord. Parts of Lambton Castle, demolished in the 18th century are kept here, built into the Grotto's walls. On ancient pillar shows the infamous Lambton Wyrm, a huge serpent dragon that terrorized the area at the time of the crusades.

Local historian and fortean researcher Mike Hallowell has unearthed a gruesome and almost unbelievable story concerning the area. According to his remarkable account, during the Danelaw, when this part of England was ruled by the Norsemen - the Vikings were in dread of a sea dragon called the 'Shoney'. They placated the dragon with human sacrifice. The longship crews would draw straws. The loser would be bound hand and foot, have their throat slashed, and were tossed into the sea, in the hope that the Shoney would eat the man and not attack the ship. Bodies would wash up all along the coast from Lindisfarne to Marsden Bay. Sometimes they were virtually untouched, and other times they were half eaten.

This practice became a sort of veneration, and was carried on by Scandinavian sailors long after the time of the Vikings as a dragon worship cult. Bodies that washed ashore in Marsden Bay were taken to the Grotto. The cellar was used as a kind of morgue on many occasions. Mike has been told that the last body was found in 1928!

If true this means that a dragon worship cult was practicing human sacrifice in England well into the 20th century. The story sounds like the script for a Hammer Horror movie. Together with David Curtis – a Fortean researcher from Seaham on Sea, Co. Durham, Mike is currently trying to gain access to police records for the period to try and verify this disturbing story. The investigation is currently being hampered by the fact that county boundaries have been changed on several occasions, and no one seems to know which police force has the records for the period. More worryingly, Mike claims that more than once he has been warned off investigating the case by anonymous phone calls. Could some vestige of such a cult still be alive?

So what manner of beasts are the reptilian sea serpents? The most popular theory is that they are decedents of prehistoric marine reptiles. In recent years this idea has gone out of fashion in favour of unknown marine mammals. I think that this is very premature. Some sea monsters are undoubtedly marine mammals; the Merhorse for example, but it is my belief that the four kinds tackled here are true reptiles.

The *plesiosaurs* and their gigantic, short-necked relatives the *pliosaurs*, have been touted as favourites in the past. Indeed the Long Necked bears a striking resemblance to the *plesiosaurs,* and the marine saurian is a dead ringer for the crocodile-like *pliosaurs.* However they belong to a family of reptiles extinct for 65,000,000 years. They died out at the end of the Cretaceous period along with non-avian dinosaurs. But there were other marine reptiles that belong to, or are very closely related to families living today.

The *mososaurs* were elongate crocodile-like predators with four flippers and savage jaws. Some - such as *tylosaurus* - grew to 12 metres (40 feet) or more in length. They were not related to the superficially similar looking *pliosaurs,* but they were closely related to the *varanids* or monitor lizards that thrive today.

Another possible sea dragon ancestor was a group of prehistoric marine crocodiles known as *thalattosuchians.* Some of these bore fins rather than feet, and some such as *steneosaurus* and *metriorychus* were capable of vertical flexation. A feature reported in the majority of sea serpent cases.

65,000,000 years of evolution could have adapted such creatures to cope with cold as well as warm water. It could also change have their body shape radically; perhaps to compete with the emerging marine mammals.

I make no apologies for the fact that my chapters on aquatic dragons have been so long. The original concept of the dragon was that of an aquatic beast. Many early legends speak of them as water dwellers. In the orient, the dragon is *still* linked with water today. The would-be modern dragon hunters would therefore be well advised to seek their quarry in the world's lakes and seas.

CONCLUSIONS

"More wriggling worms
Writh under Yggdrasill
Than any stupid ape would suppose."

Grimnismal, (Norse epic 950 AD)

hose words, written over one thousand years ago, are as true today as ever. For the past three centuries we have been conditioned by society to think of dragons as a myth, something for bedtime stories and children's books. We consign them to legend, and condemn those who believe in them as superstitious fools.

This mindset grew out of the scientific revolution that had its seeds in the Renaissance. Mankind began to concoct "laws" of nature. Something in the mental make-up of our species is inordinately fond of erecting barriers, setting limits, and putting things into boxes. In his 1748 book *An Enquiry Concerning Human Understanding,* David Hume wrote that no amount of evidence could prove the reality of an event that violated the laws of nature, as it was more likely that the evidence was wrong than that a law of nature had been overturned.

Yet these are not laws of nature, they are man-made and hence laws of man. Nature is more fluid that we small-minded humans would like to believe. Science is prone to act like a fundamentalist religion. Anything that contradicts its tenets is branded as heretical, or swept under the carpet. Many scientists themselves act like fanatical high-priests. Lord May, President of the Royal Society, and former Scientific Adviser to the government once branded cryptozoology a waste of resources. His pitiful bleating is typical of a group of "scientists" who emerged in the 20th century, the armchair scientists. After attending university, they hunker down like limpets to their comfy lecture halls and laboratories, never venturing out to do real field research. From their armchairs they proclaim that this or that cannot possibly exist, or they would have known about it. They will not consider the existence of something unless they can dissect it in a laboratory, and write a dozen peer-reviewed papers on it.

The world just doesn't work that way. The discoveries are to be made out there in the forests, seas, mountains, and deserts, not on the desk of some overpaid arrogant oaf.

During the Victorian era science enjoyed halcyon days. There was a true spirit of adventure and discovery. A genuine open mindedness existed among most scientists before the shadow of dogma took hold.

But dragons are very real. They are part of our world like it or not. We can try to explain them away with meaningless psychobabble, or slay them with the sword of science, but like the heads of the hydra the dragon grows back. People all over the world, even in this modern age, have reported encounters with dragons. Dragonlore stretches back unbroken to at least Sumerian times, and possibly far further. A cave painting 25,000 years old in Baume La-trone, France, shows a mighty fanged serpent-dragon dwarfing mammoths. Another dragon crawls across 10,000 year old rock art in Shanxi Province, China. We have always encountered these creatures.

Dragons swim in the earth's lakes and seas, they fly through its skies, and they stalk across its lands. When we deny their existence we do a great disservice to ourselves, our ancestors, and to the most remarkable creatures that roam our world.

So what can we say about these beasts? Dragonlore is a rich tapestry with many finely woven strands. There are many kinds of dragons.

- Some are known reptiles that have been taken from their homelands and brought before people who did not understand them.

- Others are known species of reptile grown to immense sizes.

- Others still, are reptiles totally unknown to science, or ones that were presumed extinct but still linger in the wilder corners of the globe.

- Yet others still, may be manifestations of paranormal entities, creatures from other plains of existence or beasts created by our own collective unconscious.

Dragons lurk inside every single one of us, hidden deep at the backs of our minds. Coiled in our race memories just waiting to live again, and bring terror to the puny cowering mammals called mankind. Think about this the next time you are away from civilization, away from the warmth of your home. Think of it when you are in the dark woods. Think of it when you are at sea. Think of it when you are sitting by the campfire like some Neolithic hunter. Beyond the circle of the fire's light is the primal darkness. It is not too difficult to fill that darkness with dragons. When your parents told you there were no such things as dragons, they lied.

Richard Freeman,
Exeter,
January 2004

APPENDIX

GEOLOGICAL AGES

ERAS	PERIODS	MILLION OF YEARS BEFORE PRESENT	A BRIEF HISTORY OF LIFE FORMS
CAINOZOIC	QUATERNARY	2.5	Modern man becomes dominant. Extinction of many large mammals
	TERTIARY	65	Early man appears. Many large mammals become extinct. Rise of mammals. Grasses become common. Widespread forests. Spread of modern bivalves and gastropods.
MESOZOIC	CRETACEOUS	135	Ammonites and many large reptiles become extinct. Almost all belemnites extinct. Mammals still small. Flowering plants develop
	JURASSIC	190	Birds and first flowering plants appear. Dinosaurs common. Ammonites and belemnites abundant
	TRIASSIC	225	Early Dinosaurs and primitive mammals appear. First scleractinian corals. Spread of conifers.
PALAEOZOIC	PERMIAN	280	Extinction of trilobites and rugose corals, Ammonites and Conifers appear.
	CARBONIFEROUS	345	Reptiles appear. Amphibians and insects become common. Non flowering plants abundant.
	DEVONIAN	395	Rapid development of land plants leads to appearance of first forests. Goniatites, amphibians and insects appear. Graptolites become extinct
	SILURIAN	430	Fish abundant. Corals brachiopods and crinoids common. First land plants appear
	ORDOVICIAN	500	Graptolites and brachiopods common. Rugose and tabulate corals appear. Armoured, jawless fish appear. Spread of molluscs
	CAMBRIAN	570	Graptolites appear. Trilobites dominant. Appearance of many invertebrate groups with hand parts
PRECAMBRIAN	ORIGIN OF EARTH	4600	Many-celled invertebrates such as worms and jellyfish appear. Algae appear about 2500 million years ago. Primitive organisms similar to bacteria. Origin of life 3500 million years ago.

BIBLIOGRAPY

- Chapter One -

Appenzella, Tim, Cantley, Donald, and Thomson, David, *Dragons* (Time Life, 1984)
Bord, Janet and Colin, *Alien Animals* (Granada, 1980)
Coleman, Loren and Clark, Jerome, *Creatures of the Outer Edge* (Warner Books, 1978)
Costello Peter, *The Magic Zoo* (Sphere Books, 1979)
Gould, Charles, *Mythical Monsters* (W H Allen & Co, 1886)
Heuvelmans, Dr Bernard *In the Wake of the Sea Serpents* (Rupert Hart-Davis, 1968)
Ingersoll, Ernest *Dragons and Dragon Lore* (Payston & Clarke, 1928)
McEwan, Graham J., *Mystery Animals of Great Britain and Ireland.* (Robert Hale, 1986)
Newman, Paul, *The Hill of the Dragon* (Kingsmead Press, 1979)
Ragache, Gillies, *Les Dragons* (Hachette, 1989)
Sant, Montse, *The Book of the Dragon* (Paper Tiger, 1992)
Shuker, Dr Karl, *Meet Mongolia's Death Worm* (in *Fortean Studies Volume 4*, John Brown Publishing, 1998)
Simpson, Jacqueline, *British Dragons* (BT Batsford, 1980)
Suckling, Nigel, *Year of the Dragon* (Pavillion Books, 2000)
Whitlock, Ralph, *Here be Dragons* (George Allen & Unwin, 1983)
Wilson, Colin, Wilson, Damon, and Wilson, Rowan, *World Famous Strange but True*

- Chapter Two -

Bassett, Michael G, *Formed Stones, Folklore and Fossils* (National Museum of Wales, 1984)
Clark Jerome, *Unexplained!* (Visible Ink, 1999)
Corliss, Richard , *Incredible Life: A Handbook of Biological Mysteries* (Sourcebook Project, 1981)
Currie, Philip J. and Padian, Kevin, *Encyclopedia of Dinosaurs* (Academic Press, 1997)
Dance, Peter, *Animal Fakes & Frauds* (Sampson Low, 1976) Mayor, Adrienne, *The First Fossil Hunters: Paleontology in Greek and Roman Times* (Princeton University Press, 2001)
Downes, Jonathan, *The Owlman and Others* (CFZ publications, 1997)
Edwards NW *The Early History of Palaeontology* (British Museum, 1976)
Gould, Charles, *Mythical Monsters* (W H Allen & Co, 1884)
Heuvelmans, Dr Bernard, *On the Track of Unknown Animals* (Rupert Hart-Davis, 1958)
Ingersoll, Ernest *Dragons and Dragon Lore* (Payston & Clarke 1928)
Needham J, *Science and civilisation in China* (CambridgeUniversity Press, 1954)
Newman, Paul, *The Hill of the Dragon* (Kingsmead Press, 1979)
Shuker, Dr Karl, *From Flying Toads to Snakes With Wings* (Llewellyn Publications, 1997)
Suckling, Nigel, *Year of the Dragon* (Pavillion Books, 2000)
Tang X, *Living Treasures. An Odyssey through China's Extraordinary Nature Reserves* (Bantam Books, 1987)
Whitlock, Ralph, *Here be Dragons* (George Allen & Unwin, 1983)

- Chapter Three -

Alderton, David, *Crocodiles and Alligators of the World* (Blandford ,1991)
Ash, James, Drewes, Robert,Howell, Kim, and Spawls, Stephen. *A Field Guide to the Reptiles of East Africa* (Academic Press, 2002)
Blashford-Snell, Colonel John, *Mysteries* (Bodley Head ,1983)
Blashford-Snell, Colonel John, *Operation Raleigh* (Colins, 1988)

Bondeson, Jan, *The Feejee Mermaid and other Essays in Natural and Unnatural History* (Cornell University Press, 1999)

Costello Peter, *The Magic Zoo* (Sphere Books, 1979)

Dinsdale, Tim *The Laviathans* (Routledge & Kegan Paul, 1966)

Eberhart, George M *Mysterious Creatures: A Guide to Cryptozoology* (ABC-CLIO, 2002)

Eberhart, George M, *Monsters:Including Bigfoot, Many Water Monsters, and Other Irreguar Animals* (Garland Publihing, 1983)

Fawcett, Brian, *Exploration Fawcett* (Hutchinson, 1953)

Furneaux, Robin, *The Amazon* (Reader's Union, 1971)

Gilroy, Rex, *Mysterious Australia* (Nexus Publishing, 1995)

Gosse, Philip Henry, *The Romance of Natural History: Second series* (James Nesbit and Co, 1866)

Gould, Charles *Mythical Monsters* (W H Allen & Co, 1884)

Guggisberg, C.W. A, *Crocodiles: their Natural History, Folklore, and Conservation* (David & Charles, 1972)

Heuvelmans, Dr Bernard, *In the Wake of the Sea Serpents* (Rupert Hart-Davis, 1968)

Holiday, FW, *The Dragon and the Disc* (Sidgwick & Jackson, 1973)

Jong, Johnson and Ritchie James, *Man-Eating Crocodiles of Borneo* (Natural History Publications, 2002)

Kearton, Cherry, *In the Land of the Lion* (National Travel Club, 1929)

Kingsley, Mary, *Travels in West Africa* (Mcmillan & Company, 1897)

Knight, Charles, *Pictorial Museum of Animated Nature* (London, 1844)

Laider, Liz and Keith, *China's Threatened Wildlife* (Blandford, 1996)

Marshall, W. H, *Four Years in Burma* (C. J. Skeet, London 1860)

MacCormic, Alex *The Mammoth Book of Maneaters* (Robinson, 2003)

Mackal, Dr Roy, *A Living Dinosaur? In Search of Mokele-Mbembe* (E. J. Brill, 1987)

Mackal, Dr Roy, *Searching for Hidden Animals* (Cadogab Books, 1983)

Minton, Sherman A & Minton, Madge Rutherford *Giant Reptiles* (Scribners,1973)

Morris, Desmond and Morris, Ramona, *Men and Snakes* (Sphere, 1965)

Ross, Charles A, *Crocodiles and Alligators* (Merhurst Press,1989)

Shuker, Dr Karl, *Mysteries of Planet Earth* (Carlton,1999)

Shuker, Dr Karl, *The Unexplained* (Carlton 1996)

Simpson, Jacqueline, *British Dragons* (B. T. Batsford, 1980)

Steel, Rodney, *Crocodiles* (Helm, 1989)

Suckling, Nigel, *Year of the Dragon* (Pavillion Books, 2000)

Tang X, *Living Treasures. An Odyssey through China's Extraordinary Nature Reserves* (Bantam Books, 1987)

Twigger, Robert, *Big Snake* (Victor Gollancz, 1999)

Waterton, Charles, *Wanderings in South America* (B. Fellows, 1839)

Willoughby-Meade, G, *Chinese ghouls and Goblins* (Constable, 1928)

Wilkins, Harold T, *Secret Cities of Old South America* (Rider and Company, 1957)

- Chapter Four -

Backer, Robert, *The Dinosaur Heresies* (Dutton Books, 1999)

Bord, Janet and Colin, *Modern Mysteries of the World* (Grafton Books, 1989)

Bord, Janet and Colin, *Modern Mysteries of Britain* (Grafton Books, 1988)

Couzens, T, *Tramp royal: The true story of Trader Horn.* (Raven Press, 1993)

Dickenson, Peter, *The Flight of Dragons* (Pierrot Publishing, 1979)

Gilroy, Rex, *Mysterious Australia* (Nexus Publishing, 1995)

Eberhart, George M, *Monsters:Including Bigfoot, Many Water Monsters, and Other Irreguar Animals* (Garland Publihing, 1983)

Fawcett, Brian, *Exploration Fawcett* (Hutchinson, 1953)

Hegeeenbeck, Carl, *Beasts and Men* Longmans, (Green and Co, 1909)

Heuvelmans, Dr Bernard, *On the Track of Unknown Animals* Rupert Hart-Davis, 1958)

Hughes, J. J. *Eighteen Years on Lake Bangweulu* (1933)

Mackal, Dr Roy, *A Living Dinosaur? In Search of Mokele-Mbembe* (E. J. Brill, 1987)
Mackal, Dr Roy, *Searching for Hidden Animals* (Cadogab Books, 1983)
Miller, Charles, *Cannibal Caravan* (L. Furman, 1939)
Paul, Gregory S Predatory Dinosaurs of the World: A Complete Illustrated Guide (Simon & Shuster, 1988)
Shuker, Dr Karl, *From Flying Toads to Snakes With Wings* (Llewellyn Publications, 1997)
Wavell, Stewart, *The Lost World of the East* (Souvenir Press, 1958)
Wilkins, Harold T, *Secret Cities of Old South America* (Rider and Company, 1957)
Wilkins, Harold T., *Monsters and Mysteries* (James Pike: St. Ives, 1973)

- Chapter Five -

Alexander, Mark, *The Devil Hunter: The Incredible Account of the work of a modern day Exorcist* (Sphere, 1978)
Bord, Janet and Colin, *Alien Animals* (Granada, 1980)
Bord, Janet and Colin, *The Bigfoot Casebook* (Granada, 1982)
Clark, Jerome and Colman, Loren *Creatures of the Outer Edge* (Warner Books, 1978)
Clark Jerome, *Unexplained!* (Visible Ink, 1999)
Coleman, Loren, *Curious Encounters* (Faber and Faber, 1985)
Coleman, Loren, *Mysterious America* (Faber and Faber, 1983)
Coleman, Loren, *Tom Slick and the search for the Yeti* (Faber and Faber, 1989)
David-Neel, Alexandra, *Magic and Mystery in Tibet* (Crown, 1937)
Downes, Jonathan, *The Owlman and Others* (CFZ publications, 1997)
Downes, Jonathan, *The Rising of the Moon* (Domra, 1999)
Eberhart, George M *Mysterious Creatures: A Guide to Cryptozoology* (ABC-CLIO, 2002)
Fortune, Dion, *Psychic Self Defence* (Aquarian Press, 1952)
Furman, Robin, *Ghostbusters UK* (Robert Hale, 2001)
Greer, John Michael, *Monsters: An Investigation into Magical Beings* (Llewellyn, 2001)
Healy, Tony and Cropper, Paul *Out of the Shadows: The Mystery Animals of Australia* (Ironbark, 1994)
Holiday, F. W, *The Dragon and the Disc* (Sidgwick & Jackson, 1973)
Holiday, F. W, *The Goblin Universe* (Llewellyn, 1986)
Holiday, F. W, *The Great Orm of Loch Ness* (Faber & Faber, 1968)
Huyghe, Patrick, *The Field Guide to Extraterrestrials* (Avon, 1996)
Keel, John, *Strange Creatures from Time and Space* (Sphere, 1975)
Lee, John and Moore, Barbara, *Monsters Among Us: Journey to the Unexplaned* (Pyramid, 1975)
McEwan, Graham J., *Mystery Animals of Great Britain and Ireland.* (Robert Hale, 1986)
North, Mark and Newland, R, *dark Dorset* (Oakmagic, 2001)
O'Siaghail, Nicail , *The Shiels Effect* (Bob Lynn / Tony Raven, 1976)
Pepper, Elizabeth and Wilcock, John, *Magical & Mystical Sites* (Harper &Row, 1977)
Randles, Jenny, *Mind Monsters: invaders from Inner Space?* (The Aquarian Press, 1990)
Shiels, Tony, *Monstrum! A Wizard's Tale* (Fortean Tomes, 1990)
Sheldrake, Rupert, *A New Science of Life* (Tarcher, 1982)
Shuker, Dr Karl, *Mysteries of Planet Earth* (Carlton, 1999)
Symonds, John and Grant, Kenneth (Editors), *The Confessions of Aleister Crowley* (Routledge & Kegan Paul, 1979)

- Chapter Six -

Bord, Janet and Colin, *Alien Animals* (Granada, 1980)
Bord, Janet and Colin, *Modern Mysteries of the World* (Grafton Books, 1989)
Bord, Janet and Colin, *Modern Mysteries of Britain* (Grafton Books, 1988)
Childress, David Hatcher, *The Lost Cities of North and Central America* (Adventures Unlimited, 1992)
Clark Jerome, *Unexplained!* (Visible Ink, 1999)

Coleman, Loren and Clark, Jerome, *Creatures of the Outer Edge* (Warner Books, 1978)

Coleman, Loren, *Curious Encounters* (Faber and Faber, 1985)

Coleman, Loren, *Mysterious America* (Faber and Faber, 1983)

Collins, Andrew, *The Brentford Griffin:The Truth Behind the Tales* (Earthquest Books, 1985)

Corliss, Richard , *Incredible Life: A Handbook of Biological Mysteries* (Sourcebook Project, 1981)

Eberhart, George M *Mysterious Creatures: A Guide to Cryptozoology* (ABC-CLIO, 2002)

Eberhart, George M, *Monsters:Including Bigfoot, Many Water Monsters, and Other Irreguar Animals* (Garland Publihing, 1983)

Fort, Charles, *LO!* (Claude H Kendal, 1931)

Heuvelmans, Dr Bernard, *On the Track of Unknown Animals* (Rupert Hart-Davis, 1958)

McEwan, Graham J., *Mystery Animals of Great Britain and Ireland.* (Robert Hale 1986)

McLoy, James F and Miller, Roy, *The Jersey Devil: 13th Child* (Middle Adlantic, 1979)

McLoy, James F and Miller, Roy, *Phantom of the Pines: More Tales of the Jersey Devil* (Middle Adlantic, 1998)

Melland, Frank H, *In Witchbound Africa* (Seeley & Service, 1923)

Percival, A Blaynet, *A Game Warden on Safari* (Nisbit, 1928)

Shuker, Dr Karl, *From Flying Toads to Snakes With Wings* (Llewellyn Publications, 1997)

Shuker, Dr Karl, *Meet Mongolia's Death Worm* (in *Fortean Studies Volume 4* John Brown Publishing, 1998)

Shuker, Dr Karl, *The Unexplained* (Carlton, 1996)

Simpson, Jacqueline, *British Dragons* (B. T. Batsford, 1980)

Whitlock, Ralph, *Here be Dragons* (George Allen & Unwin, 1983)

- Chapter Seven -

Akins, William, *The Loch Ness Monster* (Signet, 1977)

Bauer, Henry H, *The Enigma of Loch Ness: Making Sense of a Mystery* (Johnson & Bacon Books, 1991)

Bord, Janet and Colin, *Alien Animals* (Granada, 1980)

Clark Jerome, *Unexplained!* (Visible Ink, 1999)

Costello, Peter, *In Search of Lake Monsters* (Garnstone Press, 1974)

Dinsdale, Tim *The Laviathans* (Routledge & Kegan Paul, 1966)

Dinsdale, Tim, *The Story of the Loch Ness Monster* (Target, 1973)

Dinsdale, Tim, *Project Water Horse* (Routledge &Kegan Paul, 1975)

Downes, Jonathan, *The Owlman and Others* (CFZ publications, 1997)

Eberhart, George M, *Mysterious Creatures: A Guide to Cryptozoology* (ABC-CLIO, 2002)

Eberhart, George M, *Monsters:Including Bigfoot, Many Wter Monsters, and Other Irreguar Animals* (Garland Publihing, 1983)

Gaal, Arlene, *Ogopogo, The True Story of the Okanagan Lake Million Dollar Monster* (Hancock House, 1986)

Gaal, Arlene, *In Search of Ogopogo: Sacred Creature of the Okanagan Waters* (Hancock House, 2001).

Gilroy, Rex, *Mysterious Australia* (Nexus Publishing, 1995)

Harrison, Paul, *Sea Serpents and Lake Monsters of the British Isles* (Hale, 2001)

Harrison, Paul, *The Encyclopaedia of the Loch Ness Monster* (Hale, 1999)

Holiday, FW, *The Dragon and the Disc* (Sidgwick & Jackson, 1973)

Holiday, FW, *The Goblin Universe* (Llewellyn, 1986)

Holiday, FW, *The Great Orm of Loch Ness* (Faber & Faber, 1968)

Hunt, Gerry, *Bizarre America* (Berkley, 1988)

Kirk, John, *In the Domain of the Lake Monsters* (Key Porter Books, 1998)

Landsburg, Alan, *In Search of Myths and Monsters* (Corgi, 1977)

Lee, John and Moore, Barbara, *Monsters Among Us: Journey to the Unexplaned* (Pyramid, 1975)

Mackal, Roy P, *The Monsters of Loch Ness* (Macdonald and Jane's, 1976)

Mackal, Dr Roy, *Searching for Hidden Animals* (Cadogab Books, 1983)

McEwan, Graham J., *Mystery Animals of Great Britain and Ireland.* (Robert Hale, 1986)

Montgomery Campbell, Elizabeth, and Soloman, David, *The Search for Morag* (Tom Stacey, 1972)

Sanders Garner, Betty, *Monster, Monster, A Survey of the North American Monster Scene* (Hancock House, 1995)

Smith, Warren, *Strange Secrets of the Loch Ness Monster* (Zebra, 1976)
Shuker, Dr Karl, *From Flying Toads to Snakes With Wings* (Llewellyn Publications, 1997)
Witchell, Nicholas,*The Loch Ness Story* (Corgi, 1982)
Whyte, Consance, *More than a Legend* (Hamish Hamilton, 1957)
Zarzynski, Joseph W, *Champ, Beyond the Legend* (M-Z Information, 1984)

- Chapter Eight -

Bright, Michael, *There are Giants in the Sea* (Robson Books, 1991)
Clark, Bill and Clark, Bob, *The San Francisco Sea Serpent* in *Dracontonlgy Special Number 1:Being an Examination of Unknown Aquatic Animals* (Crypto, 2001)
Clark Jerome, *Unexplained!* (Visible Ink, 1999)
Dinsdale, Tim *The Laviathans* (Routledge & Kegan Paul, 1966)
Editors, Fate Magazine, *The Strange World of the Occult* (Paperback Library, 1968)
Harrison, Paul, *Sea Serpents and Lake Monsters of the British Isles* (Hale, 2001)
Heuvelmans, Dr Bernard, *In the Wake of the Sea Serpents* (Rupert Hart-Davis, 1968)
LeBlond, Dr Paul H and Bousfield, Dr Edward l, *Cadborosaurus: Survivor from the Deep* (Horsdal & Schubart, 1995)
McEwan, Graham J, *Mystery Animals of Great Britain and Ireland.* (Robert Hale, 1986)
McEwan, Graham J, *Sea Serpents, Sailors & Sceptics* (Routledge& Kegan Paul, 1978)
O'neill, J. P, *The Great New England Sea Serpent: A Account of Unknown Creatures Sighted by Many Respectable Persons Between 1638 and the Present Day* (Paraview, 2003)
Sanders Garner, Betty, *Monster, Monster, A Survey of the North American Monster Scene* (Hancock House, 1995)
Sanderson, Ivan T, *More "Things"* (Pyramid Books, 1969)
Smith, Malcomb, *Bigfoots and Bunyips: In search of Australia's Mystery Animals* (Millenium Books, 1996)

- PERIODICALS -

Animals & Men: The Journal of the Centre for Fortean Zoology
Fortean Times
British Columbia Scientific Cryptozoology Society Newsletter
World Explorer

- WEBSITES -

http://www.cfz.org.uk

http://www.forteantimes.com/

http://www.blather.net/index.htm

http://members.aol.com/karlshuker/

http://www.cryptokeeper

http://www.sommerland.org/

http://www.fortunecity.com/rivendell/krondor/1139/

http://draconomicon.com/

http://www2.prestel.co.uk/aspen/sussex/dragon.htm

http://bestiarium.net/select.html

http://www.colba.net/%7Etempest1/dragons.htm

http://www.indigogroup.co.uk/edge/dragons.htm

http://www.strangescience.net/stdino2.htm

http://www.polenth.demon.co.uk/index.html

http://www.wyrm.demon.co.uk/ukdracs.htm

http://www.theserenedragon.net/Tales/tales.html

http://www.wyrm.org.uk/

INDEX

A

B

280

H

I

Korea - *55,63,114*
Kort, Commander - *202*
Kosi, James - *169*
Koch, Dr Albert - *43, 257*
Kovach, Theresa - *218*
Kozak, Unal - *207*
Kraken - 187
Krook, Isaac - *261*
Ksoga, Lake (Uganda) - *58*
Kubu Tribe (Sumatra) - *81*
Kulta - 116
Kurodo - *34*
Kush-inada-hime (Japanese folklore) - *36*
Kussie - 211
Kutcharo, Japan - *211*
Kuykendall, Don - *257*
Kuzetsov, Vladimir Semyonovich - *160*
Kyushu (Japan) - *210-211*

L

L'Eost, Lieutenant - *242*
La Alberca - *215*
La Decidee (gun boat) - *242*
La Vibria - 14, 15
Labynkyr, Lake (Siberia) - *209*
Lacasse, Denis - *228*
Lace monitor (*Varanus varius*) - *67*
"Laddie" (dog) - *96*
Lago Grande do Salea (Brazil) - *89*
Lagoon Creek (Australia) - *116*
Lagresill, Lieutenant - *239 - 242*
Laguna Cartagena (Puerto Rico) - *173*
Laimay, Alexander - *215*
Lajan, Inch Baharuddin bin - *115*
Lambton Castle (Durham) - *268*
Lambton, Sir. John -
Lambton Worm - *42, 153, 268*
Lamon, Roberto - *84*
Landoll, Mary - *218*
Lang, Calvin - *168*
Lange, Algot - *86*
Langeland, Rolf - *206*
Langley, Major H. W. - *260*
Laos - *49, 63, 82*
Larson, Rolf - *205*
Lathangue, Neil - *227*
Lau - 77, 78
Laura (schooner) - *254*
Lausnitz, Freiherr von Stien zu - *102, 104*
Lawrence, A. R. - *202*
Lawrence, Amos - *256*

Lawson, Tracey - *175 - 6*
Le Gros - 163
Le, General Kong - *82*
Leane, Lough (Kerry, Ireland) - *127*
Leatherback Turtle; Luft (*Dermochelys coriacea*) - *210*
Le Blond, Paul - *215, 225*
Led Zeppelin - *126*
"Lee" (CIA agent) - *87*
Lee, Alice - *265*
Leeds (Yorkshire) - *133, 135, 136*
Leeds, Mrs. - *177*
Legaut, Francis - *80*
Leo, Africanus - *79*
Leonard, Steve - *198*
Lepage, M. - *96*
Leptorrhynchus crassidens - 46
Lerna (Greece) - *36*
Leslie, Captain Lionel - *125*
Lesure, Alexander - *255*
Lewanika, King - *102*
Lewis, Etherleda - *98*
Ley, Willy - *102*
Liberia - *88, 104*
Liddell, Henry - *82*
Lindisfarne - *268*
Lierde, Colonel Remy van - *78*
"Lightning snake" - *169*
Likouala-aux-Herbes River (Congo) - *105, 106*
Liles, Holly - *218*
Liles, John - *218*
Lilith - *150*
Lilius, Aleko - *236, 237*
Limpwood Nature Reserve (Australia) - *67*
Linda Banda people (northern Congo) - *103*
Lindorm - *20, 22, 32, 37, 88, 121,161, 204 - 6*
Lindsay, M. - *129*
Lingala People (Congo) - *59*
Linnaean Society - *189, 195, 255*
Lion *(Felis leo) - 57, 63, 65, 101, 143, 144, 158*
Lister, Lew - *140*
Little River County (Arkansas, USA) - *160*
Liverpool (Australia) - *83*
Llyn Tegid (Lake Bala, Wales) - *201*
Llyn-y-Gadair (Wales) - *200*
Loadstone (Australia) - *66*
Loch Ness Monster; *Nessie - 121, 122, 125, 127-9, 131, 187-199*
Lochy, Loch (Scotland) - *200*
Locke, Thomas - *226*
Loblolly Cove (Massachusetts) - *255*
Lomond, Loch (Scotland) - *200*
London (UK) - *46, 62, 98, 121, 125, 126, 139, 180,*

Richard Freeman is one of Britain's few professional cryptozoologists. His interest in unknown animals reaches back to his childhood and he has had a long and varied career working with exotic creatures. He was curator of reptiles at Twycross zoo in the Midlands.

In 1996 he took a degree in zoology at Leeds university and after graduation moved to Exeter to work full time as the Zoological Director of the Centre for Fortean Zoology, the UK`s only cryptozoological organisation. He has hunted giant snakes in Thailand, ape-men in Sumatra, lake monsters in the UK, and death worms in Mongolia. His interests include Gothic and New Wave music and the classic British Science Fiction series Dr Who.

Mark North was born in Weymouth, Dorset where he still resides. He has long been fascinated by local legends, folklore and Fortean phenomena. That he co-wrote and illustrated with Robert Newland *'Dark Dorset: Tales of Mystery, Wonder and Terror'* in 2002. As long-standing member of the CFZ team and resident illustrator, which later established him as cartoonist of *'Animals and Men'* in 1995. With popular cartoon series such as *'The Cryptozoology Files'* and *'Hopkins: The Witchfinder General'*. His work has since appeared in *'Tropical World Magazine'* and has recently illustrated the *'Monster Hunter'* by Jonathan Downes. Other interests included collecting the works of H.G. Wells and Eric Frank Russell.

Other books available from
CFZ PRESS
www.cfz.org.uk

CFZ PRESS **CFZ PRESS**

MONSTER HUNTER
Jonathan Downes

WHILE THE CAT'S AWAY
- An Exmoor Escapade -
Chris Moiser

Jonathan Downes' long-awaited autobiography, *Monster Hunter*...

Written with refreshing candour, it is the extraordinary story of an extraordinary life, in which the author crosses paths with wizards, rock stars, terrorists, and a bewildering array of mythical and not so mythical monsters, and still just about manages to emerge with his sanity intact.......

Over the past thirty years or so there have been numerous sightings of large exotic cats, including black leopards, pumas and lynx in the South West of England. Former Rhodesian soldier Sam McCall moved to North Devon and became a farmer and pub owner when Rhodesia became Zimbabwe in 1980. Over the years despite many of his pub regulars having seen the '*Beast of Exmoor*' Sam wasn't at all sure that it existed. Then the series of happenings made him change his mind.

ISBN 0-9512872-7-3

ISBN 0-9512872-1-4

Printed in the United Kingdom
by Lightning Source UK Ltd.
107379UKS00002B/235-242